WITHDRAWN
FROM
UNIVERSITY
OF
MEDWAY
LIBRARY

Programmable Logic
PLDs and FPGAs

Programmable Logic PLDs and FPGAs

R.C. Seals and G.F. Whapshott

School of Engineering
University of Greenwich

First published 1997 by
MACMILLAN PRESS LTD
Houndmills, Basingstoke, Hampshire RG21 6XS
and London
Companies and representatives
throughout the world

ISBN 0-333-65570-2

A catalogue record for this book is available
from the British Library.

This book is printed on paper suitable for recycling and made from fully managed and sustained forest sources.

8 7 6 5 4 3 2 1
04 03 02 01 00 99 98 97

Printed in Great Britain by
Antony Rowe Ltd, Chippenham, Wiltshire

Contents

Preface

This book has been produced for those people who are interested in Programmable Logic Devices (PLD) and Field Programmable Gate Arrays (FPGA) and want to find out more about how they are constructed and produced, how their architectures differ and the various programming methodologies available for design. The aim of the book is to give a broad sweep of the topic to enable a full overview to be obtained, with in-depth analysis, case studies and examples at important strategic points. Each chapter includes a problems section and a list of further reading. The problems section will require the reader to expend considerable mental effort to complete; some questions may require additional reading to obtain satisfactory answers.

Indicative solutions to the end of chapter problems may be obtained from R.Seals@greenwich.ac.uk

The authors would like to thank Holly Richards for all her assistance with the preparation of the typescript.

R.C. Seals
G.F. Whapshott

School of Engineering
the University of Greenwich
London UK

Disclaimer

The use or discussion of any component, software program or development system anywhere within this book should not be taken to be an endorsement or criticism of that product. Discussion, case studies and examples are for illustration only and may not be appropriate for real-world use. The aim is to enable readers of this book to make informed decisions of their own, based on their own particular circumstances.

Readers may obtain the most up to date information on the products mentioned in this book by contacting the manufacturers directly.

1 Introduction to integrated circuits

Microelectronics has provided an environment where many new and exciting ideas and concepts can be implemented easily and cheaply, in order to provide mankind with an improved quality of life. One aspect of microelectronics which has rapidly gained acceptance and is in widespread use is programmable logic.

1.1 What is programmable logic?

Programmable logic components are devices which are able to implement a wide variety of logic functions, both combinational and sequential. The actual logic function implemented is determined by the user, using some form of design entry software to specify the state of the internal programmable points. The internal programmable points are effectively switches which can either be selected (that is, programmed) to be closed (short circuit), or open (open circuit).

1.1.1 Permanent or reprogrammable internal programmable points

The internal programmable points can be separated into two main categories, permanent and reprogrammable. The permanent methods are based on a physical change to the internal connections using semiconductor fuses, described in chapter 2. Initially, the programmable logic components have all fuses intact: then, by applying a higher than usual voltage, large currents can be made to flow, which heat up the fusible connection until it vaporises and forms an open circuit. There is no method of reconstructing the fuses, so once they are programmed no further changes can be made. The alternative is to use reprogrammable points which do not require any permanent physical change, but use a reversible programming method such as EPROM or EEPROM, again as explained in chapter 2. The erasure method may require placement of the device in a special eraser, usually containing ultraviolet light, or it can be accomplished electronically while the device is still in circuit.

1.1.2 PLD or FPGA

The programmable logic components can also be separated into two categories based on their internal structure:

Programmable logic devices, which have a small gate count, fixed internal routing, and deterministic propagation delays.

Field programmable gate arrays, which have large numbers of gates, with user selectable interconnection (that is, routing), where the propagation delay is determined by the specific design and routing chosen. Varying the routing may vary the propagation delay.

The most important difference between the two categories is in the routing strategies.

1.1.3 Programmable logic devices

All programmable logic devices have a similar architecture consisting of a number of inputs connected to a number of AND gates. The outputs of the AND gates are connected to the inputs of a number of OR gates, and the outputs of the OR gates become the outputs of the PLD. The outputs of the OR gates produce what is called a 'sum-of-products', as the symbols used to represent logical AND and OR are the same as for arithmetic multiply and addition, as illustrated in table 1.1.

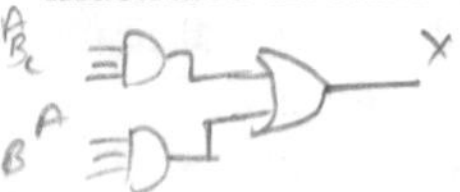

Table 1.1 Symbol meaning

Symbol	logical	arithmetic
*	AND	multiplication
+	OR	addition

The architecture of the PLD discussed so far is a simple one which is not used, as it does not contain the logical NOT function. In most PLDs there will be the opportunity to have invertors on all the inputs to the AND gates, as well as the inputs to the OR gates and the outputs of the OR gates. This would allow outputs such as

X = /(A * /B) + (C * D) + /D

to be generated. Designs such as these are known as combinational outputs, as the outputs are determined completely by the inputs at any instant.

PLD architectures can become further complicated by adding registers to the output of the OR gates; these devices are called registered PLDs, which enable sequential designs to be implemented. With sequential devices the outputs are determined both by the instantaneous inputs and the past states of the inputs. Sequential systems effectively have some 'memory'. In addition, the outputs of registered PLDs have connections back to the input of the AND gates, see figure 1.1, which are called 'buried' inputs (as they cannot physically be accessed) and provide a feedback path. The registers require the connection of a clock signal in order to make them operate. The outputs of the registers will now only change when the clock signal is applied, and between clock pulses the outputs remain constant even if the inputs change. Only the states of the inputs when the clock is present are important.

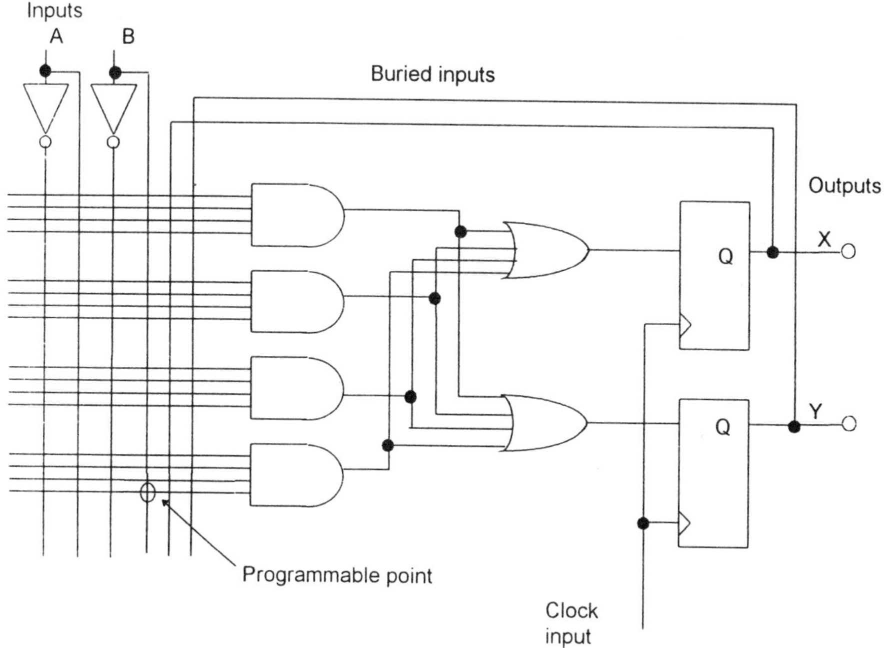

Figure 1.1 Registered PLD with buried inputs

Although a PLD may be registered, its outputs can still be used as combinational outputs as the connections can be programmed so that the register is ignored and the output of the OR gate is connected directly to the output pin of the device. Most PLDs have architectures which are some recognisable variation of this basic architecture. The architecture has a considerable number of advantages. It is well known and understood, and design software is free or cheaply available. The propagation delays are known and constant, so that the timing relationship between the inputs and the outputs can be accurately predicted and, due to the large market, prices are kept low.

There are, however, some limitations to the architecture and some applications where it would just not be suitable. The main limitations are that the fixed architecture can prevent the use of the most effective digital designs in some applications; the number of product terms is restricted, as are the number of registers and the number of inputs and outputs. In order to overcome these limitations an alternative architecture can be used, called a complex PLD (cPLD).

1.1.4 Complex programmable logic devices

The approach in the cPLD is to integrate several PLDs on to one piece of silicon, linking them together with global programmable connections as illustrated in figure 1.2. This overcomes the first two limitations by enabling multi-layer AND-OR structures to be generated so that virtually any logic function can be reproduced, and by providing many more product terms inside one package. It also increases the number of registers available as well as the number of inputs and outputs, although some applications such as microprocessor bus systems will still require more.

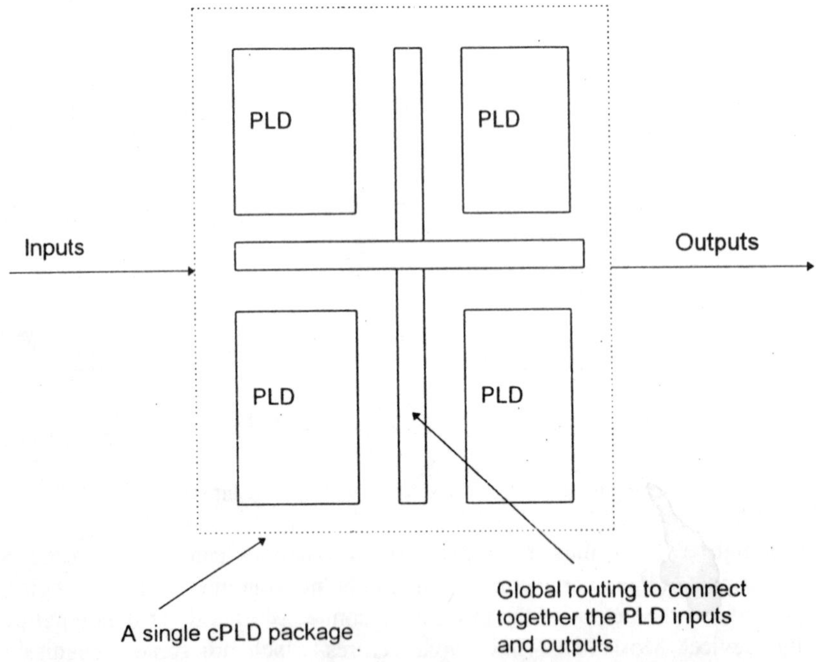

Figure 1.2 A typical complex PLD architecture

However, cPLDs have problems of their own. It is more difficult to design solutions, so the design software is more expensive, the routing between PLD blocks is highly variable between designs and the propagation delays cannot always be predicted until after the routing is completed, and there are still some limitations on the number of registers, inputs and outputs in some applications.

1.1.5 Field programmable gate arrays (FPGA)

Most of the limitations of the PLD and cPLD architectures can be overcome through the use of Field Programmable Gate Arrays (FPGAs). Instead of the fixed architecture of PLDs, FPGAs have a much more flexible architecture based on the logic block concept. A logic block consists of a small number of logic gates which is able to implement a wide variety of logic functions depending on how it is programmed, and may or may not contain a register. Figure 1.3 shows the Xilinx 2000 family logic block called a configurable logic block which contains a register.

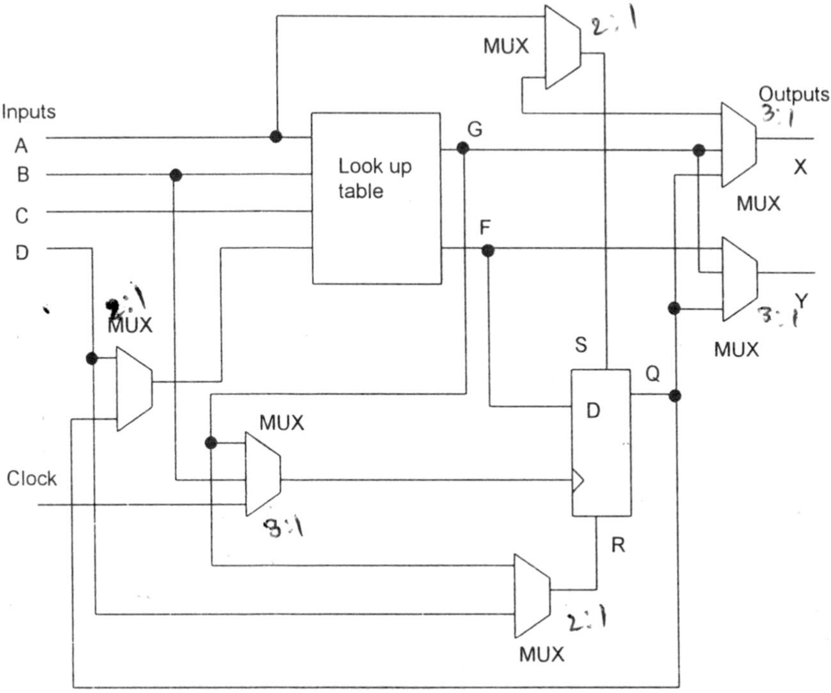

Figure 1.3 Xilinx XC2000 family configurable logic block

Each FPGA contains a large number of these logic blocks, as illustrated in figure 1.4, typically 50 to 250, sometimes more. Each logic block is connected to other logic blocks and I/O pins as required, by the programmable routing. This enables the inputs to the logic blocks to be connected to input pins or to the outputs of other logic blocks, and the outputs to output pins or to the inputs of further logic blocks.

The flexible routing between logic blocks and the wide variety of logic functions which can be implemented by each logic block provides the FPGA with its flexibility and usefulness which overcome the limitations of PLDs and cPLDs. As always, these components have their own disadvantages; the FPGAs cost more as they are more difficult and expensive to manufacture, the design development software is more expensive as the flexibility of the FPGAs make it more difficult to efficiently implement specific designs, and the propagation delays throughout the design cannot be precisely determined until after the logic blocks have been placed and all routing has taken place.

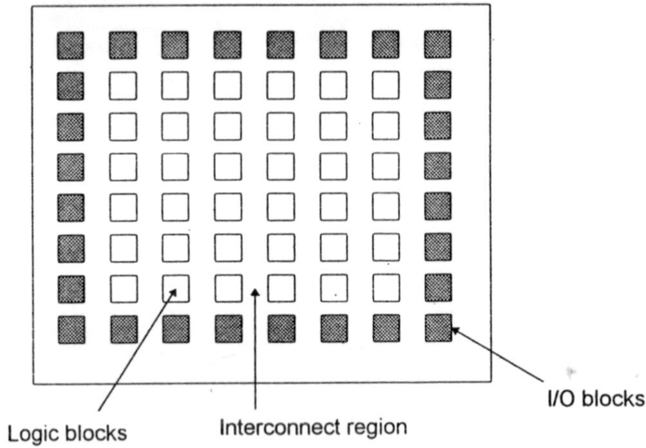

Figure 1.4 Typical layout of an FPGA

As FPGAs have many more programmable points than PLDs, a number of methods have been developed for programming them which can be divided into three main categories: EPROM/EEPROM based, fuse based and SRAM based. The EPROM based programming is essentially identical to that used in PLDs where a floating gate MOS transistor is permanently ON or OFF depending on how it is programmed; this controls whether a connection is open circuit or close circuit. By erasing the EPROM, the device may be reprogrammed. Fused based programming is almost identical to EPROM programming, except that a physical change to the circuit is made which makes a permanent open circuit or a permanent close circuit. MOS transistors are not involved, so fused based FPGAs have a higher density of logic which can make them cheaper and faster. The disadvantage is that they cannot be erased and reprogrammed and these devices are known as one time programmable.

The most interesting method of programming is for those FPGAs which are SRAM based. The programming point is controlled by a 1-bit memory, hence SRAM (Static Random Access Memory). The disadvantage of SRAM is that when the power is removed from the circuit, the contents of the SRAM is lost so that when power is reapplied the contents have to be loaded. This is achieved by storing the configuration information in a standard EPROM device. The FPGA then has a special power-on mechanism which transfers the configuration information from the EPROM into the FPGA. The advantages of this system are that the FPGAs do not require special programmers or erasers and are effectively an off-the-shelf standard part so that a stock of programmed parts does not need to be stored. In addition, there is the possibility of reconfiguring the FPGA dynamically while power is still applied so that if the product requirements change during use, different configurations can be loaded. The disadvantage is that two components have to be used instead of one so that more PCB is occupied and more solder connections made, which may make the system less reliable.

1.1.6 Application specific integration circuits (ASICs)

FPGAs have some limitations, mainly maximum speed of operation and the number of gates available for the design. These limitations can be overcome through the use of Application Specific Integrated Circuits (ASIC) where 4-10 times as many gates are available, with maximum operating frequencies 2-5 times that available from FPGA. Although ASICs are not programmable devices, each device is designed to fulfil a specific logic function. The drawbacks of using ASICs are that they are more expensive for limited component numbers and the time from design to fabricated component is much longer than for FPGA. There are many similarities between ASICs, FPGA and semi-custom design, particularly in terms of the software tools used and, apart from the two drawbacks identified, FPGA and ASIC designs can be considered as equivalent.

1.2 Semiconductor technologies

Programmable logic is dependent on the underlying semiconductor fabrication processes and this section will provide a brief overview of some of them.

1.2.1 An overview of processes used in the fabrication of integrated circuits

The term integrated circuit has been used to cover thin film, thick film, monolithic and hybrid circuits. Of these, the monolithic is the most popular and has considerable advantages over the other types. An alternative in relatively widespread use is hybrid circuits which combine thin films and monolithic circuits as well as discrete components. Figure 1.5 illustrates the main range of manufacturing technologies available. Monolithic circuits have all the components and connecting leads manufactured on or near the surface of very small (1.5 mm × 1.5 mm) silicon blocks or 'dice'. A number of active and passive components within the surface of the chip form a complete circuit; for example, an operational amplifier, or a system of circuits such as a set of logic gates. The complexity of circuits that may be produced on a simple chip of silicon is described by the number of parts that form the circuits:

- **small scale integration (SSI)**, which can be defined as fast simple circuits with between 10 and 20 passive or active components;
- **medium scale integration (MSI)**, which is used to denote circuits in which there are between 20 and 100 components;

- **large scale integration (LSI)**, which is used to indicate circuits of complexity up to a few thousand components; such circuits are most often used in computers and can be described by the number of bits that can be stored in a memory circuit of similar complexity; LSI denotes circuits of complexity in the range of 16 KBits;

- **very large scale integration (VLSI)**, which has been used to describe anything larger than LSI. Most PLDs are described as SSI or MSI and most FPGAs as VLSI.

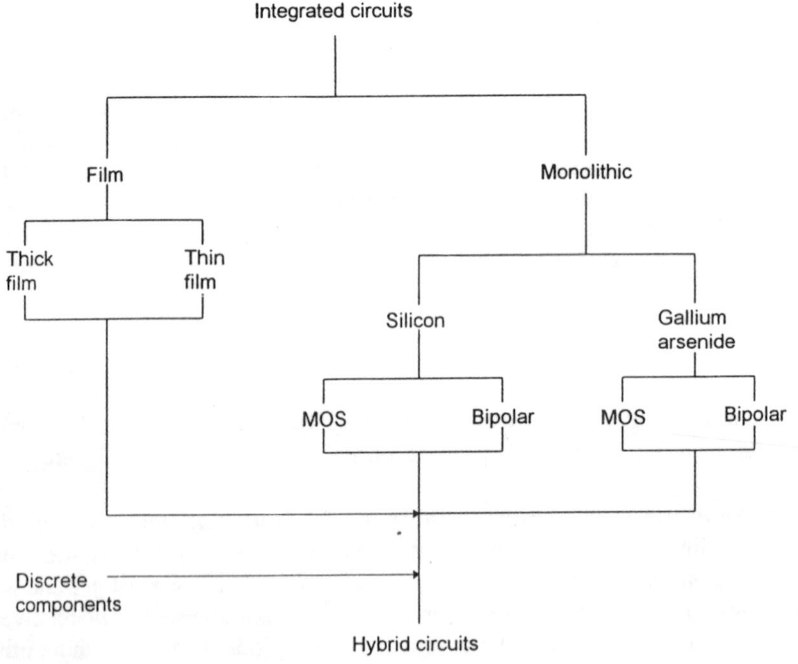

Figure 1.5 Manufacturing technologies

Thin film circuits

These have passive components (resistors, capacitors) manufactured by deposition or sputtering on a ceramic substrate with discrete active components mounted on top and connected by metallised interconnections. Only the passive components may be formed using this technology. The coated areas of the substrate are formed by apertures in the masks or by selective etching using photoresists. The required conducting leads are produced by the deposition of gold or aluminium, with the thickness of such thin film circuits being in the range 5E-10 and 1E-6 m.

Thick film circuits
These have thicknesses greater than 10E-5 m and are produced by screen printing using a suitable paste, on the selected substrate. The commonest substrate used is aluminium oxide with a purity of 96%. After the screen printing process, the paste is dried and heated in a furnace with a carefully regulated temperature-time schedule. The pastes used for the conducting leads contain precious metals such as gold, platinum, silver and palladium.

Hybrid integrated circuits
These circuits consist of several separate component parts attached to a ceramic substrate and interconnected either by wire bonds or a suitable metallisation pattern. The individual parts are noncapsulated and may consist of thin or thick film components and one or more monolithic circuits.

1.2.2 Integrated circuit production processes
Active semiconductor devices depend on the production of extremely pure silicon and to a lesser extent, germanium. Silicon needs to have in its intrinsic (that is, pure) form a number of intrinsic carriers of about 1.5E10 per cm^3 at room temperature, as compared with 2.4E13 per cm^3 for germanium. Because of this, intrinsic silicon is much more difficult to prepare than intrinsic germanium. Silicon obtained from silicon dioxide or silicon tetrachloride by normal metallurgical processes has to be further purified to reduce the number of foreign atoms to less than 1 in 1E10, in order to create silicon pure enough to be used in semiconductor devices.

The usual method of obtaining pure silicon crystals employs a technique known as Czochralski crystal pulling and involves inserting a seed crystal into a bath of molten silicon and gradually withdrawing it. In this way, a single silicon crystal of 10 to 15 cm can be obtained, with the required impurities necessary for semiconductor operation being simultaneously introduced. The cooled crystal is then divided into slices approximately 1 mm thick using diamond saws. The cut has to be aligned to a specific crystallographic direction to minimise disruption to the crystal's internal structure. However, the cutting process still introduces some surface damage and a variety of etching and polishing processes are used to remove the damaged layers; the resulting slice is approximately 0.2 mm thick.

1.2.3 Ion implantation
Certain specialised types of semiconductor devices rely on a method called ion implantation to obtain the semiconductor effect. The method implants ions into the lattice of the semiconductor crystal by bombarding the surface with impurities which have been accelerated and have energies up to 300 keV. The energy of the ion as it impacts on the surface determines the depth of implanting.

1.2.4 The integrated circuit production process

Crystal growth and the preparation of slices form the first step in the creation of integrated circuits. This is then followed by further processes:

1) epitaxial deposition;
2) oxidisation, photoengraving of the insulating diffusion;
3) oxidisation, photoengraving of the base and resistor diffusions;
4) oxidisation, photoengraving of the emitter diffusion;
5) aluminisation, photoengraving of the contacts and connections;
6) scribing and separation of the dice, followed by testing.
7) bonding and mounting.

1.2.5 Epitaxial deposition

This is one of the most important steps in the fabrication of an integrated circuit and involves the growing of a special layer, called the epitaxial layer, on the surface of the silicon slice. The various components of the IC are formed from this layer. The slice is cut in a particular crystallographic direction to facilitate the growth of the epitaxial layer, which must have the same orientation and be grown on to the underlying silicon surface. The layer is grown by placing the silicon slice into an atmosphere of silicon tetrachloride and hydrogen. By carefully controlling the conditions, a high quality single crystal is grown. A perfect crystal is essential for the correct operation of the subsequent stages. Any surface imperfections on the silicon are removed by passing gaseous hydrochloric acid over the surface. This is followed by the silicon tetrachloride and hydrogen at a temperature of approximately 1200°C.

1.2.6 Oxidisation

Oxidisation is essential to the planar process which is itself the foundation of silicon integrated device technology. When semiconductors were first being produced the oxide layer was used as a mask during diffusion of other substances, acting as a protective, passivating layer. However, more recently, oxide layers have been used as elements in active and passive devices and silicon functional blocks. The oxide layer became important for the manufacture of planar and epitaxial planar transistors which have very low leakage currents due to the junctions being formed under a layer of silicon oxide.

During the complete IC process, the surface is oxidised two or three times, which after selective etching forms a mask for the diffusion of impurity atoms, fabrications or connections. One method of oxidisation used is to pass oxygen over the surface of the silicon at a temperature of 1200°C to produce oxide layers which are typically 5E-7 m thick. The oxide layers produced in this way have high quality physical properties, uniform thickness, freedom from imperfections and high DC isolation. The process is illustrated in figure 1.6 and typically 10 silicon slices would be simultaneously processed in this way, with each slice having the potential to create 200 monolithic circuits.

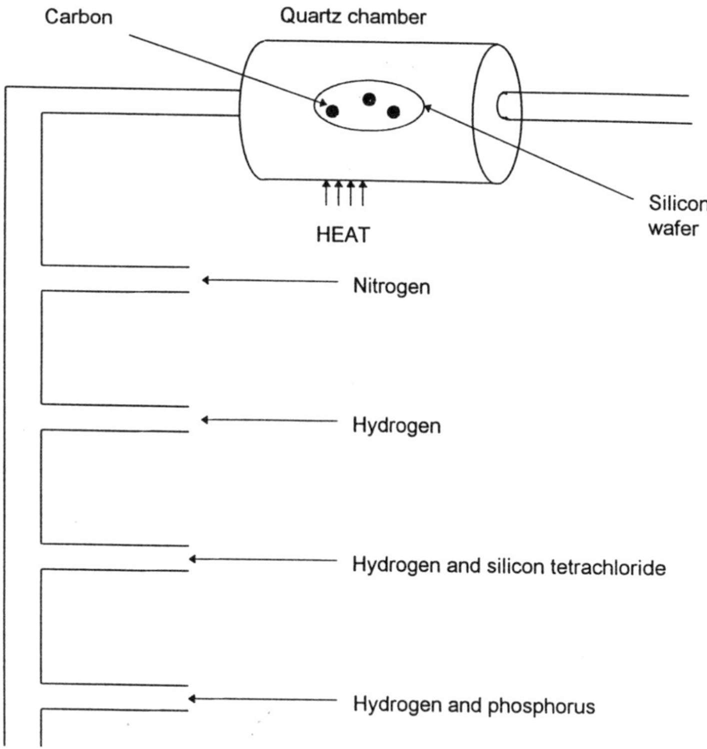

Figure 1.6 Epitaxial deposition

1.2.7 Photo-engraving

Photo-engraving is a process which involves two operations; the preparation of the photographic mask and the etching of the silicon dioxide to cut the windows which allow the diffusion of subsequent stages to take place.

1.2.8 Mask production

The photographic mask comprises a large number of identical elements, each of which is a reduced version of the original mask layout. Due to limitations in photographic equipment, several stages of reduction are required and a typical sequence would consist of the preparation of artwork originals, photographic reduction, step-by-step contact printing and finally rephotographing. The resulting mask would typically have 200 or more images within a circle of 15 cm diameter.

1.2.9 Photo-etching

When the photographic mask has been prepared the processing of the slice may be started. Initially, the surface of the slice is covered with a thin layer of photo-

photo-resist which can be painted on, although a better method is to rotate the slice at 800 rpm and drop photoresist on the surface. Centrifugal force then spreads the light sensitive emulsion evenly over the slice. The photoresist is then allowed to dry in an oven, after which the photographic mask is placed in the exact position required and then exposed to ultraviolet light. This causes the photoresist to polymerise and harden with the opaque areas corresponding to the areas to be etched. The slice is then developed so that the photoresist is removed in these areas, with the polymerised areas being untouched. The polymerised photoresist forms a coat that is resistant to hydrofluoric acid which is used to etch the base silicon away.

1.2.10 Diffusion

In the preparation of integrated circuits there are always at least three diffusion stages and it is possible to produce complete ICs in this way. However, the usual method involves a combination of epitaxial deposition and diffusion. The diffusion process takes place through the holes etched in the silicon dioxide and the choice of the diffusant must be such that it diffuses easily into the silicon itself, but not into the silicon dioxide. Boron and phosphorous are the usual impurities. The time and concentration of the diffusant, or 'impurities', are accurately controlled to obtain the diffusion depths required by the specific transistor design.

1.2.11 Evaporation

Evaporation is a process which is suitable for producing the prepassivation of the ohmic contacts and the construction of interconnections. Aluminium is usually used for this, but gold and nickel can also be used. The main problem associated with the process is to avoid changing the nature of the semiconductor material when the aluminium is added. The process takes place in a vacuum, with aluminium rods being evaporated to produce a thin layer over the entire surface. Then, by masking and etching, only the desired aluminium configuration remains to form the contacts and interconnections.

1.3 Packaging

Once a slice of semiconductor has been processed it is cut into individual circuits. This is achieved by drawing a diamond-tipped tool across the surface of the slice, after which it is easily broken into separate 'chips'. The individual chips are now ready for mounting and encapsulation.

1.3.1 Mounting, bonding, testing and encapsulation

Mounting is performed by holding the chip by its edges in a vacuum chuck and pushing down on to a gold plated mounting area on the encapsulation 'header', which will have been preheated. A gentle 'scrubbing' motion is used to form a gold-silicon alloy which gives a good mechanical bond when cool. Connections are made between the terminal posts on the header and the aluminium bonding areas on the chip. Usually, a fine gold wire is used and a typical process is called 'nailhead' bonding. This involves passing the gold wire through a heated capillary tube with a hydrogen flame used to form a small ball of gold at the end of the wire. The tube is then located over the aluminium pad and pressed down. The heat and pressure form a 'thermo-compression' bond, which has all the necessary electrical and mechanical properties. The tube is then raised, leaving a connection shaped like a nailhead and moved until it is over the terminal post. When the connection is created the capillary is raised again and the wire is cut by the hydrogen flame to leave a gold ball ready for the next connection.

Initial testing using multi-electrode probes takes place before the chip is separated from the complete slice. This allows any faulty parts to be marked so that they are not encapsulated. Faulty parts are discarded, as it is not possible to 'repair' silicon chips. The bonded chip is then completely encapsulated in a suitable protective substance, dependent upon the type of use. For commercial use with a limited temperature range, plastic is used, whereas for military use some form of ceramic material will be used, which has a much greater temperature range and is more resistant to thermal and mechanical shock. The final production stage is to seal the packages by soldering, after which the IC (integrated circuit) may be tested again to ensure that the encapsulation was successful; it is then ready for use.

In order to protect the silicon chip from its operating environment and to make it easier to incorporate in products, different packages are used. Two main types of package fixing are the pin-through-hole and the surface mount.

1.3.2 Pin-through-hole mounting

When integrated circuits were first developed, they were all pin-through-hole, where the ICs had solder or gold plated legs or pins, which were inserted into holes drilled through the printed circuit board (PCB). For double or multi-layer boards, the holes were internally plated with copper so that when soldered in position, there was an electrical connection between the pin of the IC and all of the layers of copper. The printed circuit board was used to physically fix all the components and the copper tracks were used to make the signal connections. With multi-layer boards, where there are two or more layers of copper tracks in between the insulating board material, plated through holes are used to ensure a good solder connection to the pins and to connect signal tracks on both sides of the board.

The components have a minimum pin spacing of 0.1 inches to provide sufficiently large holes for the IC legs to fit through without weakening the PCB by having many holes close together. Obviously, this restricts the number of legs that a package can have, with old style packages using dual-in-line (DIL) rows of pins, and modern style using a pin grid array (PGA). Dual-in-line have two rows of pins with the pins spaced at 0.1 inches and the rows spaced at 0.3 inches for pin counts up to 24, and 0.6 inches for pin counts up to 48 pins, see figure 1.7(a). For total pin counts above 48, the PGA was developed, as this minimises the PCB area required; the pins are arranged on a square matrix, spaced in rows, with the pins 0.1 inches apart and the rows 0.1 inches apart. The PCB area required for a 48 pin DIL is approximately

$$\begin{aligned}\text{total area} &= (\text{number of pins} \times \text{pin spacing}) \times \text{row spacing} \\ &= (24 \times 0.1) \times 0.6 \\ &= 1.44 \text{ in}^2\end{aligned}$$

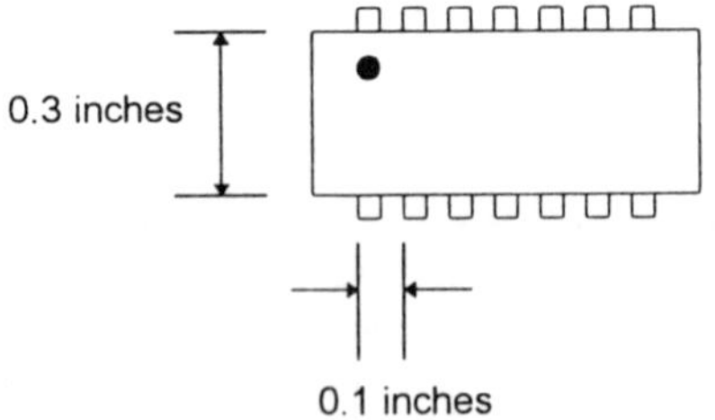

Figure 1.7(a) 0.3 inch spaced DIL

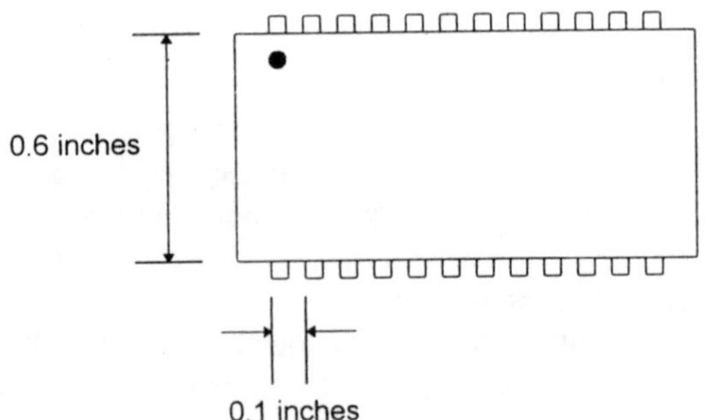

Figure 1.7(b) 0.9 inch spaced DIL

The smallest PGA made, the 68 pin package, has two rows of pins on each of the four sides of the square package. With the pins spaced at 0.1 inches the PCB area required for a 68 pin PGA is approximately

$$\begin{aligned}\text{total area} &= (\text{number of pins in a row} \times \text{pin spacing})^2 \\ &= (11 \times 0.1)^2 \\ &= 1.21 \text{ in}^2\end{aligned}$$

The result is that a package with 42% more pins occupies 16% less PCB.

Pin-through-hole packages have a number of other disadvantages when compared with surface mount packages, such as higher resistance, higher inductance, high capacitance, and thermal creep when socketed.

Thermal creep is an interesting problem which only affects those pin-through-hole packages which have been placed in sockets and usually DIL packages. The problem is caused by a repeated power on/power off cycling, which causes the package legs to expand slightly due to heating when power is applied. The expansion creates a force which forces the pin out of the socket. When power is removed and the pin shrinks it does not return to its original position. The actual movement is very small, but over a large number of power on-off cycles it can be sufficient to cause one or more pins to be intermittently connected after power on, or even completely disconnected. The problem can be compensated for by using sockets which have a higher insertion force and hence a higher retraction force, which prevents the thermal creep.

When pin counts become too high, such as for high pin count (200+ pins) PGAs, the subsequent insertion forces become too high and there is an increased probability of pin damage. To overcome this problem, the individual socket pin insertion force is reduced which means that the surface tarnish on the pins may not always be penetrated. This problem is overcome by using gold-plated pins, as these do not tarnish, although unfortunately it has the disadvantage of making the components more expensive. The result of all the difficulties has been to make pin-through-hole packages unpopular and instead surface mount packages have become much more popular.

1.3.3 Surface mount packages

Surface mount packages are available in a variety of different styles, mainly the J lead and the chip carrier concepts, as illustrated in figures 1.8 (a) and (b). All the connections are arranged around the edge of the package, with pin spacing of 0.05 inches, half that of pin-through-hole packages, and they are mounted directly on to the surface of the PCB on copper pads. The advantages of the surface mount packages are as follows: a smaller PCB area is required hence the product is cheaper, the pins are smaller so capacitance and inductance are reduced, large pin counts are possible without the need for large insertion forces, or weakened PCBs, the packages are suitable for machine placement, the packing density of devices on a PCB is higher and both sides of the PCB can be used.

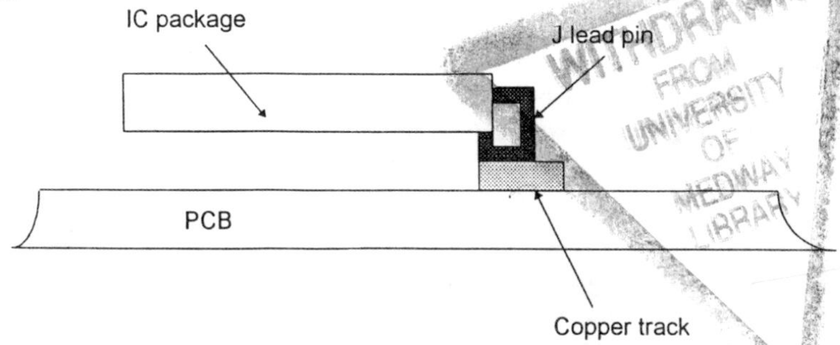

Figure 1.8(a) J lead package (cross section)

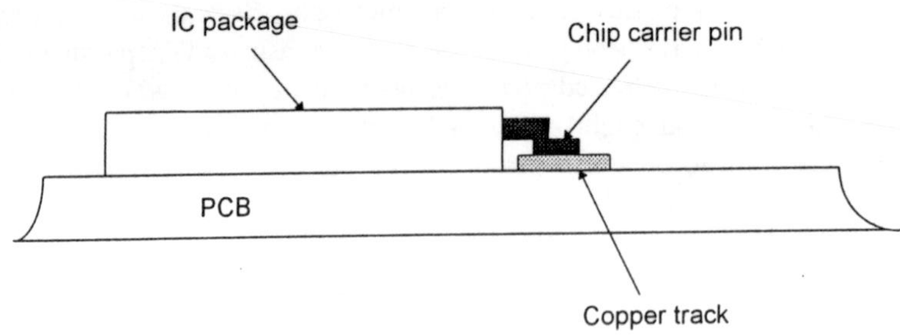

Figure 1.8(b) Chip carrier package (cross section)

The disadvantages of surface mounts are that it is more difficult to place components accurately due to smaller pin spacing. Machine placement is essential, which is expensive, as hand soldering is too unreliable. These drawbacks make the method unsuitable for small production runs due to the expense. Solder faults are more difficult to avoid, due to smaller tolerances, the chip carrier pins are more liable to damage during assembly, due to the small pin dimensions, and large pin counts and pin probing for testing is no longer feasible, thus alternative testing methods have to be used, such as boundary scan.

There are also some indirect problems with surface mount technology. For example, the packing density of components is much higher, particularly if both sides of the PCB are used and heat dissipation may become a problem. However, modern components tend to generate less heat due to the use of CMOS and other power-saving methodologies which, coupled with methods of using the PCB substrate as a heat sink and the fixing of heat sinks directly to significant heat sources, reduce the problem to manageable levels.

For very large pin counts, typically those above 200 pins, the pin spacing is reduced even further to 0.020 inches, giving 50 pins per inch, which enables the size of the component to remain at a size of less than 1.4 inches on each side. Much higher pin counts may be required in the near future and pin spacing may be reduced even more. However, the limits of production technology are being reached and although the technology can be improved it may not be possible to obtain the pin densities along the edge of the component that will be required.

Alternative assembly technologies will be required and one which is becoming increasingly popular is solder bump. This is a combination of pin grid array and surface mount, with the pins replaced by solder bumps. This allows much larger 'pin' dimensions, making production much easier and in addition the devices are also self-aligning when soldered. For other types of surface mount the components are held in place during soldering, often by the solder paste. However, if there is misalignment during placement, which is easy with 0.020 inch pin spacing, the device is soldered incorrectly. It is possible to correct such soldering defects, but it would be better if they did not occur. With solder bump the surface tension of the melted solder is such that it 'pulls' the device until it is correctly aligned. Misalignment is much less of a problem, as the bump spacing is larger than for high density chip carriers; this, combined with the self-aligning mechanism, makes them easier to place correctly.

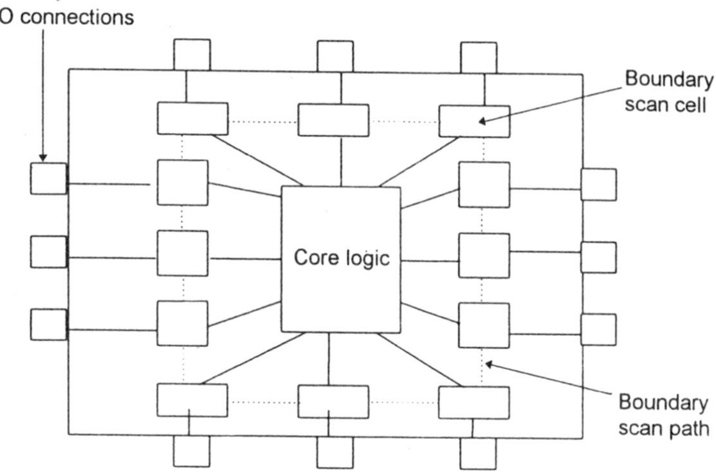

Figure 1.9 Device with boundary scan cells

The drawback of the solder bump connection method is that the majority of the connections are under the device package and cannot be physically accessed, as there are no through holes as there are with pin grid arrays. During testing of the assembled product it has been usual to make physical connections using probe pins to the product PCB tracks, so that each connection and signal can be tested. With pin spacings of 0.020 inches on chip carrier surface mount devices this has become increasingly difficult and with solder bumps it becomes physically impossible. The result is that new techniques of testing are being introduced, which do not depend on making physical contact with test points on the PCB, but use electronic means to test connections. The most popular at the moment is called boundary scan which is an IEEE standard. The components need to have boundary scan cells between the I/O pins and the internal core logic, as illustrated in figure 1.9. During normal operation the boundary scan cells are transparent and have no effect on device operation but, during testing, the cells isolate the logic core. The scan path is used to pass information and the results of tests into and out of the device, so that testing of the PCB becomes possible.

1.3.4 Environmental considerations

So far, only the functional operation of the devices has been considered, but there are a number of important environmental parameters that need to be understood in order to obtain the maximum operating reliability, humidity, reliability, inductance/capacitance and thermal characteristics.

1.3.5 Humidity

The humidity does not have an effect on the semiconductor itself but on the protective packaging material. The plastic package seals and protects the semiconductor from the environment, but its surface may contain microscopic cracks. If moisture enters these cracks due to high humidity, then when soldering takes place, typically machine soldering which immerses the components in molten solder, the sudden temperature rise causes the moisture to vaporise, creating a significant rise in pressure. If sufficient, this can crack open the packaging and cause the device to fail.

Typical recommendations are that the packages are dried for 24 hours at approximately 120°C before being inserted on to PCBs and soldered. As an alternative, the manufacturer can supply the devices already dried, in moisture-sealed bags containing a desiccant. The devices will keep for up to 12 months if the bags are not opened and the devices should be soldered within 48 hours of the bag being opened. Provided that these guidelines, or similar ones issued by the manufacturer, are followed, there should be no failures caused by humidity.

1.3.6 Reliability

Devices are produced for a variety of different types of product which have different reliabilities and operating conditions. Typical categories are:

1) commercial (temperature range 0°C to 70°C)
2) industrial (temperature range −40°C to 85°C)
3) military (temperature range −40°C to 100°C)

In addition, the components are tested for different reliability conditions, such as mechanical shock, thermal shock and burn-in.

Mechanical shock subjects the components to a variety of rapid acceleration and deceleration forces to identify components which have loose internal and external connections. These could be large, one-off forces, or a smaller but periodic force.

Thermal shock testing involves rapidly raising and lowering the external temperature, usually periodically, to identify if there are any weak points in the physical construction of the device which thermal shock will cause to fail.

Finally, burn-in is used to prematurely age the component by running it at higher than normal temperatures, typically 100°C, in order to induce weaknesses in the semiconductor structure to turn into identifiable faults. This is because it is known that at the beginning and end of a device's life cycle, the probability of a failure is higher, as illustrated in figure 1.10. Burning in enables those components which are going to fail in their youth, to be identified before they are shipped to customers.

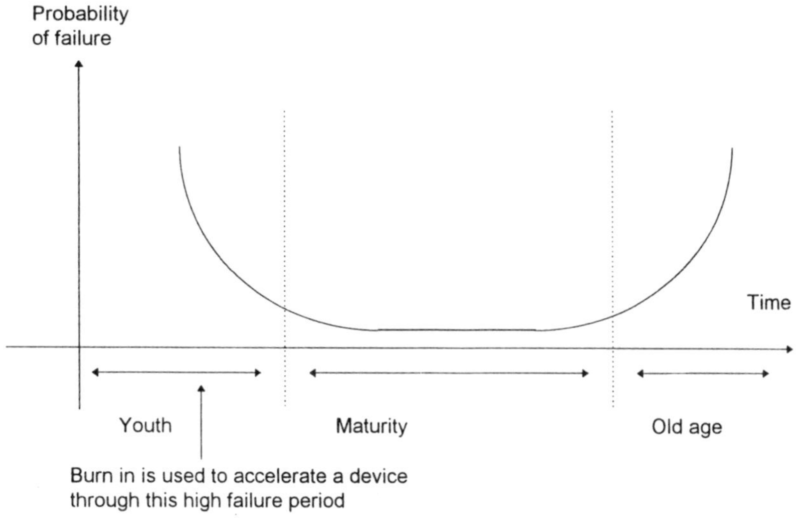

Figure 1.10 Failures against life cycle

In addition to the thermal shock tests and burn-in devices are also subjected to thermal cycling. This involves raising and lowering the environmental temperatures to the cool and hot extremes. The rate of change of the temperature is controlled to avoid the extremes of thermal shock.

1.3.7 Inductance and capacitance

Almost every electronic components exhibit some inductance and capacitance effects which have to be allowed for when designing high speed systems. At low frequencies the effects are negligible and can be ignored, but at high frequencies they contribute to limit the maximum frequency of operation.

Inductance is exhibited by almost every wire connection, including device pins, PCB tracks and internal bonding. The designer only really has control over the PCB layout and there are techniques for reducing inductance. For the device, it is the packaging which determines the inductance, so that DIL and PGA packages have a higher inductance than J lead surface mount and PLCC packages, due to the large size of the pins. The packaging does have some effect on capacitance, but the majority capacitance effect is due to the transistors themselves. The majority of programmable devices use nMOS and CMOS transistors to construct the circuit which have the gate connection separated from the drain and source by an insulating layer, effectively constructing a capacitor. These capacitors are called parasitic capacitors; they limit the operating frequency and have a typical value between 5 and 15 pF.

1.3.8 Thermal calculations

Once a system has been designed, it is necessary to perform some thermal calculations to determine whether the devices will remain below their maximum operating temperature, or whether additional cooling is required. In designs where additional cooling is not possible or desirable, it may be necessary to use low power versions so that the amount of heat to be dissipated is reduced. The calculation of the maximum power which can be dissipated is a simple one, determined by a number of quantities:

$\max T_A$ maximum ambient temperature (this is also the maximum operating air temperature allowed)

θ_{JA} thermal resistance (junction to ambient)

$\max T_J$ maximum allowable junction temperature.

If the temperature of a semiconductor *pn* junction becomes too high, the device ceases to operate correctly and may be destroyed. A safe value to use is approximately 65°C, although higher values up to 85°C can be used for some industrial specification devices. The maximum power which can be dissipated is calculated from

$$\max P = (\max T_J - \max T_A)/\theta_{JA}$$

For a device used in free air, a typical $\max T_A$ is 20°C, with 25°C being taken as a more conservative value. The thermal resistance is determined by the specific device and can be found from the data sheets. For a medium sized FPGA a typical value is 45°C/W

$$\max T_J = 65°\text{C}$$
$$\max T_A = 25°\text{C}$$
$$\theta_{JA} = 45°\text{C/W}$$

Therefore

$$\max P = (65 - 25)/45 \text{ W} = 0.89 \text{ W}$$

Power dissipated is the product of the voltage and the current required by the device. For most devices the voltage is 5.0 V.

$$\max P = VI$$

$$
\begin{aligned}
I &= \text{maxP/V} \\
&= 0.89/5.0 \text{ A} \\
&= 178 \text{ mA}
\end{aligned}
$$

Therefore, the maximum current allowed for an average FPGA in free air conditions is 178 mA. New versions of the standard FPGA architectures are being introduced which operate from 3.3 V supplies which would allow a maximum current of 270 mA.

1.3.9 Packaging materials

There are two main types of packaging material commonly used, moulded plastic and hermetic. Moulded plastic packaging is cheaper, but still provides good electrical and environmental properties and is suitable for use in most commercial products. The silicon chip is mounted on a copper frame to provide low inductance and impedance connections to the PCB. This is then enclosed in a non-conducting plastic moulded material. Moulded plastic devices can be surface mounted. The external leads are coated with solder for reliable solder connections and require no preparation before soldering. Hermetic devices use a silicon chip mounted on a ceramic base and a metal lid which is fitted to make a completely air-tight connection. The copper leads are brazed to the ceramic base and have improved inductance and impedance characteristics. The leads can be solder plated or gold plated for more reliable connections and require no preparation before soldering. The ceramic base provides improved heat dissipation, improved environmental and reliability characteristics, and is suitable for use in industrial as well as commercial products. When properly specified, ceramic devices may also be used in military applications.

1.4 The development environment

The process for the development of designs for programmable logic is outlined in figure 1.11 and consists of four basic steps:

1) the generation of the specification,
2) design entry,
3) design checking,
4) synthesis, simulation and verification.

which may need to be iterated in order to achieve a final product that works to the specification. The process of design, implementation and testing may well result in changes to the specification, if the specification was incorrect, incomplete or vague, although this should be avoided if possible as it leads to wasted design effort.

The generation of the specification is beyond the scope of this book, as it will usually be produced by the customer and it will be up to the designer to interpret it to produce the design solution.

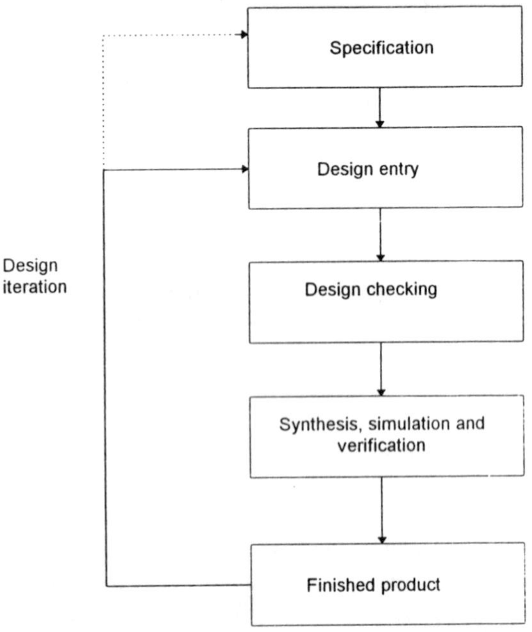

Figure 1.11 The design process

1.4.1 Design entry

There are four main design entry methods: three text-based methods, fuse, HDL and VHDL, and one pictorial, schematic. Some development environments allow two or more different design methods to be combined into a single design so that the most appropriate method can be used for different parts. There is also a hierarchy of complexity of the programmable devices used for the methods, as well as a historical trend, as illustrated in figure 1.12. When PALs first became available, there were few software tools available and it was necessary to edit fuse maps directly, which was a time-consuming and error-prone method. This approach was soon replaced when better software tools called Hardware Description Languages (HDL) became available which provided a more abstract and symbolic method of design entry. However, HDLs were manufacturer specific and limited in their capability and were not suitable for FPGA development. Schematic entry methods became the norm for FPGAs, but these suffered from the long design entry times and the difficulty of retargeting to different manufacturers. To overcome these problems, a manufacturer and device independent method called VHDL was developed. VHDL is a sophisticated and function rich design and simulation language. Although it can be used for the design of virtually any electronic system, it has become particularly popular with FPGA designers as it provides a quicker method of design entry which is not manufacturer specific. Any VHDL program produced in one development environment can be transferred virtually unchanged to another, and it can be retargeted to different FPGAs and different manufacturers FPGA with minimal effort.

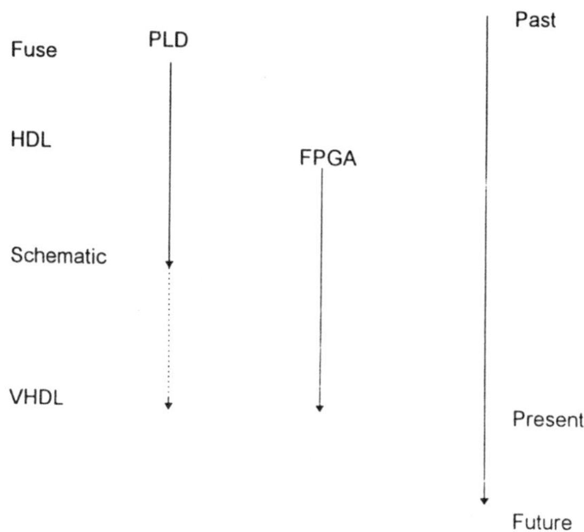

Figure 1.12 Design entry trends

VHDL does have some disadvantages in that the hardware implementation of apparently correct designs may not always produce the same results as the functional simulation. That is, the realised gate level performance is different from the functional simulation.

1.4.2 Fuse based design

Each PLD and FPGA has a specific number of programmable connection points which identify the particular logic function to be implemented. Ultimately, all design entry methods will result in a description of the fuses indicating which ones are to make connections and which ones are not. The description of the fuse maps were standardised when PALs and PLAs were first introduced by what is known as the JEDEC standard; this is a textual method of describing the number of programmable points in a PLD and whether they are to be programmed as conductive or non-conductive. This standard is described more fully in Chapter 8.

Knowing which fuse controls which logic function, and its position in the JEDEC map, allows specific designs to be generated. It is worth noting that for most PLD simulators the entry of the logic design into the simulator is through the JEDEC description and not the HDL program or the schematic. In addition, there are a number of software utilities available which will convert JEDEC descriptions back into HDL program descriptions. These are mainly designed to help convert old PAL and PLA designs into PLD or FPGA designs without having to redesign, resimulate and retest. This approach should no longer be used and is not recommended for new designs. However, a number of modern development environments do have the ability to incorporate old designs based on JEDEC files, and to combine multiple JEDEC designs into a single PLD or FPGA solution.

1.4.3 HDL design entry

Fuse map editing is a difficult design entry method and was soon superseded by the use of Hardware Description Languages (HDL). Early versions of HDLs were fairly primitive, being essentially programs to convert Boolean equations, which described the logic system to be implemented, into the correct fuse map. This was a considerable improvement and was a major contribution to the uptake of PLDs in new designs. These first HDLs also introduced some of the first functional simulators so that the logic could be tested before being programmed, since early PLDs were one-time-programmable. If the logic implemented was incorrect then the programmed device had to be thrown away.

The simulators were only functional and so did not contain any timing information. However, this information was not really necessary as the PLDs were completely deterministic and timing calculations could be performed independently of the logic implemented.

The HDL compilers were still proprietary and if devices from different manufacturers were used then different compilers had to be used. However, most PLDs had standard architectures, even from different manufacturers, so that if the architectures were the same it was usually possible to use different manufacturers' devices and still obtain satisfactory results. In addition, a number of general purpose compilers became available which were not tied to a specific manufacturers' devices, the most popular of which was PALASM (PAL Assembler) which is still in use and can be used as a design entry route for FPGAs. Gradually the programming languages became more abstract, so that behavioural descriptions of the logic designs could be implemented, as well as functional designs if necessary. The following program fragments illustrate the difference between behavioural and functional designs for a 4-bit counter.

```
count[0] = /count[0];
count[1] = count[1] % count[0];
count[2] = count[2] % (count[1] * count[0]);
count[3] = count[3] % (count[2] * count[1] * count[0]);
```

where / represents logical not operation, % represents logical exclusive or operation, and * represents logical and operation.

The behavioural version of this program is

```
count = count + 1;
```

where + represents arithmetic addition.

PLDs were becoming more complex and capable of implementing sophisticated logic functions and were no longer completely deterministic, so some timing information had to be included in the simulator. Also, as the HDLs became more sophisticated, it became much easier to develop logic designs which were almost independent of the target component, so that they could be implemented on a variety of PLDs with minimal changes to the programs. The complexity of the PLDs and the abstract level of the programming languages required optimised place and routing software, known as a 'fitter', the use of which is typically supplied by the PLD manufacturers as they have the detailed knowledge of the internal operation of the devices.

1.4.4 Schematic design entry

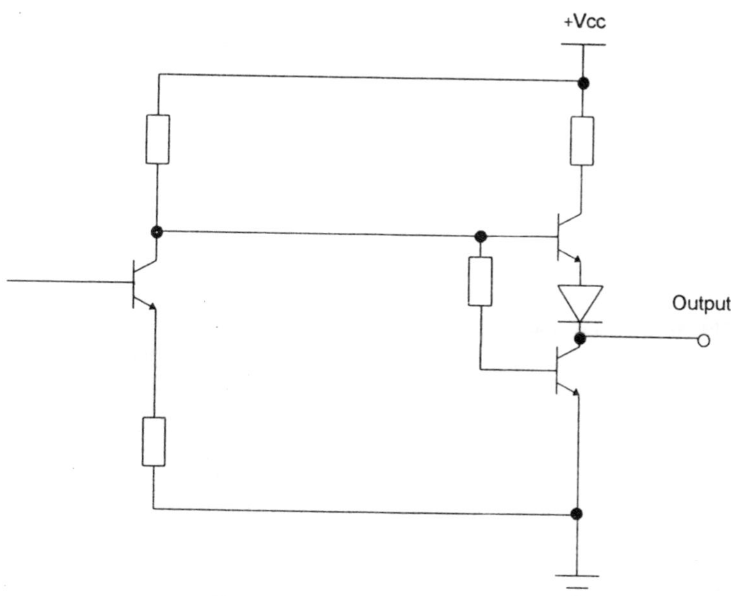

Figure 1.13 A simple schematic

As the PLDs became more complex and FPGAs were introduced, schematic entry tools were produced based on those used for the creation of ASICs, as the HDLs were limited in their ability to describe complex logic systems. In addition, logic system designers were more comfortable with the schematic entry method as it more closely corresponds to circuit diagrams based on standard components. Figure 1.13 illustrates a simple schematic for a logic system.

Schematics also have the advantage of allowing hierarchical structures so that top-down designs can be performed, simplifying the schematics in sub-systems, thereby assisting the design process.

The use of macros which are standard logic functions such as counters, flip-flops, multiplexers and so on, also makes the schematic design entry method powerful. Each FPGA manufacturer provides libraries of macros which when included will compile to fast and efficient gate level designs. This frees the designer from the need to work at a low level such as the gate level, so that a more productive higher level can be used.

1.4.5 VHDL design entry

The increasing sophistication, and the desire to design at a higher abstract level than that provided by schematic entry, led to the development of VHDL. VHDL is a high level HDL designed specifically to describe and simulate hardware systems and has become popular for large logic designs. It is an IEEE standard and is therefore manufacturer independent and allows for the easy reuse of modules of code and the retargeting of designs to different FPGAs and different manufacturers' FPGAs, although libraries specific to each FPGA to be used are still required.

VHDL provides two additional levels of design abstraction to those available for other HDLs:

HDL	**VHDL**
1) Functional;	3) Architectural;
2) Structural;	4) Behavioural.

Architectural design considers the operation of the entire system and is used to demonstrate that the algorithms being used are correct. Generally the implementation is not considered, so that high levels of abstraction are involved. This is then converted into a VHDL description, usually at the functional level rather than the behavioural. Behavioural descriptions may not be easily implementable as they are more abstract and not necessarily compatible with the target hardware and it may be necessary to convert by hand into a functional VHDL description.

1.4.6 Synthesis

Synthesis is the process by which the design entry is converted into a specific implementation at gate level. This involves placing the logic function into the macro cells or logic blocks of the particular FPGA being used and then routing all the interconnections. The particular design entry method used will determine exactly how it is implemented. There are two parts to synthesis, the placing of logic on to macro cells, followed by the routing of the connections between macro cells.

Most FPGAs have some form of macro cell structure which is capable of implementing a wide variety of logic functions. Once a logic function has been mapped to a macro cell, that macro cell is no longer available for use by any other logic functions, even if all of its capability has not been utilised. Therefore, the placing mechanism has to ensure that each required logic function is mapped to a suitable macro. A suitable macro is one where the maximum capability of the macro cell is utilised. This leaves the maximum amount of macro cells free for future mapping and implements the maximum amount of logic in the minimum amount of hardware. The most efficient mapping attempts to achieve the highest utilisation of an individual FPGA, as that produces the most cost effective solution. That is, use the smallest FPGA possible as this will be the cheapest device, requiring the minimum amount of PCB area and consuming the least amount of power.

Many FPGAs have two types of macro cells, the I/O macro cells and the hidden or buried macro cells. The I/O macro cells have a physical connection to an external pin on the FPGA package and therefore have an input/output capability. For small FPGAs it is common for there to be only I/O macro cells and there is no need for the mapping algorithm to distinguish between macro cells, that is, all macro cells are equal. For larger FPGAs it is common to have more macro cells than I/O pins, so that some macro cells do not have a physical connection to an I/O pin and are called hidden macro cells.

Due to the mismatch between a standard macro cell logic capability and the logic functions actually required, it is unusual to obtain designs which utilise more than 75% of the total resources available. It is also dependent on the design entry method used. Gate level entry is the most efficient, with schematic entry a close second. At present, VHDL is the least efficient due to its general purpose nature which results in inefficient logic implementations. However, as VHDL is becoming more widespread, the implementations are becoming more efficient.

A second feature which has an effect on the maximum utilisation is the routing. FPGAs have a number of macro cells available and an amount of interconnection possible, that is, the routing. However, it is not usually sufficient to allow each macro cell to be connected to every other macro cell, as would be required to guarantee interconnection once placement has taken place. Therefore, placement also has to take into account the interconnection of the logic function placed into a macro cell, with the other logic functions in the design. The ideal would be to place logic functions which are interconnected on to adjacent macro cells. This is not always possible if the logic functions have a large amount of interconnections and some macro cells may have a limited interconnection ability, such as I/O macro cells, as they are placed at the edge of the component, see figure 1.14. One final consideration which affects place and routing is the propagation delay of the interconnections. Although it is not a linear relationship, it can be considered that the longer the interconnect, the longer the propagation delay, so that if macro cells which have to be connected are too far apart, the propagation delays introduced may mean that the system may not operate at the frequency required.

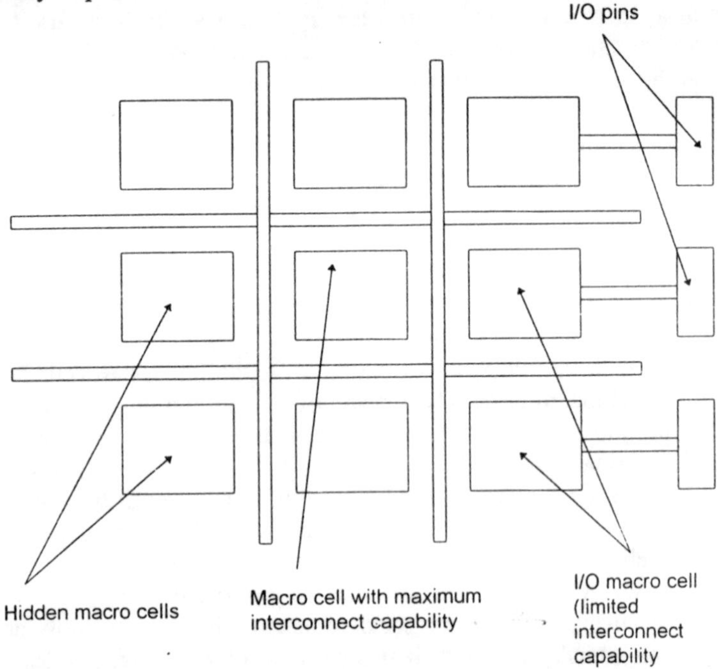

Figure 1.14 Interconnection resources for macro cells

The result of all these restrictions is that place and route is a difficult and time consuming process and there is a non-linear relationship between the time taken for place and route and the amount of FPGA resources used. There are three place and route methodologies:

1) automatic,
2) manual,
3) interactive.

Automatic place and route is preferred, as it frees the designer from the task, but the drawback is that the FPGA utilisation is lower, typically 50% to guarantee 100% place and route. If a high utilisation of FPGA resources is required, then manual place and route is still the preferred method but it is time consuming and requires skilled users. The alternative is to allow the automatic place and route to complete as much of the implementation as possible, usually somewhere around 85% to 90%, and then complete the remaining routing manually, using an interactive mode. Table 1.2 gives an approximate description of the timescales involved for an average design.

Table 1.2 Place and route timescales

Place and route method	Timescale	Utilisation
Automatic	2-3 hours	50%
Interactive	1 day	75%
Manual	1 week	95%

So far, only FPGA synthesis has been considered, as synthesis for PLD implementation is much more straightforward. Typically, a PLD will allow all inputs to be connected to all macro cells as they have a much simpler structure, and any feedbacks from the macro cell outputs can also be connected to any input. In addition, because of the simpler architecture, PLD timing is deterministic, that is, it is virtually independent of the place and routing of the logic. Timing calculations can be performed independently of the actual implementation. Complex PLDs are a little different, as there is some propagation delay involved with some of the routing, but this is usually easy to add to the place and route algorithms. However, for PLDs and cPLDs, the parameter which determines whether a logic design can be implemented in a particular device is the number of macro cells required. Routing is rarely a problem.

1.4.7 Simulation

To ensure that the logic design implemented performs the required functions, simulators are used to verify that the expected inputs produce the expected outputs, without the need to program the device. There are essentially two methods of simulation used, the functional and the gate level approaches. Functional simulation is concerned with the high level implementation VHDL or schematic and is used to verify that the logical operation of the design is as required. The simulation is performed by software which 'executes' the logic specification given and enables errors to be identified and rectified through an interactive process. Once the functional simulation process has verified that the design performs as required, then the design is synthesised for a particular programmable architecture, usually a specific manufacturer's FPGA. This converts the logic specification into a gate level equivalence with the necessary routing and interconnection connections. Due to inaccuracies in the synthesis process the gate level implementation may not produce exactly the same functionality of operation as the functional level so that further simulation is required. The differences between the functional and gate level simulations would not be expected to be large and, if they do exist, are likely to be due to timing differences caused by the place and route. Usually, the user will have to manually intervene at the gate level layout level to correct the timing differences. If it proves to difficult to correct these differences, usually because of a high gate utilisation which restricts the changes that can be made, then there are two options available, to use a larger FPGA and resynthesise, or to redesign the functional level program to induce an alternative synthesis using different logic.

The drawback of using a larger FPGA is usually the cost element, particularly if a different pin out device is used which will require changes to the PCB. This problem can be avoided by leaving the PCB design until after the gate level synthesis. However, in most designs this will not be possible, as FPGA design and PCB design proceed in parallel in order to reduce the time to market. Redesigning at a functional level means altering the original design which will require further functional simulation before resynthesising. There is no guarantee that this approach will be successful, as a good understanding of both the FPGA architecture and the synthesis process are required in order to be able to influence synthesis from the original functional design.

When the simulation process takes place, a mechanism for identifying input values with their expected outputs or results is required. This is achieved using test vectors which are used in two forms, discrete logic values and waveform entry.

If the timing for the programmable device being used is completely deterministic, then discrete values can be used as they are simpler to produce and the simulators are simpler and hence cheaper. Their drawback is that they do not provide a 100% accurate simulation and a design which appears to simulate correctly may not operate as required when implemented. Most PLDs and cPLDs use this type of simulator due to their deterministic timing. For combinational designs, where all outputs are explicitly defined by the instantaneous inputs, the sequence of multiple test vectors is not important. However, when a design is sequential and contains registers, which provide a form of system memory, the sequence of the test vectors can become very important as the outputs now become dependent on both the instantaneous inputs and previous input and output values.

When the synthesis of the design can affect the timing of signals an alternative form of test vectors are used, called waveform test vectors where the values of the inputs are continuously specified. The outputs are not specified, but simply displayed, so that the simulator cannot identify when an error has occurred. It is then up to the designer to interpret the waveforms and determine whether they are correct or not.

1.5 Case study: Selecting an FPGA development environment

One method of improving one's understanding of programmable logic is to work through a number of complete problem solutions, or case studies, to better appreciate how conflicting demands of the specification and product parameters can be optimised satisfactorily.

1.5.1 Introduction

In order to include the widest range of elements requiring consideration in the selection of a development environment for programmable logic, a university electronics department will be used in the case study. The university has a large electronics department teaching a wide range of undergraduate courses. Programmable logic has been introduced quite recently to fulfil two different perspectives. Final year lecturers have been interested in integrated circuit (IC) design and have been designing application specific ICs for some time in order to be able to produce physical designs cost effectively. First and second year lecturers have been looking at methods of shortening the time required by students to design and implement digital designs requiring tens of logic gates and a few registers. The present method effectively utilises SSI components and is felt to be no longer relevant to common industrial practice.

1.5.2 ASIC design

The ASIC design was previously based around a package called Silvar Lisco running on Apollo workstations. Owing to the cost of producing the final designs, up to four students had to share each layout, having a quarter of the available I/O pads and internal gates available for their use. In line with many other universities the mainframe has been replaced with networked workstations which, unfortunately for the electronics department, were standardised on SUN SPARC stations. This meant that the Apollos would no longer be centrally maintained or supported and would have to be replaced by SUNs at the end of their working life. This meant looking around for an alternative ASIC design package. In addition, the number of students choosing the ASIC design option has increased significantly and there was a desire by the lecturers to allow students to perform a complete design. This virtually eliminated the ASIC approach. The alternative was to look for some form of programmable gate array.

1.5.3 Logic design

Students entering the first and second year of the courses were being introduced to digital design but had only limited access to practical implementations,as these were laboratory based with limited opening hours and restricted access. The aim, therefore, was to provide easy access to some form of digital design which could be used by large numbers of students. The university has an extensive PC network and the obvious approach would be to have a PC based software system. Taking this approach would require the use of a simulator to check that the designs would operate as required. It would also be useful if the final designs could be easily implemented for testing in the laboratory. One final restriction was that whatever was chosen had to be extremely cheap, as over 100 students per year were expected to need whatever system was chosen.

1.5.4 The ECAD initiative and CHEST

One significant factor which made the selection process easier was the existence of two UK nationwide initiatives for universities. The first was the ECAD initiative, which aimed to encourage and promote the use of industry standard ASIC and FPGA design and verification tools within universities by negotiating directly with manufacturers to obtain favourable terms, typically only 10% of the normal prices, for educational establishments. The second initiative was CHEST which has a similar aim but which applies to almost every area of software products, not just digital design.

1.5.5 The initial choices

Because the two requirements were thought to be so diverse the decisions as to which systems to choose were taken independently. The low level digital design group of lecturers choose to use PLDs programmed using a language called PLPL (Programmable Logic for Programmable Logic), which has many similarities to C and Pascal programming, which the students were already familiar with. This was available under CHEST in the form of a site licence for a small fee. In addition, it supported the 22V10 PLD architecture which is a well known and flexible architecture, available from a wide range of manufacturers, on OTP (One Time Programmable) and reprogrammable versions. The 22V10s could also be programmed by virtually any programming device so that special programmers were not required. The components were relatively cheap as well as being reprogrammable, so the students could implement their own designs.

PLPL had a further advantage of being an abstract description of the logic functions required. The built-in minimiser enabled the students to concentrate on the problems to be solved, without becoming too involved in minimisation methodologies. For the high level designs, Mentor Graphics design entry was chosen which was a schematic entry methodology using logic blocks that students were already familiar with, such as flip-flops, adders, counters and so on. It was an industry standard which executed on SUN SPARC stations and was available under the ECAD initiative at approximately 10% of its usual price. It was also possible to target the implementation at different manufacturer's products such as Xilinx and Altera. The Xilinx family of FPGAs were chosen as the main implementation device, as their configuration information is stored in a standard EPROM which is automatically uploaded when power is first applied. This enabled a standard programmer to be used, thereby avoiding the cost of a dedicated programmer. In addition, the components could be reused, thereby reducing the running costs. Finally, as the university had a network of SUN machines, access to the software was increased.

1.5.6 The next step

Once the low level and high level systems had been implemented a natural convergence took place. The introduction of new PLD architecture and low end FPGAs made the choice of which design approach to take, more difficult. In addition, there was the desire that the low level designs should be convertible into a suitable format and transferred to the high level system. However, fundamental differences between the two methodologies made this difficult. One was an abstract program language description and the other used circuit schematics. The solution to this dilemma arrived in the shape of VHDL (Very high speed IC Hardware Description Language).

The language being used for PLD designs, PLPL, was a HDL (Hardware Description Language) but was specific to a particular manufacturer, so to start using VHDL was a natural and easy transition to make. However, the transition from schematic capture to VHDL was conceptually more difficult. The advantage of VHDL is that it is an IEEE standard language and is independent of any manufacturer. Within a short period of time two VHDL compilers were available; WARP2 for PCs and Viewlogic which executes on SUN SPARC stations and can be integrated with the Mentor Graphics schematic capture and simulation environment already available. Students were then able to start in the first and second years of digital system design courses using VHDL on an easily accessible PC network and then transfer in the final year to the SUN network with the more powerful development and testing environment, being already familiar with the design methodology and the language.

1.5.7 Summary

In real life the process of deciding on a programmable logic development environment is never straightforward. The reasoning behind any original decision can quickly change due to the rapidly changing demands of the market place, coupled with the extremely rapid developments in the technology itself. Any system chosen could quite easily be superseded by a cheaper, faster and better one, even before the first system has been fully commissioned and integrated into a company's product development strategy. Development systems need to be in a constant state of review to ensure that the optimum development environment is available and this may require quite radical changes over a short period of time, which may well render existing equipment and methodologies redundant.

1.6 Problems

1. a) List the factors which can be used to differentiate PLDs from FPGAs. Why is this differentiation important?
   b) Using the factors you have outlined above, should complex PLDs be treated as PLDs or FPGAs?

2. The waveforms shown in figure 1.15 (a) were produced by applying the test vectors shown in figure 1.15 (b). Is the logic design correct? [It is not necessary to known what the logic design is.]

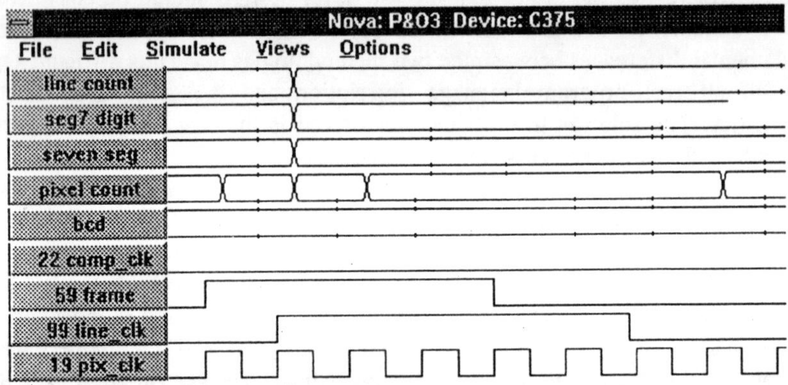

Figure 1.15(a) Simulation waveforms

```
NOVA Vectors produced: Sun Mar 17 00:27:11 1996
 *
N00000 000000000111111111122222222223333333333444444444455555555556666666666
N00001 123456789012345678901234567890123456789012345678901234567890123456789
N00002 ------------------------------------------------------------
V00001 NNNNNNNNNNNNNNNNNN1NN0NNNNNNNNNNNNNNNNNNNNNNNNNNNNNNNNNNNN0NNNNNNNNNN
V00002 NNNNNNNNNNNNNNNNNN1NN0NNNNNNNNNNNNNNNNNNNNNNNNNNNNNNNNNNNNUNNNNNNNNNN
V00003 NNNNNNNNNNNNNNNNNN1NN0NNNNNNNNNNNNNNNNNNNNNNNNNNNNNNNNNNNN1NNNNNNNNNN
*
```

Figure 1.15(b) Typical test vectors

3. An FPGA with a thermal resistance of θ_{jA} = 58°C/W has a 5.0 V supply and a maximum current requirement of 293 mA. The device is to be used in an enclosed product where the ambient temperature may rise to 35°C. Is a heat sink required? If so, which of the three available heat sinks listed below is the optimum and why?

Heat sink	Thermal resistance °C/W	Physical volume cm^3	Cost (£)
1	25	1.0	0.50
2	12	4.0	1.00
3	6	16.0	2.00

1.7 Further reading

Actel, *FPGA Data Book and Design Guide*, Actel Corporation, 955E, Arques Avenue, Sunnyvale, CA 94086.

Hands on FPGA design project (part 1), EDN 9th April 1992, pp 98-121.

Hands on FPGA project (part 2), EDN, 23rd April 1992, pp 120-152.

Xilinx, *The Programmable Logic Data Book*, 2100 Logic Drive, San Jose, CA 95124, USA.

York, T. A., 'Survey of Field Programmable Logic Devices', *Microprocessors and Microsystems*, vol 17, no. 7, 1993.

2 Programmable technologies

Before looking at the construction of the programmable elements, some of the basic sub-components which are used to construct them, such as conductors, diodes and transistors will be considered. All these sub-components are constructed using similar methods and processes which have been described in chapter 1. Following this, the programmable technologies themselves will be considered, along with how they are structured; finally, the chapter will close with a case study which examines some of the important parameters used in selecting programmable logic for a specific problem.

2.1 Creating passive circuit components

A number of what can be regarded as passive components are required by most ICs at some point. There are four main passive component types: conductors, resistors, capacitors and inductors. At present, it is quite difficult to obtain semiconductor inductances of useful values and if inductance is required, it is normal to use alternative approaches to achieve the same effect. Fortunately, inductance is not a requirement for programmable logic, so it is unnecessary to consider those techniques here.

2.1.1 Conductors

Although interconnections are in general evaporated on to the surface, it is necessary in some instances to have cross-overs. In such cases additional conductors have to be fabricated. This is achieved by oxidisation, photo-etching and n-type diffusion which creates a conductor in the silicon surface layer itself, followed by the usual evaporation of the aluminium conductors to produce a cross-over.

2.1.2 Diffused resistors

A resistor can be produced in a similar fashion to a conductor, being essentially only a variation on a conductor. The initial n-type epitaxial deposition and isolating diffusion is followed by a p-type diffusion of the actual resistor profile, followed by the evaporation of contacts to enable it to be connected to the rest of the circuit. These stages can all be accomplished at the same time as other devices are being fabricated. The resistance R of a resistor is given by the formula:

$$R = pl/A$$

where:

p is the resistivity of the semiconductor
l is the length of the resistor, and
A is the cross-sectional area.

This equation can be simplified by making the width equal to the length so that the equation becomes:

$$R = p/d$$

where d is the depth of the diffused layer.

Hence for a given value of d, the resistance R of a square of material is independent of the length of the sides. This allows the resistance to be quoted in ohms per square. This is common in ICs, with typical values of 100 to 200 ohms per square obtained with diffusion depths of 2.5E-6 m. The design of resistors in ICs is then based on the idea of a square or a number of squares. By putting 10 such squares in a line, a resistance of 1000 to 2000 ohms is obtained. In practice a compromise is reached between the area that the resistors occupy and the accuracy of the photo-engraving process used, which limits resistance to a maximum value of approximately 25 kΩ.

2.1.3 Thin film resistors

The disadvantages of diffused resistors are their limited value, high temperature coefficient of resistivity, susceptibility to radiation and the fact that they cannot be adjusted individually. These disadvantages can be overcome by using thin-film resistors. Thin film resistors are produced by depositing nichrome or tantalum on the silicon dioxide. The advantage of tantalum is that it is a single element and not an alloy so that there is no danger of composition changes during fabrication. The method of deposition for thin film can be plating, evaporation or sputtering with the latter being the easiest to manufacturer due to it being performed at a lower temperature.

2.1.4 Diffused capacitors

A capacitor is formed from the inherent capacitance of a p-n junction and as with diffused resistors there is a higher limit on the value of capacitance that can be achieved. The construction process follows the same process as for diodes, which is described later, except that the impurity gradient and hence the value of the capacitance can be increased by using a buried n layer. An area of approximately 0.6 mm^2 corresponds to about 2.5 pF and capacitances of 1000 pF can be achieved, although it is more normal to limit the value to 300-400 pF.

2.1.5 Metal oxide capacitors

Junction capacitors have a relatively low parallel resistance which will restrict their use in many instances. A more suitable alternative is the metal oxide capacitor which is formed by using silicon dioxide as the dielectric between the semiconductor and an aluminium layer. The parallel resistance of this type of capacitor is approximately 10 times that of a junction capacitor and, in addition, better tolerances can be obtained.

2.2 Active circuit components

As well as the passive circuit components described above, ICs also contain active components, with most ICs having many more active components than passive ones.

2.2.1 Diodes

The simplest active component is the diode, which is a single p-n junction that essentially operates to let current flow easily in one direction, but not in the other; they are effectively unidirectional. Although diodes consist of only two materials, a p-type and a n-type, they have to be constructed with three layers in order to obtain the isolation between devices. The structure of a diode is illustrated in figure 2.1.

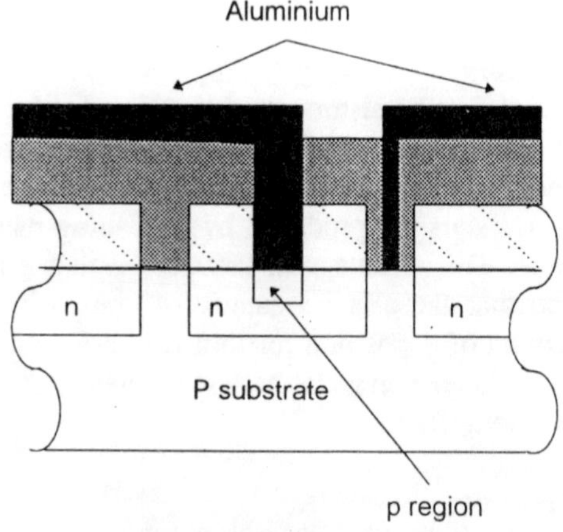

Figure 2.1 Structure of a diode

2.2.2 Transistors

Since a diode in an IC is a three layer device, it then intuitively follows that a transistor consisting of effectively two diodes back to back is constructed from four layers. The most popular type of transistor is the epitaxially grown one, although diffused collector and triple diffusion methods are also used.

2.2.3 Diffused collector transistor

Figure 2.2 illustrates the structure of a diffused collector transistor in an integrated circuit. After the oxidation of the substrate, windows are etched and n-type diffusions made. This is followed by the addition of the aluminium contact depositions to complete the device.

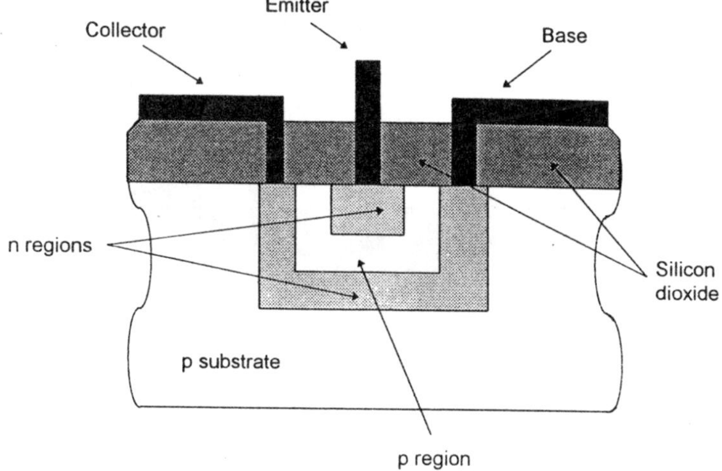

Figure 2.2 Complete diffused collector transistor

2.2.4 *Triple diffused transistors*

An alternative is the triple diffused transistor which is created by diffusing p-type into a n-type substrate from both sides of the dice slice. The lower layer is diffused evenly over the entire surface to form what is effectively a p-type substrate. A mask is used on the upper side to allow isolated n-type regions to be produced and the rest of the transistor is fabricated by additional diffusions of n and p-types as appropriate to obtain the complete transistor structure.

2.2.5 *Epitaxially grown and diffused transistor*

By growing an epitaxial n-type layer on a p-type substrate, the epitaxially grown transistor is created. The starting process has the substrate and the epitaxially grown n-type layer. Then the silicon oxide layer used for masking is added and the p-type regions and diffused to join up with the p-type substrate. A new layer of silicon dioxide is added and the p-type layer diffused into the n-type pocket. This is followed by another p-type layer to form the p-n-p sandwich required and finally the metallisation.

2.2.6 *Field effect transistors*

The construction of junction FETs follows much the same pattern as for junction bipolar transistors. For a p channel device the stages in construction are the growth of an n-type epitaxial layer, followed by a p-type insulating diffused layer, followed by a p-type channel diffusion, followed by a final n-type gate diffusion and evaporation deposition of aluminium contacts. A complete device is illustrated in figure 2.3. An insulated gate FET with an n channel enhancement is obtained by diffusion of an n-type drain and source into a p-type substrate, followed by the oxidation and evaporation and evaporation deposition of the aluminium gate electrode contacts, and source and drain contacts. This sequence of processes results in a transistor with the cross-sectional layout illustrated in figure 2.4.

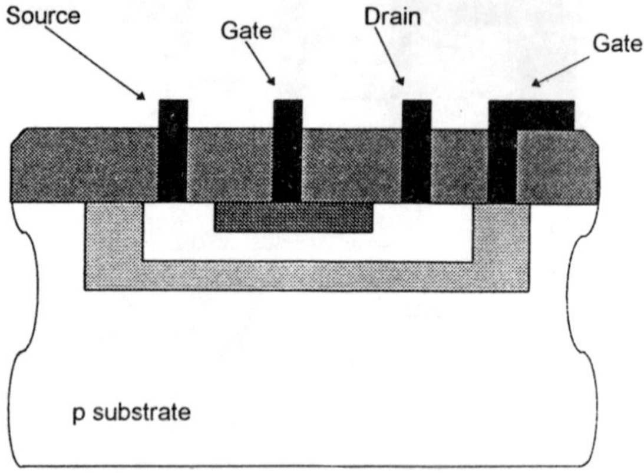

Figure 2.3 The Field Effect Transistor

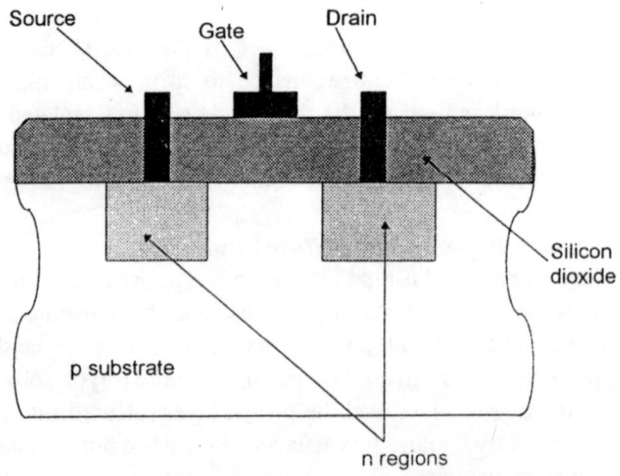

Figure 2.4 The insulated gate Field Effect Transistor

2.2.7 Bipolar and metal oxide semiconductor (MOS) technologies

Throughout the years, a number of different technologies have been adopted in the production processes used to make integrated circuits, particularly those based on silicon. Figure 2.5 shows a selection of silicon processes used in the fabrication of integrated circuits. The major division is based on the type of transistor, MOS or bipolar, used as the active element. The use of bipolar technologies has led to the creation of transistor-transistor logic (TTL), integrated injection logic (IIL or I^2L) and emitter coupled logic (ECL) families. For the metal oxide semiconductor (MOS) process there are two basic circuit types: n-channel MOS (nMOS) and complementary MOS (CMOS) where both p- and n-channel devices are used.

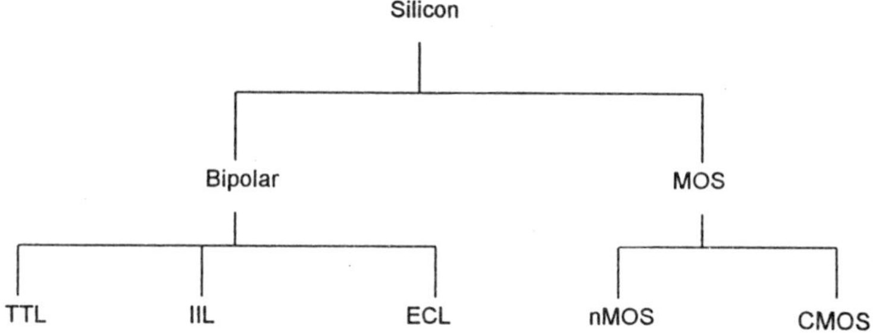

Figure 2.5 A hierarchy of silicon based IC production techniques

2.2.8 Bipolar technologies

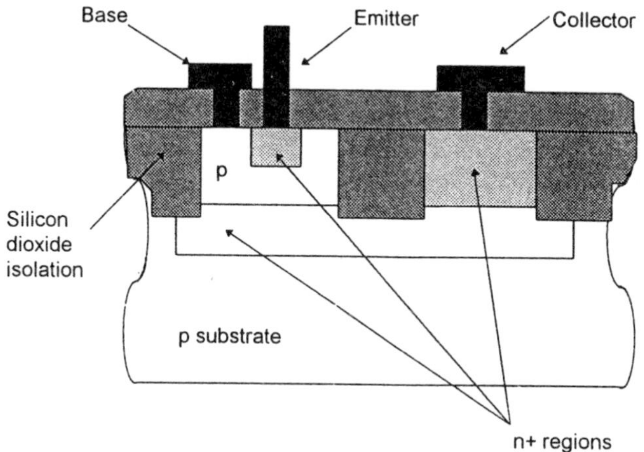

Figure 2.6 The integrated bipolar transistor structure

The integrated bipolar transistor is shown in figure 2.6. First, an oxide is grown on a p substrate and an opening made using the first mask for the diffusion of a buried n+ collector region. The buried layer has two functions; it isolates the transistor from the underlying p-region by the n+p-junction formed and gives a highly conducting path for the collector current. Following this, an epitaxial layer is grown and an Si_3N_4/SiO_2 composite film is deposited. This film is etched away, except for the areas where the base emitter and collector are to be formed. Part of the epitaxial layer in the unprotected areas is etched away and SiO_2 is regrown. It grows downwards to join the n+ buried layer, completing the isolation of the transistor, and upwards to give an approximately plane surface. A window is opened over the collector to diffuse an n+ contact down to the buried layer. Another opening is required for the implantation of the n+ emitter and the emitter region is implanted with phosphorous. The base contact mask is used to implant p+ ions in the base contact region. The base itself is the original epitaxial p-layer but, to make a low resistance contact, it is necessary to increase the p-type density in the region of the contact. Contact windows for the base, emitter and collector are grown using another mask, followed by the aluminium contact pattern using the final mask.

2.2.9 Transistor transistor logic (TTL)

A typical circuit for a TTL logic gate is shown in figure 2.7, where the totem pole output circuit of the gate results in active pull-up and active pull-down and reduced rise and fall times of the output voltages. The propagation delay for such a circuit is in the range of 15-20 ns. The circuit is available in different forms such as low power and high speed. One special form of the TTL circuit is the three-state or tri-state TTL output in which the output can take one of three states; logical 1 (usually a high voltage), logical 0 (usually a low voltage) or open circuit, sometimes called high impedance.

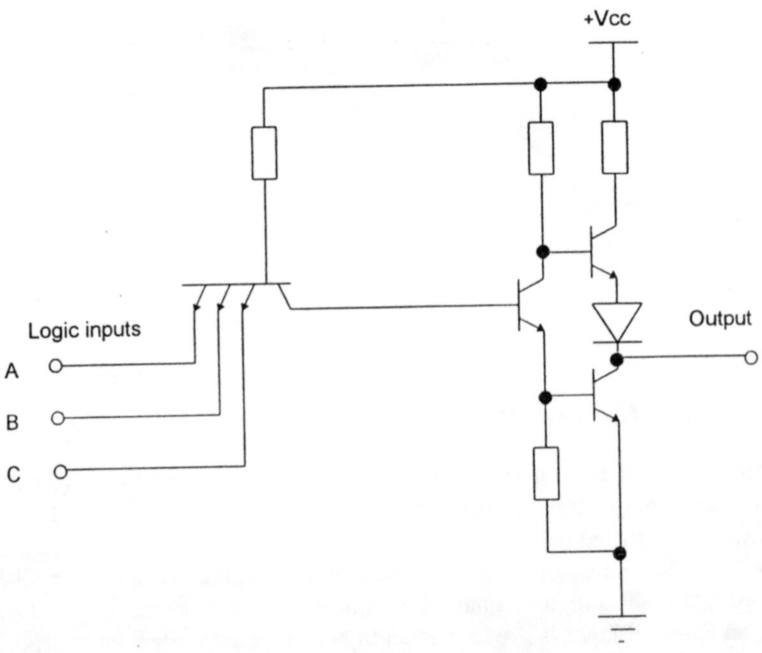

Figure 2.7 3 input TTL NAND gate

2.2.10 *Integrated injection logic (IIL)*

The basic diffused transistor is called a vertical transistor and the name indicates that charges injected into the emitter pass through the base which is directly below it, see figure 2.6. In order to integrate many devices on to a single chip it would be necessary to provide all transistors' connections on the surface. This leads to increased complexity as each transistor has to be isolated.

The so-called lateral transistor was developed with the expectation of low power consumption and high packing density. To increase the density of packing, the base region of each transistor has to be as narrow as possible. Additionally, the narrow base increases the speed of operation due to the shorter time required by the injected charge carriers. The advantages of IIL are high packing densities and low power consumption. The disadvantages are poor transistor efficiency and transistor saturation.

2.2.11 *Emitter coupled logic (ECL)*

The ECL circuit is used where fast devices are needed and the propagation delays are in the region of a few nanoseconds. The advantages of ECL are low propagation delays, the availability of complementary outputs and an implicit wired logic capability. The disadvantages are the high power consumption, the low packing densities and the logic voltage levels which are incompatible with other logic families.

2.2.12 *Metal oxide semiconductor (MOS)*

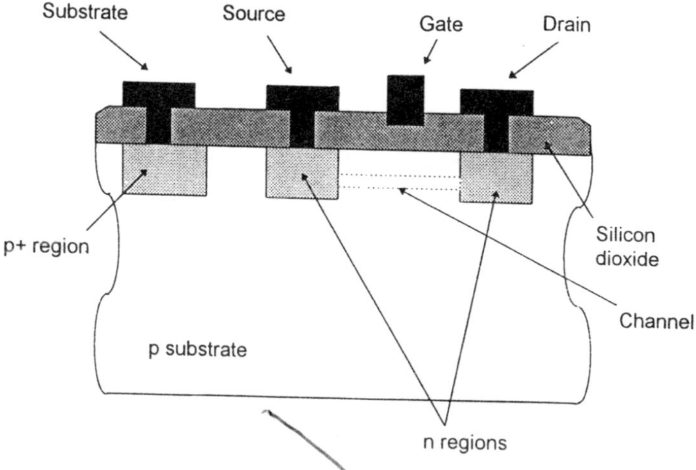

Figure 2.8 A MOS transistor structure

A simple form of the MOS transistor is shown in figure 2.8. Depending on the potential applied to the gate an n-type layer is induced in the channel region. It connects the two n-regions forming the source and drain. The resistance of the channel is controlled by the gate voltage. Alternatively, the channel region may exist in either an OFF state when the induced n-region is not present, or an ON state where a strong n-region is present. In these situations the device operates as a switch and may be used as a binary logic element. The whole of the conducting n-region (source – channel – drain) is surrounded by a p-region. The pn junction formed in this way acts as a barrier to the flow of electrons into the p-region. This effectively electrically isolates the element from any other components so that a separate isolation layer is not required.

For the correct operation of the MOS transistor, it is necessary that the channel extends between the source and the drain. Because of the alignment tolerance between masking levels it is possible that the edges of the gate region may not overlap the source or drain, unless a sufficient margin of error is allowed. This leads to the overlap being larger than ideally necessary and introduces parasitic capacitance to the junctions, which increases the transistor switching times and hence the propagation delay of the element as a whole. In order to avoid the disadvantages introduced by this problem, a silicon gate nMOS transistor was developed, which has the gate electrode formed from polycrystalline silicon. It can withstand high temperatures and is present during the source and drain diffusion. The sideways movement of the impurities at the gate edges ensures that the gate region always overlaps source and drain. At present the silicon gate n-channel process is the industry standard.

In digital circuits the switching transistor is either in an OFF or ZERO state, or an ON or ONE state. During the ON (conducting) state, the current results in heat dissipation and such dissipation can be significant, especially when the number of transistors is high. CMOS technology was developed to reduce this heat dissipation problem by utilising p- and n-channel MOS transistors. The p-type MOS transistor operates in a similar way to the nMOS except that it reverses the gate voltages. A positive voltage on an nMOS transistor turns it ON, whereas a positive voltage turns a pMOS transistor OFF. By using a pair of MOS transistors, one p and one n, a circuit can be constructed which does not consume any current when stable in either the ON or OFF state. Current is only consumed when the transistors are actually switching from one state to the other, with the net result being that average current consumption is virtually zero. Because of this, CMOS has low power dissipation and is used in low power applications.

The n-channel transistor has to have a p-type semiconductor under the gate which is formed by a localised ion implantation or diffusion. To ensure that all diodes formed between the source/drain and background material are reverse biased, the p-well is connected to the most negative potential, usually ground, and the n-type substrate to the most positive, usually called Vdd. To produce these transistors, several masks are necessary to define the areas where particular processes are to be conducted and this is the main disadvantage of CMOS technology, as there are more production processes than for nMOS and more silicon area is used because of the p-well.

2.2.13 3 V logic circuits

3 V logic systems can be considered to be 5 V logic systems used at 3 V. For standard logic this will result in a lower maximum frequency of operation, but it does lead to approximately 50% reduction in power consumption. By optimising the transistor design, higher maximum frequency of operation is possible due to the reduced voltage swings and a further reduction in power consumption to 25% of the 5 V versions. A drawback is that this type of logic is more susceptible to electrical interference and crosstalk making the design of the PCB a more demanding task. Increasing numbers of manufacturers of digital components are using 3 V logic and it seems to be the emergence of a new standard.

2.2.14 Silicon manufacturing alternatives

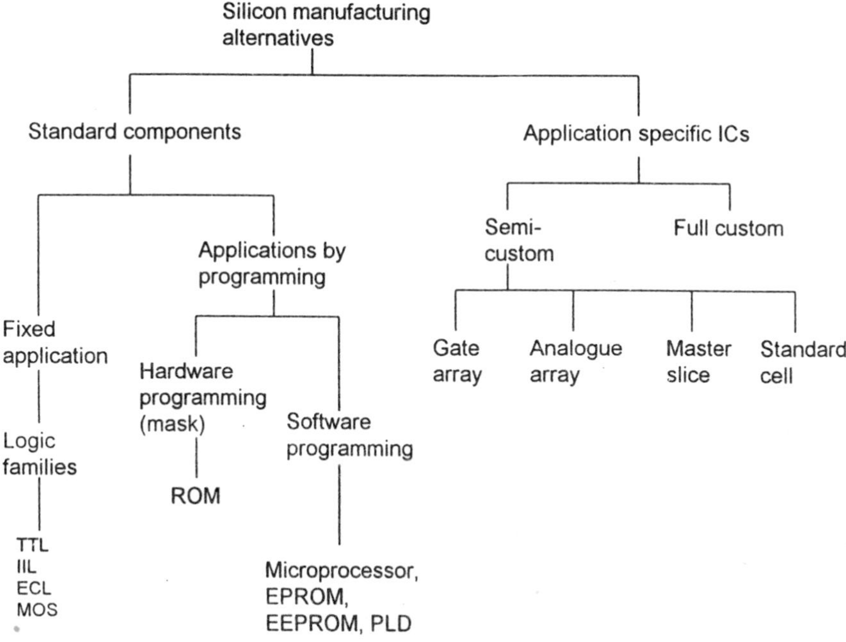

Figure 2.9 Silicon manufacturing alternatives

In the fast development of integrated circuits design it is possible to determine three noticeable trends in the fabrication of circuits; first, the use of standard components, second, the use of application specific integrated circuits (ASIC) and finally the use of standard components representing product lines for fixed applications, or for those circuits to be programmed during production processes. The ASICs are designed specifically to meet the requirements for a particular application. The diagram in figure 2.9 shows the main divisions and the types of design in each group. Full custom designs the circuits for particular functions down to transistor level and this also provides improved reliability and minimised silicon area. Custom designed circuits increase the cost of the development which becomes more suited for high volume production. Semi-custom design means that the active element inside the IC is partially designed and only needs to be connected in different ways to provide solutions to different designs.

There are four types of semicustom circuits which can be classified as follows:

Gate array	A chip that contains an unconnected pattern of gates. By specifying interconnections between the gates, the gate array can be customised to provide individual circuits.
Analogue array	A prefabricated IC that contains a range of analogue circuit elements, which are interconnected into an analogue circuit by a customised mask for metallisation.
Master slice	A combination of analogue and gate array. It is a prefabricated IC which allows the digital and analogue functions to be customised by masks.
Standard cell	Software is employed to define logic or analogue functions. There is no prefabrication and each designer extracts from the software library the circuit functions required, and composes them on to the silicon to form the required system.

2.3 Programmable circuit elements

A programmable logic device is a circuit which can be configured by the user to perform a logic function. Programmable logic devices (PLDs) may be considered as a compromise between the standard products and custom or semicustom circuits. PLDs offer a general structure which users can adapt to their own specification by inducing permanent or reversible physical changes in selected parts of the PLD. Most PLDs consist of an AND array followed by an OR array, with either, or both, having programmable inputs and/or outputs. Inputs are fed into the AND array which performs the desired AND functions and generates the 'product terms'. The product terms are then fed into the OR array. In the OR array, the outputs of the various product terms are combined to create the required outputs.

Programmable read only memory (PROM) devices are usually thought of as memory elements. However, the PROM can be thought of functionally as a fixed AND array (that is, the inputs to the AND array cannot be programmed), followed by a programmable OR array, see figure 2.10, with the inputs to the

AND array being the address inputs. Each different binary address combination is effectively the inputs to one AND gate, so that a 1 KByte PROM with 10 address line inputs is functionally 1024 × 10 input AND gates. The data outputs act as the OR gate outputs, so that the 1 KByte device has 8 data outputs, hence 8 OR gates, with each OR gate having 1024 inputs, one from each of the AND gates.

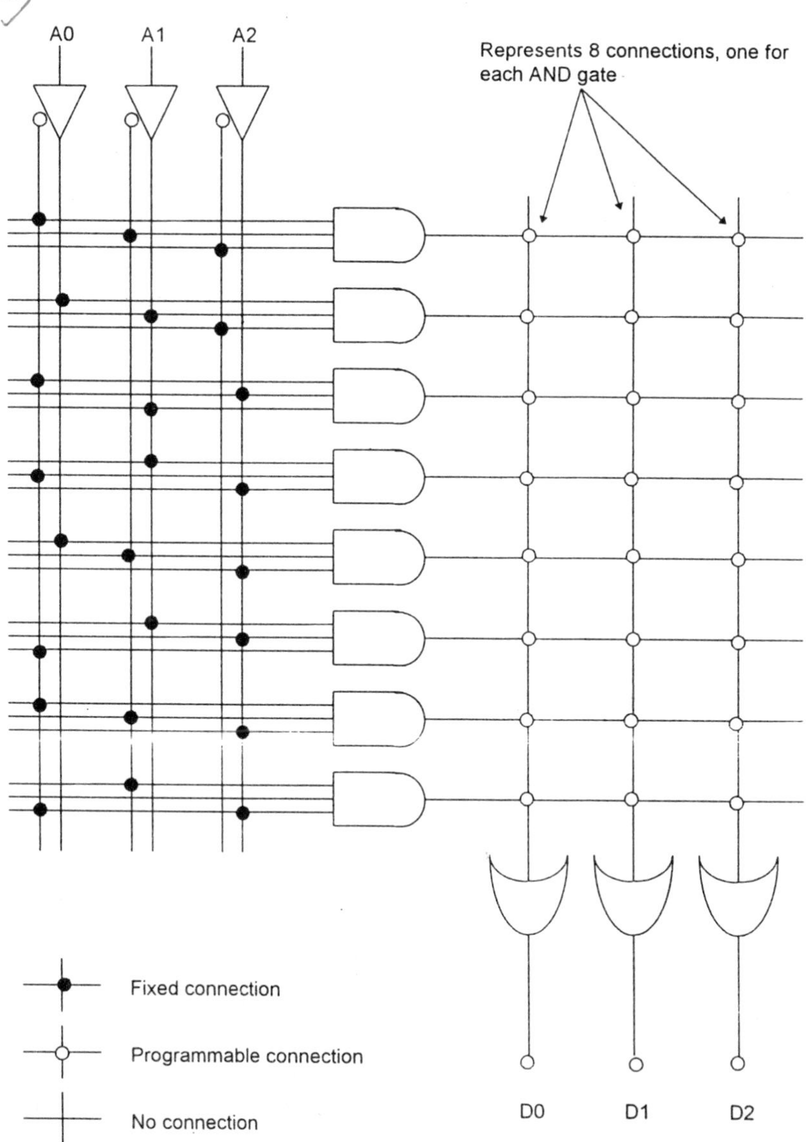

Figure 2.10 PROM functional logic structure

The large number of AND gates and OR gate inputs allows virtually any logic function to be implemented, but it does have the disadvantage that the outputs are not specially designed to remain constant when the inputs are changing, as PLDs are, so that the outputs can contain small 'glitches' (unwanted logic output values of a few nanoseconds duration) which can affect system operation. For each of a given set of input combinations (that is, addresses), it generates a value which has been programmed into the device. This type of memory is available with all its conductive elements intact. Each bit position in the memory consists of a transistor switch, bipolar or MOS, connected in series with a small fuse. The circuit diagram of one bit of a typical bipolar PROM is shown in figure 2.11. The major disadvantage of this type of programmable device is that it cannot be programmed more than once. The programming of information into PROMS may be performed either by the user or the manufacturer.

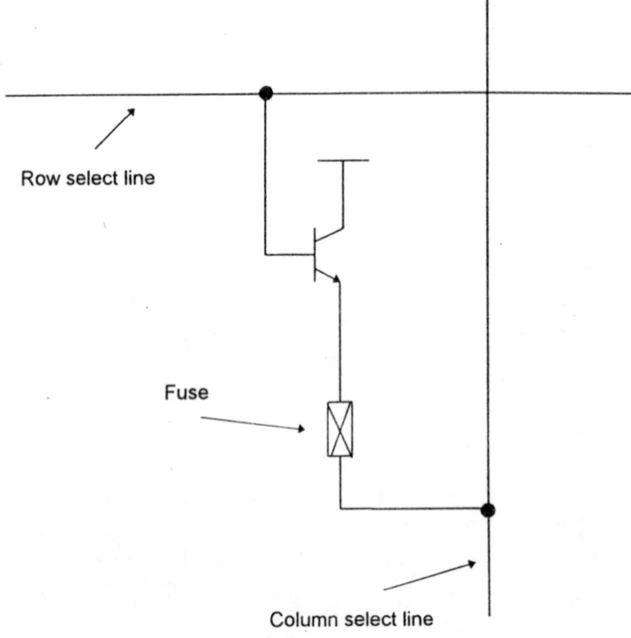

Figure 2.11 A typical bipolar PROM circuit

2.3.1 *Fuse*

The fuses themselves are made from nichrome (early types), titanium tungsten or polycrystalline silicon. The fuses break open when current flowing through exceeds a certain limit, as the fuses starts to heat up, reducing its resistance, which rapidly increases the current flow causing further rapid heating until the fuses is vaporised to form an open circuit. A transistor with a 'blown' fuse will represent one logic state, and a transistor with an intact, or unblown fuse, represents the other logic state, as Boolean logic systems only have two logic states, although output drivers sometimes include the tri-state form for interfacing purposes. The use of nichrome as the fuse element creates difficulties, as it deposits extremely thin films of nichrome over the surface of the IC chip as fuses are programmed. This occasionally leads to unreliable circuit operation. Finally, the blown fuses occasionally 'remake' after a period of time as the nichrome vaporises and recondenses to remake the link. To prevent the 'regrowth' of fuses, polycrystalline silicon fuses are used in place of the nichrome. With this type of fuse, a series of current pulses, increasing in energy, is passed through the fuse, melting the silicon until it forms an insulating silicon dioxide barrier which cannot grow back.

2.3.2 *Antifuse*

In a recent development, an antifuse has been introduced which has several advantages over the standard fuse. When a high voltage is applied across it, its resistance changes from high to low, providing a low resistance path between connection points. Effectively, when programmed the antifuse makes a connection and the fuse breaks a connection.

2.3.3 *(E)PROM*

An alternative to the PROM based on fuse technology, which is a non-reversible programming technology, is the use of a technique known as avalanche injection programming. Such devices are called Floating gate Avalanche injection MOS (FAMOS), and the structure of such a transistor is shown in figure 2.12. EPROMs are supplied by their manufacturer with all locations at the same logic level, 0 or 1, depending on their type. The logic level at any specified programming point may be changed by applying a programming potential (Vpp) via the appropriate read and select signals. The potential is applied between the drain and the source of the MOSFET switch and causes an avalanche breakdown of the drain. The result is the injection of high energy current carriers from the surface of the avalanche region into a floating gate. Since the gate is floating, a charge is accumulated which produces an inversion layer (n-type) at the substrate surface which holds the MOSFET switch in the ON state. Once the applied voltage is removed, no path exists for the floating charge on the gate to leak away and it is retained, typically for a duration of 10 years. Therefore, once the MOSFET switch has been programmed ON, it remains ON permanently. The big advance of the FAMOS device is that it can also be erased by exposure to ultraviolet light (UV) so that it can be reprogrammed with new data at a later time, hence the abbreviation, UVEPROM, Ultra-Violet Erasable Programmable Read Only Memory.

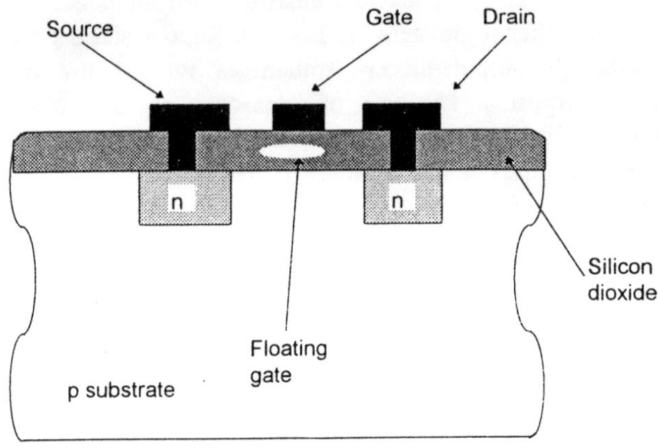

Figure 2.12 Typical structure of a FAMOS EPROM

The EPROM is erased by exposing the entire chip to UV light for a recommended period of time, typically 15-20 minutes at a distance of 2.5 cm from the UV tube. A quartz window is provided on each EPROM IC to enable the chip to be exposed. Some devices are constructed without the quartz window using a plastic encapsulation which is considerably cheaper. Obviously, such devices cannot be erased and are known as one-time programmable. The advantage that one-time programmable devices have over fuse programmable devices is that the EPROM technology is much more widely available and the components tend to be cheaper. Also, EPROM devices can be used during development work when reprogrammability is a necessity; then, when the product goes into production, the cheaper one-time programmable devices can be substituted with no other changes, even the same programmer can be used if necessary. The action of the UV light which is high energy light, is to transfer to the trapped electrons, sufficient energy to enable them to escape from the floating gate. Once all the electrons have escaped from the gate, the transistor will once again be in the OFF state, and can be reprogrammed as required.

The reason why the programming only lasts for approximately 10 years is that at any temperature above absolute zero, each electron trapped in the floating gate will eventually gain enough energy through thermally generated collisions so that it is able to escape. Once enough electrons have escaped from the gate, the transistor is no longer permanently ON. This effect is speeded up if the quartz window is left uncovered, as normal daylight and particularly sunlight contains a significant proportion of UV. Thus production use of EPROMS will always use one-time programmable devices which only have thermally generated leakage. Alternatively, the quartz window can be covered with an opaque label. During development, when the time between programming and erasure is limited, it is not necessary to keep the quartz window covered. Each programmable point in a FAMOS EPROM consists of a complete transistor, whereas the fuse and anti-fuse programming points consist only of the fuse, which is physically smaller. Because of this, fuse and antifuse devices have the advantage of a higher packing density, that is, more logic circuits per millimetre of silicon, whereas EPROMs have the advantage of being erasable and then reprogrammable.

2.3.4 *Electrically alterable ROM (EAROM)*

The threshold potential required to switch on a MOSFET is typically 3-4 V. This threshold can be reduced by replacing its silicon dioxide insulating layer with silicon nitride. This does have a side effect which is to produce different OFF to ON and ON to OFF thresholds, known as hysteresis. The hysteresis is caused by charges tunnelling from the substrate into the nitride layer and then being trapped there. This effect is utilised by the EAROM device as a method of storing data in a non-volatile manner. The silicon dioxide is made very thin, approximately 25 Angstroms (25E-10 m) so that normal gate potentials do not cause tunnelling to occur, hence there is no hysteresis effect. However, by increasing the gate potential to the order of −25 to −30 V, electrons are driven out of the silicon dioxide/nitride interface into the substrate material with the result that a positive charge is stored in the 'trap site' at the interface. Since the silicon dioxide and silicon nitride are good insulators, the trapped charges are retained for a long time. A trapped positive charge has the same effect as a positive gate basis on a MOSFET and holds the transistor in the OFF state. This positive charge must be overcome by externally applied negative gate signals, with the result that the switching threshold is raised to approximately −12 V. An EAROM device may be erased to produce a low threshold, making it easy to turn ON, by applying a positive potential to its gate, as this has the effect of attracting electrons from the substrate into the silicon dioxide/nitride interface to trap a negative charge there. This trapped negative charge has the same effect as a negative bias on the MOSFET to help the normal negative gate bias, with the result that the transistor is held in an ON state, with a switching threshold of approximately −2 V.

Information is stored in an EAROM in a similar manner to that for a PROM. The difference is that the trapped charges are induced by gate potentials and not by the avalanche effect. An EAROM may be selectively erased and reprogrammed, since all gates are electrically accessible via the address matrix decoding. The disadvantages of EAROMs are that they are more expensive, the packing density is not as high as for PROMs and the number of erasures is limited, at present to approximately 10,000 erase/program cycles.

2.3.5 *Electrically erasable PROM (EEPROM)*

The Electrically Erasable PROM has a similar structure to the UV EPROM and the devices are programmed using similar electrical pulses. The difference is that the programmed values can be erased electrically, so that both programming and erasing can be accomplished without disturbing the chips in the host system.

Erasing can be performed either as single bytes or as a block. In the block mode, the entire component has to be erased. The most important features of EEPROMs are the endurance and data retention capability. Currently produced EEPROMs are designed to be used in applications which can have up to 10,000 program/erase cycles during the life of the equipment, and data retention is specified to last for 10 years. As a quartz window is not required, a less expensive encapsulation can be used.

2.3.6 SRAM based

A number of semiconductor memories are designed using MOS technology. One of them is Random Access Memory (RAM) which allows access to each bit of information stored in the memory. In order to provide the access, the RAM is constructed in the form of a matrix with two sets of signals to select a particular memory cell, see figure 2.13. A memory cell is connected to the address lines arranged in an horizontal (row address) and vertical (column address) structure, which determines the address of the memory cell. A memory cell is selected when both the row and the column lines are activated.

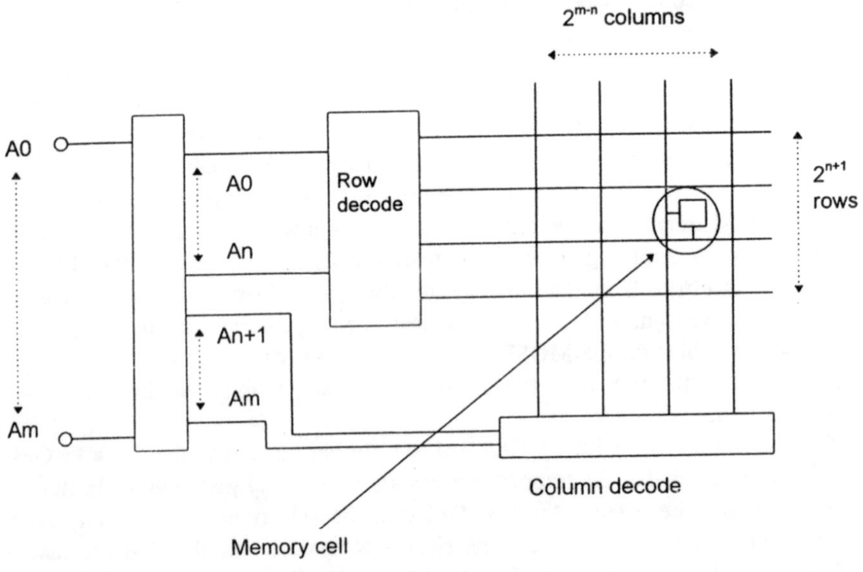

Figure 2.13 Organisation of a RAM matrix

Each memory cell consists of six nMOS transistors employed as a pair of cross-coupled invertors, called a flip-flop, two active transistors acting as pull-up resistors and two transistors that transmit logic signals to the memory cell. The construction and connections of such an nMOS memory cell are shown in figure 2.14.

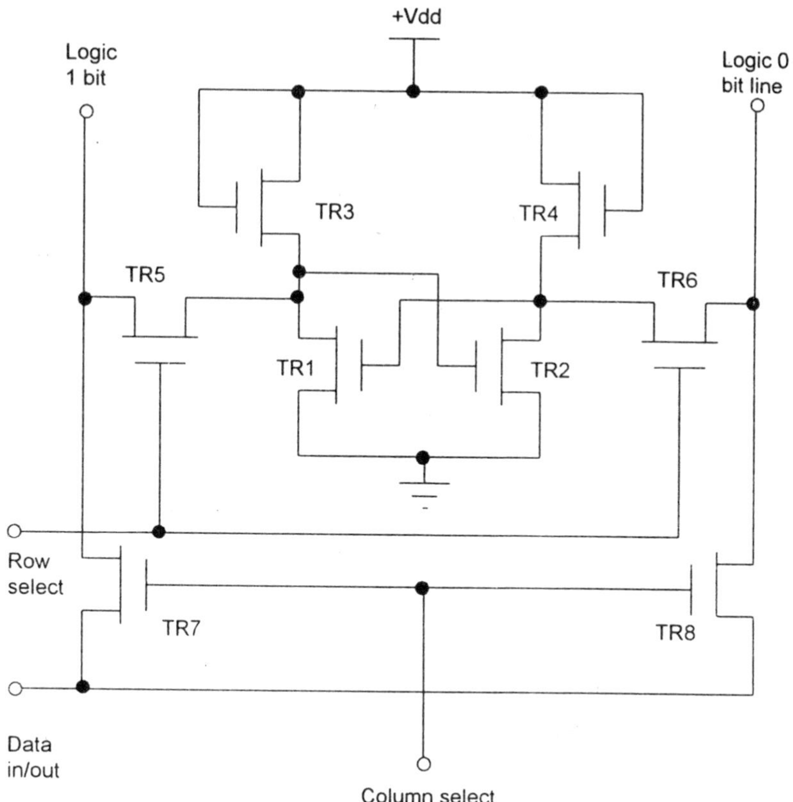

Figure 2.14 NMOS RAM cell

The 0-bit and 1-bit lines are connected to every cell in the same column. Transistors TR1 and TR2 are the cross-coupled switching transistors and transistors TR3 and TR4 are used as the active pull-up resistors. Transistors TR5, TR6, TR7 and TR8 are controlled by the row and column select signals. When a particular column is selected, transistors TR7 and TR8 are conducting and the selection of a particular row activates transistors TR5 and TR6. Only the memory cell at the intersection of the selected row and column is activated. If a logic 1 is applied to the DATA IN/OUT connection, a positive potential is applied to transistor TR2 gate through transistor TR5 and TR7. The positive potential enables TR2 to conduct, so that its drain potential is reduced to zero volts. This results in transistor TR1 becoming non-conducting and its drain voltage remains at $+V_{DD}$ (logic 1) after the input signal is removed. This process stores a logic 1 on the drain of transistor TR1 so that the memory cell is storing a logic 1.

The static CMOS RAM is similar in structure and operation to the nMOS RAM, Four transistors are used as cross-coupled CMOS invertors to create the flip-flop circuit. Further nMOS transistors provide the data path into and out of the memory cell. The memory cell stores data in the same way as the nMOS RAM cell. CMOS technology requires the implementation of both the p- and n-channel transistors so that more silicon area than for the nMOS RAM cell is required. However, the big advantage of the CMOS RAM cell is that it requires much less power, due to the fact that one of the transistors is always off.

2.3.7 Summary

In the early 1970s programmable devices based on the fusible link technology were all bipolar technology, were expensive, had low packing densities and consumed high levels of power generating large amounts of heat. Second generation devices were based on a variety of technologies, such as polysilicon fused technology, antifuse technology, erasable CMOS devices based on ultraviolet erasable and electrically erasable methods and static RAM. The most important advantage of erasable devices is that they can be fully tested before being delivered to the customer. Functions are programmed into each device and tested in an automatic tester. If the device is satisfactory, the contents are erased and it can be supplied to the customer as if new, but with the added guarantee that it has been tested and works correctly.

2.4 Introduction to JTAG

Most of the semiconductor technologies outlined previously rely on some form of special programmer to transfer the digital design into the programmable device. This is usually inconvenient and can require costly programmers. An alternative which is starting to gain in popularity is to use the JTAG port added to FPGAs for testing purposes, as a means of downloading the design in the programmable device via the serial port of a PC. This allows every user to have their own individual 'programmer' at very little additional cost. The JTAG port would have been added to the device and the PCB anyway, so using it for programming purposes is effectively cost free. At present, there is no standard for the use of the JTAG port for programming purposes and each manufacturer has their own approach; however, it is probable that before too long an extension to the JTAG standard will be proposed to incorporate it.

2.4.1 Description of JTAG

JTAG stands for Joint Test Action Group and is used to describe the IEEE Standard 1149.1-1990 for a serial test interface. This was amended with a 'Supplement A' in 1990. JTAG, or boundary scan to give it its proper name, was designed to provide a means of testing populated PCBs as an alternative to the use of bed of nails fixtures. As the name suggests, a bed of nails is a two-dimensional array of nail-like, spring-loaded electrical connectors which, when pressed on to a PCB, enable unpowered continuity tests and powered voltage tests to be made, to ensure that the board has been made correctly and is operating correctly.

A number of difficulties with bed of nails testing have arisen, due to new technologies which allow more components to be placed on to a PCB, with ICs having pins much closer together. This prevents the use of the bed of nails, as the nail connectors are too large to make direct connections to the IC pins. In addition, there is usually insufficient space to provide special test pads elsewhere on the PCB. Because of this, alternative technologies have been developed to overcome these problems and boundary scan is one of them.

2.4.2 Boundary scan

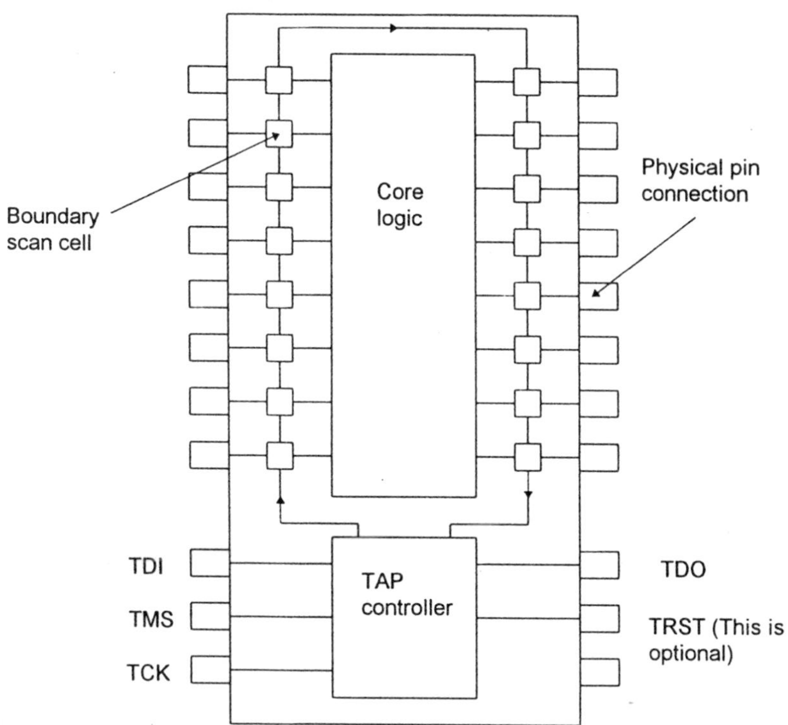

Figure 2.15 An IC with boundary scan cells

Boundary scan is a means of testing interconnection between powered digital ICs by isolating the internal function of the device from its physical pin connections, using boundary cells, see figure 2.15. All the boundary cells are connected in a serial chain to a boundary scan interface which defines how signals are passed into the serial array of boundary cells and how results are passed out. Boundary scan can be used to test individual ICs or complete populated PCBs. At present it can only be used on digital devices. Only relatively few devices contain the boundary cells, so the testing of complete boards is still limited. However, as new devices are designed they are likely to include the boundary scan interface and over the next few years the percentage of devices containing the boundary scan interface is likely to increase significantly. Once a reasonable percentage of the devices on a PCB contain boundary scan, it becomes possible not only to test individual components, but also to test for physical interconnection between them. Because the approach is based on a simple serial interface, the cost of bed of nail fixtures is avoided and changes can be made to PCB layout without needing to produce another test fixture. Testing is effectively performed using software.

The boundary scan interface defines:

1) input pins,
2) output pins,
3) logic control functions,
4) instructions.

The interface consists of a four-wire interface with an optional fifth wire, see table 2.1.

Table 2.1 The boundary scan connections

TCK (test clock)	Controls the state machine and data transfer operations.
TMS (Test Mode Select)	Selects the boundary scan test mode and controls the state machine.
TDI (Test Data Input)	Serial input data stream containing instructions and test data.
TDO (Test Data Output)	Serial output data stream containing instructions and data for daisy chained devices and/or the results of tests performed.
TRST (Test Reset) This signal is optional.	Can be used to reset the state machine to a known initial state. Technically, this signal is not required.

The boundary scan interface contains three important elements, the state machine, the instruction register and the data register. The synchronous finite state machine is the heart of boundary scan, controlling every action taken and is shown in figure 2.16. It may appear to be a complex design, but it only has to implement a limited number of operations. The difficult part, which is the generation and analysis of the test data, is performed off-line on a PC or other automatic test equipment (ATE). The state machine controls the registers which make up the JTAG interface and identifies whether the interface is in reset mode, receiving an instruction, receiving data or idle. The operation being performed is determined solely by the value of TMS (and the previous sequence of values of TMS) on the active edge of the clock signal, TCK. The four (or five) signals connected to the device constitute what is called the Test Access Port (TAP) which contains the state machine described above. The TAP controls the JTAG registers based on the current state of the state machine and the TMS value. Incoming data appears on TDI, passes through the TAP and exits on TDO.

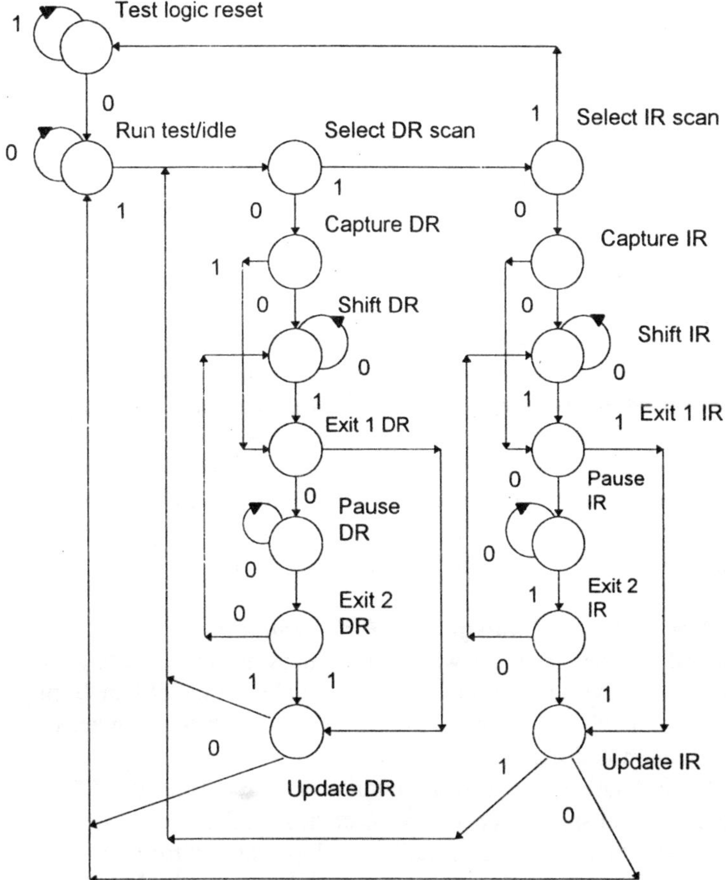

Figure 2.16 The boundary scan state machine

2.4.3 Reset mode

On power on the TAP is forced into the reset mode. Then clock pulses and TMS values are used to move from state to state. If part way through an operation a reset is required, a maximum of five successive 1's on TMS are necessary to return the TAP to the reset mode.

2.4.4 Instruction mode

The TAP contains an instruction register of a length selectable by the device manufacturer, provided that it can implement the minimum instruction set required.

2.4.5 Data mode

The data mode encompasses a variety of operations, some related to boundary scan functions, which are:

1) Boundary scan register,
2) IDCODE register,
3) USERCODE register,
4) Bypass register (1 bit).

The boundary scan register length is determined by the number of boundary scan cells, typically one per pin, excluding power pins. A boundary scan cell has the ability to disconnect the internal logic from the physical pin. They are all connected in series to allow test values to be shifted in to every pin and subsequent result values from every pin to be shifted out.

The IDCODE is manufacturer specific, containing a manufacturer's identifying code, a component code and any revisions to the component code. This can only be viewed by the user; it cannot be altered. The USERCODE register may be programmed to contain a user specified value which identifies the design implemented. The use of this register is optional. The final register is the bypass register, which is only one bit long. This is used to provide the shortest route from TDI to TDO when data values are being passed to further components in the scan path which contain the boundary scan interface.

2.4.6 Use of the JTAG interface by FPGA manufacturers

The boundary scan interface was developed as an aid to testing, but FPGA manufacturers have adapted it to provide a simple method of transferring a logic design from a PC to the device connected to the PCB. Each manufacturer's implementation is different and few details are available. The reasons for using the JTAG interface in this way are numerous: it avoids the need for expensive programmers and special adapters for each new component, it allows in-circuit programming, it provides a versatile development environment which avoids constant programming and erasing, it avoids damage to the FPGA due to static and handling damage to fragile pins, and it provides each designer with a complete programming and test environment. The technique operates by the designer downloading the JEDEC created as normal with the standard design software (compiler, simulator, and so on), using a simple cable connecting the PC printer port and the JTAG port on the PCB containing the FPGA. The design will then start to execute and can be tested as normal, using oscilloscopes and logic analysers.

2.5 The main producers

Programmable logic devices are manufactured under a variety of different names. These include:

PLA Programmable Logic Array
PAL Programmable Array Logic
PGA Programmable Gate Array
FPGA Field Programmable Gate Array
EPLD Erasable Programmable Logic Devices
PLS Programmable Logic Sequencers
FPAD Field Programmable Address Decoders
MAX Multiple Array Matrix
GAL Generic Array Logic.

At present, PLDs can contain a whole spectrum of logic gates equivalent from a few tens to 40,000 or more, which is still considerably less than ASICs which can contain 200,000 to 500,000 logic gate equivalents or more. Some of the devices are considered to be application oriented and may occasionally be referred to as Programmable Logic Device ASICs (PLDASIC).

Each vendor tends to concentrate on one particular technology, such as anti-fuse, or SRAM based, and produces a range of components which match what they perceive as the market need. Some of the main manufacturers of PLDs are:

Actel Semiconductor Corp.
Advanced Micro Devices Inc.
Altera Corporation
Atmel Corporation
Cypress Semiconductor
Excel Microelectronics Inc.
Gazelle Microcircuits Inc.
Gould Semiconductors Inc.
Harris Semiconductors
Intel Corporation
International CMOS Technology
Lattice Semiconductors
Monolithic Memories Inc.
National Semiconductors/Fairchild
Panatech Semiconductors
Phillips/Signetics
PLX Technology
Samsung Semiconductor Inc.
Seeq Semiconductors Ltd
Seiko Semiconductors Ltd
SGS Thompson
Sprague Solid State
Texas Instruments Inc.
VLSI Technology Inc.
Wafer Scale Integration Inc.
Xilinx Incorporated.

2.6 Problems

1. Using the circuit diagram shown in figure 2.7 for a 3 input NAND TTL gate, design all the masks required for the production processes. State any assumptions that you make. [Hint: Use graph paper to help with the mask designs, so that they will overlay correctly.]

2.
(a) Explain the meaning of the following terms:
(i) JTAG port; (ii) TAP controller; (iii) Boundary scan cell.

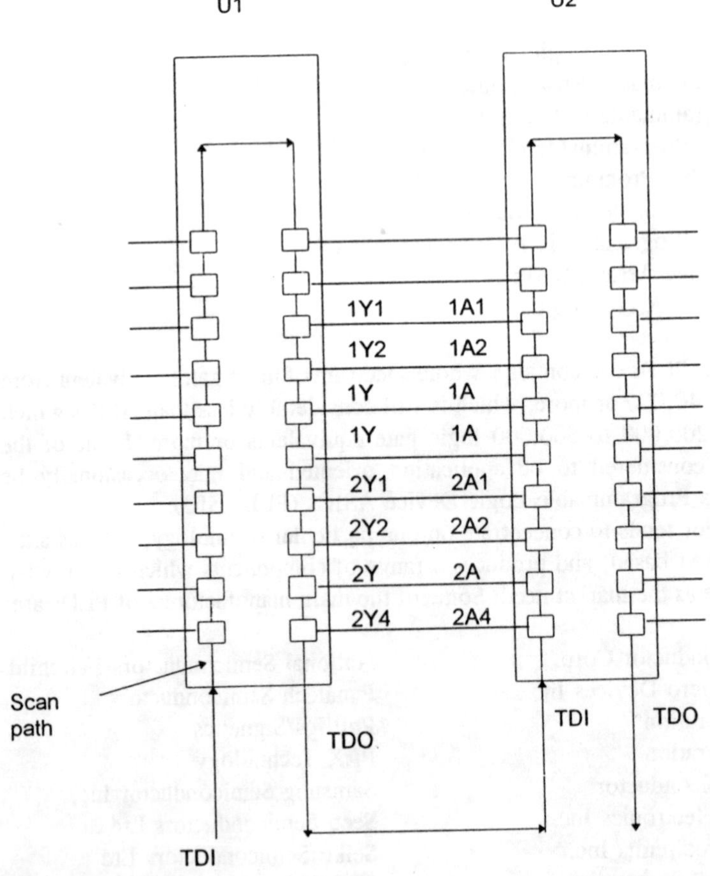

Figure 2.17 Circuit containing boundary scan devices

(b) The JTAG state machine for the TAP controller is shown in figure 2.16.

(i) Explain the two main functions performed by the JTAG state machine,
(ii) Given the TMS stream 1111111010000011111, what action is performed?

(c) The two components shown in figure 2.17 contain boundary scan ports. What TDI sequences are required to test the physical connections between pins 1Y1, 1Y2, 1Y3, 1Y4, 2Y1, 2Y2, 2Y3, 2Y4 on device U1 and the corresponding pins 1A1, 1A2, 1A3, 1A4, 2A1, 2A2, 2A3, and 2A4 on device U2. Explain how you arrived at the TDI sequences and predict the expected TDO sequences. The instructions available are shown in table 2.2.

Table 2.2 JTAG instructions available

Bypass	11111111
Sample/preload	10000010
Extest	00000000

2.7 Further reading

Bernella, G.,'A new generation of programmable logic devices (PLD)', *Electronica Oggi*, Iss 44, pp 65-69, July 1992.

Burskey, D., 'In-system programmable logic keeps delays short', *Electronic Design*, Vol 39, Iss 12, pp 137-141, June 1991.

Greiger, R., Allen P. and Strader, N., *VLSI Design Technology*, 1990, McGraw-Hill, NY.

IEEE Standard Test Access Port and Boundary Scan Architecture. IEEE Std 1149.1-1990.

Jagar, J., 'The development of programmable logic devices', *Electronic Entwicklung*, Vol 25 Iss 1-2, pp 8-11, Feb 1990.

Koumis, L.S., 'Optimised PLD architecture for high speed system design, Electro/90 conference record, pp 106-108, May 1990, Boston, USA.

Morgan, D.V. and Board, K., *An Introduction to Semiconductor Microtechnology*, 1995, John Wiley and Sons, Chichester.

Pucknell, D.A. and Eshraghian, K., *Basic VLSI Design Systems and Circuits*, 2nd edition, 1988, Prentice Hall, NJ.

Wong, R. and Gordon, K., 'Evaluating the reliability of the QuickLogic antifuse', *Electronic Engineering*, Vol 64, iss 786, pp 49-56, June 1992.

3 Programmable logic devices

3.1 The basic architecture

In the development of integrated circuits the programmable logic devices are positioned between the standard logic gates and custom or semi-custom designed circuits. All programmable logic devices have a similar architecture consisting of an array of AND gates and an array of OR gates as described in chapter 1. However, in order to enhance the performance of programmable logic devices, a number of additional features are added to the basic structure. The use of registers and feedback circuits in programmable logic devices enables them to be used in the designs of state machines and sequential logic circuits. Additionally, the inclusion of macrocells in programmable logic devices provides the opportunity to emulate the output structure of many existing devices. The internal configuration between the inputs and outputs create the different types of PLDs which will be described in this chapter. Generally, the programmable logic devices provide cost-effective solutions to digital problems as they replace a large number of combinational logic families.

3.1.1 Programmable logic devices

There is a wide range of programmable logic devices available which have different architectures designed to fulfil specific needs. These are described by the part number. The part number consists of three essential sections, with a preceding manufacturer code and a following technology and speed code. The three essential sections are the number of inputs, the internal architecture and the number of outputs. Therefore a typical part number might be:

DMPAL10H8-15

DMPAL	indicates that this is an AMD bipolar component
10	maximum number of inputs
H	high active high outputs
8	maximum number of outputs
−15	speed of operation (normally this would mean 150 ns)

Note: The device may not simultaneously allow the maximum number of outputs and the maximum number of inputs. Some signals can be programmed for input or output, but not both at the same time.

The standard part used for most examples is the 22V10 which has a flexible architecture that can be used to implement most PLD types. The 22V10 has a maximum of 22 inputs (in a 24 pin dual-in-line (DIL) package) and a maximum of 10 outputs. There are 11 dedicated input only connections, one input only or clock input and 10 input/output connections. The other two connections are power connections. The 10 input/output connections are usually programmed to be input only or output only, as required by the design. It is possible to have these connections perform input or output dynamically under the control of the logic design implemented in the component. However, this is complicated and is rarely done.

3.1.2 Registered

PLD architectures are further complicated by adding registers to the outputs of the OR gates; such devices are called registered PLDs which enable sequential designs to be implemented. With sequential devices the outputs are determined both by the instantaneous inputs and the past states of the inputs. Sequential systems effectively have some 'memory'. In addition, the outputs of registered PLDs have connections back to the input of the AND gates, see figure 1.1, which are called buried inputs. They cannot physically be accessed but provide a feedback path. The registers require the connection of a clock signal in order to make them operate and the outputs will now only change when the clock signal is applied. Between clock pulses the outputs remain constant even if the inputs change, as only the states of the inputs when the clock is present are important. Although a PLD may be registered, its outputs can still be used as combinational outputs, as the connections can be programmed so that the register is ignored and the output of the OR gate is connected directly to the output pin of the device.

The architecture has a considerable number of advantages: it is well known and understood, the design software is free or cheaply available, propagation delays are known and constant so that the timing relationship between the inputs and the outputs can be accurately predicted, and due to the large market, prices are kept low. Most PLDs have architectures which are some recognisable variation of this basic architecture.

The design software is used to develop and simulate the design, based on particular integrated circuits. Some software aids are produced by manufacturers to support their own devices; other software is designed to support all available programmable devices of different manufacturers. The software packages are of two types: assemblers or compilers. When an assembler type is used in design it is necessary to define the input/output pins and their logic equations. The compiler type requires only truth tables or a state diagram description.

The propagation delay is the time that is necessary for a change at the input of a signal path to produce a change at the output of the path. The total propagation delays of a design can be calculated from the manufacturers' data giving the time delay for each element of the circuit. The main limitations are that the fixed architecture can prevent the use of the most effective digital designs in some applications, the number of product terms is limited, the number of registers is limited and the number of inputs and outputs is limited. In order to overcome these limitations an alternative architecture can be used, called a complex PLD (cPLD) or an advanced PLD.

3.1.3 Macrocells

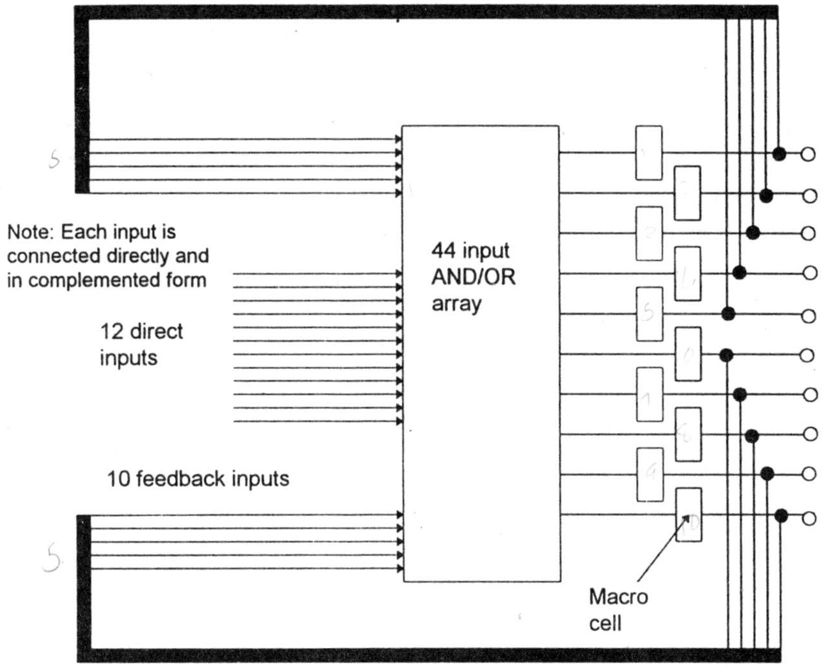

Figure 3.1 The 22V10 block architecture

A macrocell is a dedicated part of a programmable logic device placed between the AND-OR array and the output pin. The use of macrocells increases the flexibility of a device. It can be programmed to implement a variety of registered and non-registered output functions. The 22V10 device consists of a 44 input AND-OR array connected to 10 macro cells, as shown in figure 3.1. The macro cell is illustrated in figure 3.2 and consists of a D type register, a feedback selector, an output selector and an output buffer. The D type register has a single data input which is obtained from an associated OR gate output in the AND-OR array. Therefore, as there are 10 macro cells, the AND-OR array contains 10 OR gates. The D type register has a rising edge-triggered global clock signal which is synchronised with all the D type registers, which means that the Q output changes on the rising edge. The register has an asynchronous clear, enabling the output to be set to logic 0 at any time, independent of the clock signal. This is a global signal connected to all the registers. The synchronous preset is used to set the Q output to logic 1. This is also a global signal connected to all the registers but is only effective on the rising edge of the clock signal, that is, it is synchronised to the clock, and overrides any value on the D input. The feedback selector is a 2 input multiplexer, taking one input from the output of the D type register (the complement of Q) and the other input from the physical pin connection. A multiplexer (MUX) is a combinational circuit element that selects data from one of the possible inputs and directs it to a single output. The output from the feedback selector then provides both the true and complementary versions of the selected signal, which are connected back into the AND-OR array. The output selector has 4 inputs: the true and complementary versions of the related output of the OR gate in the AND-OR array and the true and complementary Q outputs of the D type register. The output of the output selector is passed through a non-inverting tri-state buffer to the physical pin connection. The control of each output buffer is asynchronous, that is, it is not related to the clock signal, is local so that it is independent of all other macro cell buffer, and is one output from the AND array. Because the output is only from the AND array and not from the AND-OR array, this signal consists only of a single product term, that is, it does not contain any Boolean OR operations. The use of the selectors enables the macro cell to implement registered active high outputs (with feedback), or registered active low outputs (with feedback), or combinational active high outputs (this can be bi-directional), or combinational active low outputs (this can be bi-directional), or combinational input or registered input. This provides considerable flexibility when implementing logic designs.

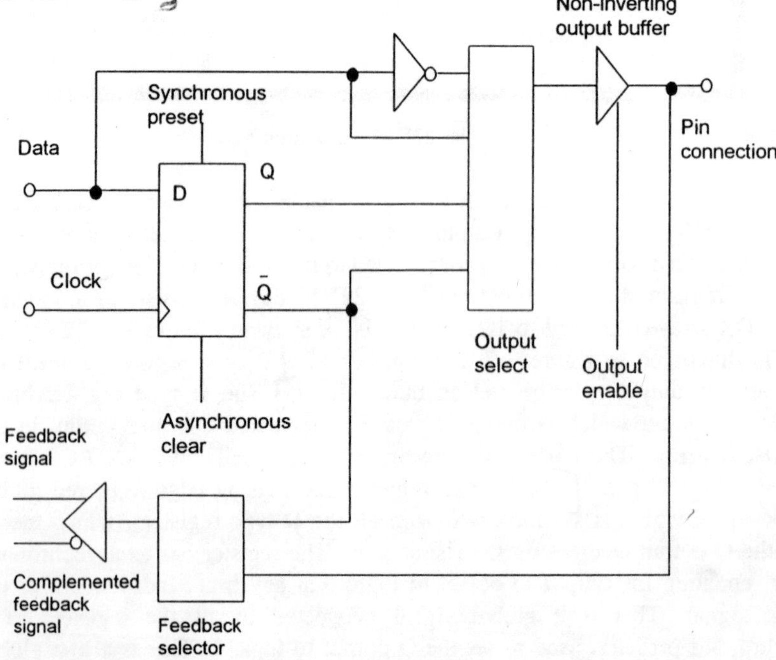

Figure 3.2 The macro cell

Each D input to the register is obtained from an OR gate output in the AND-OR array and enables multiple product terms to be used, that is, both AND and OR logic functions can be contained in a single Boolean equation. Note that exclusive OR Boolean equations are implemented using AND and OR primitives, as illustrated below:

A :+: B = /A*B + A * /B

where :+: represents the exclusive OR logic function. This results in exclusive OR equations being inefficiently implemented. This becomes a problem if high bit value counters are being implemented as it is most efficient to use exclusive OR functions in the equations, as illustrated below:

Q0 = Q0
Q1 = Q1:+:Q0
Q2 = Q2:+:(Q1*Q0)
Q3 = Q3:+:(Q2*Q1*Q0)

The macro cells are arranged in pairs with each pair having a different number of product terms, as illustrated in table 3.1. Alternative architectures are provided if efficient implementation of exclusive OR equations is required. Each product term is effectively implemented by a 44 input AND gate connected to an OR gate. Any input which is not specifically controlled in the equation for each OR gate output defaults to a logic 1, so that the operation of the AND gate is not affected. The distribution of product terms in this way enables the efficiency of utilisation to be maximised by implementing equations requiring only a few product terms on macro cells with the smaller product term availability.

Table 3.1 Product term distribution for 22V10

Macro cell pin numbers	Number of product terms
23 and 14	8
22 and 15	10
21 and 16	12
20 and 17	14
19 and 18	16

3.1.4 Complex programmable logic devices

The approach in the cPLD is to integrate several PLDs on to one piece of silicon connected together with global programmable connections, as illustrated in figure 1.2. This overcomes the first two limitations by enabling multi-layer AND-OR structures to be generated so that virtually any logic function can be generated, and by providing many more product terms inside one package. It also increases the number of registers available as well as the number of inputs and outputs, although some applications such as microprocessor bus systems will still require more. However, cPLDs have problems of their own; it is more difficult to design solutions, so the design software is more expensive, the routing between PLD blocks is highly variable between designs and the propagation delays cannot always be predicted until after the routing is completed, and there are still some limitations on the number of registers, inputs and outputs in some applications.

3.2 Development software

A wide variety of support tools are available for use in designing with programmable logic devices which simplify the design process. The design software consists of a high level language (HLL) used to describe the hardware functions to be implemented. A suitable compiler converts this text description into a format that can be used to program the PLD with the required logic functions. The aim of the compilers is to simplify the design process, which they achieve by enabling an abstract level of design to be used; that is, design as much as possible without any specific reference to the hardware that will be used, or to how the description will be converted into a PLD format. In addition, most PLD compilers include a simulator which enables the compiled design to be tested before programming the physical device, to ensure (as much as possible within the accuracy limitations of the simulator) that the required logic function has been implemented.

3.2.1 Hardware description languages

There are two basic types of language, those aimed at PLDs, which are called hardware description languages (HDL) and those aimed at gate arrays, which use VHDL. The main difference between the two types is the ability for VHDL to include timing information, which most HDLs do not: the introduction of hardware description languages (HDLs) as a design entry method greatly improved the use of PLDs in modern designs. Early versions of HDLs were essentially programs to convert Boolean equations, which described the logic system to be implemented, into the correct fuse map. These first HDLs also introduced some of the first functional simulators so that the logic could be tested before being programmed as early PLDs were one-time-programmable. If the logic implemented was incorrect then the programmed device had to be thrown away. The simulators were only functional and so did not contain any timing information. However, this information was not really necessary, as the

PLDs were completely deterministic and timing calculations could be performed independently of the logic implemented. The HDL compilers were still proprietary and if devices from different manufacturers were used then different compilers had to be used. However, most PLDs had standard architectures, even from different manufacturers, so if the architectures were the same it was usually possible to use different manufacturers' devices and still obtain satisfactory results. In addition, a number of general purpose compilers became available which were not tied to a specific manufacturers' devices, the most popular of which was PALASM (PAL assembler) which is still in use and can be used as a design entry route for FPGAs. A superset of the PALASM language called MACHXL is used for the PLD examples that appear in this book. Appendix A gives a brief overview of the language and chapter 6 illustrates a number of example designs. Gradually, the programming languages became more abstract, so that behavioural descriptions of the logic designs could be implemented as well as functional designs. Also, the PLDs were becoming more complex and capable of implementing sophisticated logic functions and were no longer completely deterministic so that some timing information had to be included in the simulator.

As the HDLs became more sophisticated, it became much easier to develop logic designs which were almost independent of the target component, so they could be implemented on a variety of PLDs with minimal changes to the programs. The complexity of the PLDs and the abstract level of the programming languages required optimised place and routing software, typically supplied by the PLD manufacturers as they have the detailed knowledge of the internal operation of the devices. Once a specification has been devised, it is necessary to select the device to be used. Sometimes this step may be left until later although it is common nowadays for the hardware and software designs to take place in parallel. This requires the specific device and the pin out to be defined as soon as possible in the design cycle. Selecting the optimum component can be difficult, as there is a desire to use the smallest and hence cheapest device, but there is always the possibility that the estimated size is too small and a larger device is required. It may be considered safer to select a larger device than predicted to ensure that the design can be fitted inside. There are a number of software tools available which are designed to make it easier to vary different parameters, such as power, speed, and so on, in order to determine what effect they might have on the size of component required. However, most of these are restricted to only select a particular manufacturer's components.

Having selected a device, it is then necessary to convert the specification into logic equations. This is where the majority of the design effort is required. There are four main types of logic entry for PLDs: Boolean equations, truth tables, state machines and hardware description languages. Not all PLD compilers implement all of these. If it is a simple combinational design, that is, a design where the outputs are always, explicitly and instantaneously defined by the inputs only, then it is usual to use Boolean equations or truth tables. If the design has feedback from the output to the input, contains registers, or is dependent on what may have happened in the past, that is, the circuit has a memory of some kind, then state machines may be of use.

3.2.2 Simulation

Once a design has been implemented, it is worthwhile attempting to verify that it will execute as required before actually programming the device. This avoids the cost of disposing of one-time programmable devices where the design was not correct, or the waste of time and effort involved in erasing reprogrammable components. This is achieved through the use of simulators. Simulators are software programs that emulate the operation of the selected device which, when programmed with the design to be implemented, replicate the operation of the physical device. Unfortunately, most of these simulators can never be 100% accurate due to the difficulties of simulating physical device operation down to the atomic level. However, most simulators will be 95-99% accurate and provide a great deal of confidence that the design will execute as required. The inputs and outputs to the simulated design are provided by test vectors which specify the outputs expected for a given set of inputs. For combinational designs, each set of inputs is completely independent of any other set of inputs, so the sequence of test vectors is not important. However, for designs which have a memory, then the sequence of test vectors also becomes important. The design of the test vectors used to verify correct operation can be almost as difficult as the design of the logic equations. It is important that the set of test vectors exercises the simulated design with all possible data combinations that the real device will encounter in order to have a high degree of confidence in the design. For some complex designs, this may be virtually impossible if a very long simulation period is to be avoided. Careful thought is required to minimise the number of test vectors to reduce simulation time as much as possible, but to ensure that all possible logic paths are tested.

3.2.3 Fitting the design into the PLD

The majority of software packages require the user to perform the allocation of signals (and hence equations) to pin numbers. This means that the user must be aware of the architecture of the PLD being used and any inherent restrictions. It also means that the languages being used to describe the logic system to be implemented, are not completely independent of the device used. This becomes a problem when designing without knowing the PLD to be used, or when a design for one PLD has to be converted to an alternative, perhaps more modern PLD. The preferred design language is one which is totally abstract, that is, completely independent of the PLD or any programmable device used to implement it. As the design languages are becoming increasingly abstract they require the use of a fitter. A fitter is a piece of software which takes the compiled abstract language description of the design, which will be in a standardised format, and attempts to allocate it to the programmable device selected. When using a fitter, the target device has to be specified, but if the device is changed, only the fitter has to be executed again. The compilation of the description in the abstract language remains unchanged.

Some programming languages for PLDs are starting to allow abstract designs, that is, a design not specific to a particular PLD or a design where the allocation of signals and hence logic equations to physical pins is not user specified. A fitter will then be used to allocate the signals to physical pin numbers in order to achieve the maximum utilisation of resources, typically product terms and macrocells. Even with the use of abstract design and fitters, product term utilisation of over 75% is very difficult to obtain. However, their advantage is that utilisation in the 50%-75% region is simplified, as the fitter performs the difficult task of manipulating the logic equations to make them fit the available resources. Sometimes, even with low utilisation, a design cannot be implemented on the selected PLD. This occurs when the number of product terms for any one equation exceeds those available on any one OR gate, or there are too many equations with large numbers of product terms in each of them. Some PLDs have a mechanism for what is called product term sharing, where unused product terms from adjacent OR gates can be transferred. This enables an OR gate to be constructed with more product terms than an initial inspection would suggest.

3.3 Programming

There are a variety of techniques for programming the design into the PLD: one-time programmable, reprogrammable and in-circuit programming. The technology involved in these techniques is described in earlier chapters. The essential difference between the three techniques is that one-time programmable technology enables denser integrated circuits to be constructed which are then cheaper and more reliable. Reprogrammable devices enable changes to be made to the design without the need to use new devices, but they do have a slightly reduced reliability which can lead to partial erasure after a long period. In-circuit programming avoids the need to maintain stocks of programmed devices for manufacture. In addition, the hardware can be manufactured before the design is completed and the same ready-made hardware can be used in a variety of different products by using different logic designs when programming. Increasingly, PLD manufacturers are moving towards the use of in-circuit programmed devices, for the reasons outlined previously, but also because it enables them to offer low cost development software which requires no expensive special programmer. All that is needed is a simple cable between a personal computer, usually the parallel port, and a standard 4 or 5 pin connection on the device or board being programmed. This process has been speeded up by the JTAG interface, which is a 4 or 5 pin connection used for in-circuit testing of densely packed PCBs that is also being used for in-circuit programming. Once the programmed device is installed in the product, there is a need to test the complete system; this is achieved by a system of tests designed to ensure that the specification has been completely and accurately implemented. The design of these tests and the equipment required is beyond the scope of this book.

3.4 Standardised file formats for programming PLDs

Each PLD and FPGA has a specific number of programmable connection points which identify the particular logic function to be implemented. Ultimately, all design entry methods will result in a description of the fuses indicating which ones are to make connections and which ones are not. The description of the fuse maps were standardised when PLDs were first introduced by what is known as the JEDEC standard.

3.4.1 JEDEC JC-42.1 Standard

This particular JEDEC standard describes how the fuse information for PLDs is saved in a format which can be sent to the programmer. The data is saved in files as mainly printable characters with the addition of four non-printing characters listed below:

02H Start of transmission <STX>
03H End of transmission <ETX>
0AH Line feed
0DH Carriage return

3.4.2 File structure

The file structure consists of a number of lines of text with the following structure:

1) <STX>
2) file header (any number of lines which are usually ignored by the programmer).
3) lines starting with * describe the fuse map data.
4) fuse checksum
5) [optional test vectors]
6) <ETX>
7) Transmission checksum

Note: All commands are terminated by the * character which must be on the same line as the command.

There are a number of commands which can be placed after the * character and these are listed below. Later versions of the JEDEC standard may use additional letters.

C fuse checksum
D Device type. This command is rarely used.
F Default fuse state. Not all fuses are explicitly defined in the JEDEC file, and this command gives the state of all undefined fuses:
  0 Low resistance link
  1 High resistance link
G Security fuse. Those PLDs which have a security bit to prevent unauthorised reading of the fuse configuration require this command.
  0 Disables programming of security fuse
  1 Enables programming of security fuse
L Link fuse data
P Pin order. Indicates the ordering of pins on the device to be programmed. When used in conjunction with the Q command, it identifies the maximum number of pins on the device.
Q Value.
V Test vector. When used in conjunction with the Q command, it indicates the number of test vectors. When used alone, it indicates a test vector to be applied to the device. Test vectors are optional in the JEDEC file and are only useful for programmers who also have a test facility. Some simulators may also take the test vector information from the JEDEC file. Test vector characters:

  C clock input (LOW-HIGH-LOW)
  K clock input (HIGH-LOW-HIGH)
  O low input
  I high input
  L expected low output
  H expected high output
  Z expected high impedance output
  X don't care: if input is undefined, if an output it is untested.
  P preload registers

A complete example of a JEDEC file containing a fuse map and test vectors is given below.

```
18      PLD [p22v10] Device Map for
        Design [and]*
QF5828*
QP24*
F0*
L0044 1111 1111 1111 1111 1111 1111 1111 1111 1111 1111 1111 *
L0088 1111 0111 0111 1111 1111 1111 1111 1111 1111 1111 1111 *
L5808 11 *
C0AE7*
QV4*
```

```
N Vectors from File [and] for PLD [p22v10]*
X0*
V0001 X00XXXXXXXXNXXXXXXXXXXXLN*
V0002 X01XXXXXXXXNXXXXXXXXXXXLN*
V0003 X10XXXXXXXXNXXXXXXXXXXXLN*
V0004 X11XXXXXXXXNXXXXXXXXXXXHN*
^C6000
```

3.4.3 Fuse checksum

As it is important to ensure that the fuse map data is not corrupted, a fuse checksum is used at the end of the fuse data which is guaranteed to identify single errors. It may not identify multiple errors as they could cancel each other out in the checksum. The checksum, which is a 16-bit hexadecimal value, is obtained by converting the binary fuse map pattern into 8-bit hexadecimal numbers and then adding them together. The fuse patterns are converted into hexadecimal numbers by taking the first bit of the first L command and treating that as the LSB of the 8-bit value and then counting another 7 bits to make up an 8-bit binary number. This is then easily converted to a hexadecimal value. If the result of the sum of these values is more than four hexadecimal digits, then only the least significant four digits are saved.

Example

Given the following fuse map pattern calculate the fuse check sum.

L0000	0001	0011	0000	0000
L0016	1101	1110	1111	0111

First convert to 8-bit binary, then to hexadecimal

1100	1000	=	0C8H
0000	0000	=	000H
0111	1011	=	07BH
1110	1111	=	0EFH
and add together		Total	0232H

3.4.4 Transmission checksum

As well as checking that the fuse map information is correct, a second checksum, the transmission checksum, is applied to the entire file to ensure that no other information has been corrupted. This is generated by adding together all the character ASCII hexadecimal values, including <STX> and <ETX>. This includes the other non-printing characters of line find and carriage return. Again, only the least significant four digits of the checksum are included. This is guaranteed to detect single errors in the file. If the checksum contains an error then an error signal will be generated even though there is no error in the data itself. The error occurs in the error checking. As errors rarely occur this is not usually a problem and only requires the file to be downloaded to the programmer again. New programmers should have been designed to operate with all previous versions of the JEDEC standard up to the date that the programmer was designed. Care should be taken when using a new software package with old programmers. The JEDEC format may include newer commands that the old programmer is not familiar with, which may then either be ignored or cause a file load error. Either way, something that was required to happen may not take place. However, this kind of incompatibility is rare. By knowing which fuse controls which logic function and its position in the JEDEC map, specific designs can be generated. It is worth noting that for most PLD simulators, the entry of the logic design into the simulator is through the JEDEC description and not the HDL program or the schematic.

3.4.5 Decompiling JEDEC files

There are a number of software utilities available which will convert JEDEC descriptions back into HDL program descriptions. These are mainly designed to help convert old designs into PLD or FPGA designs without having to redesign, resimulate and retest. This approach should no longer be used and is not recommended for new designs. However, a number of modern development environments do have the ability to incorporate old designs based on JEDEC files, and to combine multiple JEDEC designs into a single PLD or FPGA solution.

3.5 Designing test vectors

When a digital system has been designed using a hardware programming language such as MACHXL, it is best to simulate its operation before programming the real device. This helps to identify any faults in the design and to increase confidence that the design will execute as required. This is achieved through the use of test vectors which are essentially a description of the inputs to be applied and the expected outputs. There are two main types of logic design: combinational (that is, those which do not contain feedback or memory) and registered. The test vectors required for each type of design are different.

3.5.1 Test vectors for combinational designs

With combinational designs, the outputs are always the instantaneous combination of the inputs, as specified by the logic equations. Therefore, for a simple two input AND gate implemented by the MACHXL program shown below the test vectors are relatively easy to design.

```
;---------------------------------- Boolean Equation Segment ------
EQUATIONS

Z = A * B
```

All the possible input combinations are listed with the expected outputs, as illustrated below:

```
;---------------------------------- Boolean Equation Segment ------
EQUATIONS

Z = A * B

;---------------------------------- Simulation Segment ------------
SIMULATION

trace_on  A B Z

setf /A /B
setf /A  B
setf  A /B
setf  A  B

trace_off

;-----------------------------------------------------------------
```

However, for designs which contain larger numbers of inputs, the possible number of test vectors becomes large as it is the power of two of the number of inputs:

T_{max} maximum number of test vectors required for 100% testing.
N number of inputs to combinational logic design.

$$T_{max} = 2^N$$

For N = 6, this would require 64 test vectors, which is a considerable number, but for large numbers of inputs the number required becomes too large to be realistically implemented. For example, with 16 inputs, which is not uncommon, the maximum number of test vectors is 1 million!

3.5.2 Testing critical paths

Because of the difficulties of obtaining 100% testing, it is necessary to identify the critical paths or critical elements within a design and then ensure that they have a number of tests applied to obtain some confidence in the design. Usually, all possible boundary conditions plus a few random intermediate values are tested.

3.5.3 Boundary conditions

Boundary conditions for combinational designs are usually identified from the extremes of the binary inputs. For example, a 6 input AND gate could be considered to have the boundary conditions shown in table 3.1.

Table 3.1 Boundary conditions for a 6 input AND gate

Input A	Input B	Input C	Input D	Input E	Input F	Output Z
0	0	0	0	0	0	0
1	1	1	1	1	1	1

This would provide some testing and would identify that the output was not stuck at one logic value, either logic '0' or logic '1'. However, it does not identify all possible faults. For example, it may be that two of the inputs have been 'accidentally' stuck together and this type of error could be identified by what is called a walking logic 0, as illustrated in table 3.2.

Table 3.2 Walking logic zeros for a 6 input AND gate

Input A	Input B	Input C	Input D	Input E	Input F	Output Z
0	0	0	0	0	0	0
0	1	1	1	1	1	0
1	0	1	1	1	1	0
1	1	0	1	1	1	0
1	1	1	0	1	1	0
1	1	1	1	0	1	0
1	1	1	1	1	0	0
1	1	1	1	1	1	1

This would identify if any adjacent inputs are connected together, provided that the inputs were adjacent in the sequence:

A,B,C,D,E,F

If the sequence was altered which would not be unusual, as illustrated below:

A,D,F,B,E,C

then the walking logic zeros illustrated in table 3.2 will not uncover the fault. Therefore, the user has to ensure that the walking logic zeros pattern used matches the actual sequence of inputs.

3.5.4 Complex logic equations

For more complex logic equations, it is important to ensure that each product term is tested. For example, the equation given below contains three product terms, each of which should be tested separately, rather than just doing the boundary conditions testing on the number of inputs.

Z = A.B.C + /C.D + A./B.E

This equation has five inputs so that a comprehensive testing would require 32 test vectors. A more cost effective set of test vectors would test each product term in sequence, as illustrated in table 3.3.

Table 3.3 Testing A.B.C

Test vector	Input A	Input B	Input C	Input D	Input E	Output Z
1	0	0	0	0	0	0
2	1	1	1	0	0	1
3	0	1	1	0	0	0

By setting the D and E inputs to logic zero, the last two product terms have no effect on the output, so that only A, B and C have any effect on Z. Then test vector 1 checks the boundary condition when the inputs are logic 0, test vector 2 tests when the logic inputs are logic 1, and test vector 3 provides one non-boundary condition test. Then a further three test vectors would be required for the second product term, with three more for the final product term. These are illustrated in table 3.4.

Table 3.4 The optimum set of test vectors

Test vector	Input A	Input B	Input C	Input D	Input E	Output Z
1	0	0	0	0	0	0
2	1	1	1	0	0	1
3	0	1	1	0	0	0
4	0	0	1	0	0	0
5	0	0	0	1	0	1
6	0	0	0	0	0	0
8	0	1	0	0	0	0
8	1	0	0	0	1	1
9	1	1	0	0	1	0

Vectors 4, 5 and 6 provide the tests for the /C.D product term and vectors 7, 8 and 9 the tests for the A./B.C product term. This optimum set of test vectors is now only 9 long rather than 32, making a considerable saving on the generation of the test vectors and also on the simulation time. They do not provide 100% testing or 100% confidence, but they do provide a reasonable degree of testing with a high degree of confidence. For designs containing a larger number of inputs the savings in time and effort obtained can be considerable.

For designs containing a number of equations, such as those illustrated below, test vectors for each equation need to be generated.

X = A.B.C + C.D
Y = /A./C.F + /C.D + A./B.E
Z = A.B

When simulating, however, there are two approaches that can be taken, to use separate test vectors for each equation or to use combined test vectors.

3.5.5 Separate test vectors for multiple equation logic

If each equation is to be tested in isolation, then a test vector program has to be generated for each equation. The program listed below implements the three equations, but only tests X.

```
;------------------------------------- Boolean Equation Segment ------
EQUATIONS

 X = A*B*C + C*D
 Y = /A*/C*F + /C*D + A*/B*E
 Z = A * B

;------------------------------------- Simulation Segment ------------
SIMULATION

trace_on  A B C D  X

setf /A /B /C /D
setf  A  B  C /D
setf /A /B  C /D
setf /A /B  C  D
trace_off
;-------------------------------------------------------------------
```

Note that only four test vectors were required to test out the two product terms, as there is an overlap between the boundary conditions for the first and second product term for the all logic zeros boundary and random input conditions selected for each product term. Therefore, instead of requiring six test vectors, only four were needed. Similar programs would be required to test Y and another one for testing Z. These are listed below.

```
;------------------------------------- Boolean Equation Segment ------
EQUATIONS

 X = A*B*C + C*D
 Y = /A*/C*F + /C*D + A*/B*E
 Z = A * B

;------------------------------------- Simulation Segment ------------
SIMULATION

trace_on  A B C D E F  Y

setf  A /B  C /D /E /F ;First test /A*/C*F
setf /A /B /C /D /E  F
setf  A /B /C /D /E  F
setf /A /B  C /D /E /F ; Now test /C*D
setf /A /B /C  D /E /F
setf /A /B  C  D /E /F
setf /A  B /C /D /E /F ; Finally test A*/B*E
setf  A /B /C /D  E /F
setf  A  B /C /D /E /F
trace_off
;-------------------------------------------------------------------
```

For this particular example, all nine test vectors were required for the three product terms, as there was no overlap between them.

Program for testing Z

```
;--------------------------------- Boolean Equation Segment ------
EQUATIONS

 X = A*B*C + C*D
 Y = /A*/C*F + /C*D + A*/B*E
 Z = A * B

;--------------------------------- Simulation Segment -----------
SIMULATION

trace_on  A B  Z

setf /A /B
setf /A  B
setf  A /B
setf  A  B

trace_off
;--------------------------------------------------------------
```

When testing Z which only has two inputs and one product term, a comprehensive set of test vectors was used as there would be little saving in using a reduced set. It is also worth noting that only the inputs involved in the testing of Z need to be identified in the test vectors.

3.5.6 Combined test vectors

It is time consuming to create separate programs to test each equation and it can be difficult to keep all the various versions of the program up to date if changes are made. The preferred solution is to test all of the output equations simultaneously in one set of test vectors, as illustrated below.

```
;--------------------------------- Boolean Equation Segment ------
EQUATIONS

 X = A*B*C + C*D
 Y = /A*/C*F + /C*D + A*/B*E
 Z = A * B

;--------------------------------- Simulation Segment -----------
SIMULATION
```

```
trace_on  A B C D E F  X Y Z

setf /A /B /C /D /E /F
setf  A  B  C /D /E /F
setf /A  B /C /D /E /F
setf /A /B /C /D /E /F
setf /A /B  C  D /E /F
setf /A /B /C  D /E /F
setf  A  B  C /D /E /F
setf /A  B /C /D /E  F
setf /A  B  C /D /E  F
setf /A  B  C /D /E /F
setf /A  B /C  D /E /F
setf /A  B  C  D /E /F
setf /A  B  C /D /E /F
setf  A /B  C /D  E /F
setf  A  B  C /D /E /F

trace_off
;-----------------------------------------------------------------
```

Only 15 test vectors are required to provide a high confidence in the design, rather than the maximum 64 required for 100% testing. Note that the equation for Z can be tested using some of the same values used for testing the other two equations as they have the same values. As the outputs are independent, it does not cause any problems simultaneously to use the same values of inputs for different outputs. It should also be noted that two of the test vectors used for testing different product terms in the equation for X are the same, that is, test vectors 1 and 4. This is not unusual as the same conditions will often apply to several different equations. The difference in outputs between these two vectors is not significant as the X in vector 4 for Z, indicates a don't care situation and could be considered to be a L. With multiple Boolean equations it is more difficult to design the test vectors to ensure that all possible product terms and equations are tested, but the saving in time and effort can be considerable. An important feature of combinational test vector design is that the sequence in which the test vectors are applied has no effect on the outputs obtained, as the outputs are produced only by the instantaneous inputs and are not affected by any past input values.

3.5.7 Test vectors for registered designs

The second type of logic design which contains registers requires a different approach to the design of test vectors. Because registered designs will often incorporate the effect of what the inputs and outputs have been in the past, the sequence of the test vectors is of great importance. This is the major difference between the design of test vectors for combinational logic registered logic designs. An example of a registered design is given below, which consists of a

3-bit binary up counter. This is a relatively simple design which has been implemented using a CASE statement. The test vectors have been included with all the outputs shown as don't cares. This avoids the need to know what the outputs are for the initial state. This is important as the start-up value for the outputs for the device may not be known and it can cause a large number of (apparent) errors. By using don't cares, the errors are avoided, but the user does have to read the simulator output listing carefully to identify that the correct outputs are being produced in the correct sequence. It should also be noted that there are eight possible output states from a 3-bit binary up counter, but that 10 test vectors have been included. This ensures that the counter will return to the zero value (#b000) correctly, once the largest value has been output. 10 values, rather than 9, are used for this to ensure that the boundary condition is passed correctly. That is, the values #b000 and #b001 can be considered to be special values because they comprise a boundary condition (#b000) and the value next to a boundary condition (#b001). Testing past this point increases the confidence in the design.

```
;---------------------------------- PIN Declarations --------------
PIN  ?        cnter[2..0] registered
PIN  ?        clk                                  ;

;---------------------------------- Boolean Equation Segment ------
EQUATIONS

cnter[2..0].clkf = clk

  case (cnter[2..0])
    begin
      #b000: begin
              cnter[2..0] = #b001
            end
      #b001: begin
              cnter[2..0] = #b010
            end
      #b010: begin
              cnter[2..0] = #b011
            end
      #b011: begin
              cnter[2..0] = #b100
            end
      #b100: begin
              cnter[2..0] = #b101
            end
      #b101: begin
              cnter[2..0] = #b110
            end
```

```
    #b110: begin
            cnter[2..0] = #b111
           end
    #b111: begin
            cnter[2..0] = #b000
           end
  end

;------------------------------------ Simulation Segment ------------
SIMULATION

trace_on  cnter[2..0] clk

setf /cnter[2..0]
clockf clk
clockf clk
clockf clk
clockf clk
clockf clk
clockf clk
clockf clk
clockf clk
clockf clk
clockf clk

trace_off
;-----------------------------------------------------------------
```

This particular design produced the simulation listing shown below. By a careful study of the three outputs it can be seen that they are producing the correct output sequence.

```
MACHXL 1.3 MACHSIM (05-15-94)
 (C) - COPYRIGHT ADVANCED MICRO DEVICES INC., 1993, 1994

MACHXL SIMULATION SELECTIVE TRACE LISTING

Title     : three bit counter        Author   : R C Seals
Pattern   : 1                       Company  : University of Greenwich
Revision  : 1                        Date     : 23/10/95

MACH445
Page : 1

               gc  c  c  c  c  c  c  c  c  c
 CNTER[2]      HHHHHLLLLLLLLLLLLHHHHHHHHHHHHLL
 CNTER[1]      HHHHHLLLLLLHHHHHHLLLLLLHHHHHHLL
 CNTER[0]      LLHHHLLLHHHLLLHHHLLLHHHLLLHHHLL
 CLK           LHHLHHLHHLHHLHHLHHLHHLHHLHHLHHL
```

For this design, all possible output states were produced by the test vectors; this is 100% testing. For counters with large numbers of bits it may become difficult and time consuming to generate test vectors for all possible output states. For example, an 8-bit counter will have 256 different output states, requiring at least 256 + 2 = 258 test vectors. For simple counters it is not difficult to decide on the test vectors, but for more complex registered designs such as an up/down counter it can be difficult, as there are virtually an infinite number of possible combinations. An example of a simple 3 bit up/down binary counter implemented using a CASE statement is shown below.

```
;---------------------------------- PIN Declarations ---------------
PIN  ?        Q[2..0] registered
PIN  ?        up                          ;
PIN  ?        clk                         ;

;----------------------------------- Boolean Equation Segment ------
EQUATIONS
Q[2..0].clkf = clk    ; Associate the clock with the registers

  case (Q[2..0])
    begin
      #b000: begin                        ;For a count of zero, determine if
             if (up) then                 ;it is an up count or a down count.
              begin                       ;Repeat for each count value.
               Q[2..0] := #b001;
              end
             else
              begin
               Q[2..0] := #b111;
              end
           end
      #b001: begin
             if (up) then
              begin
               Q[2..0] = #b010;
              end
             else
              begin
               Q[2..0] = #b000;
              end
           end
      #b010: begin
             if (up) then
              begin
               Q[2..0] = #b011;
              end
             else
```

```
                begin
                 Q[2..0] = #b001;
                end
            end
    #b011: begin
               if (up) then
                begin
                 Q[2..0] = #b100;
                end
               else
                begin
                 Q[2..0] = #b010;
                end
            end
    #b100: begin
               if (up) then
                begin
                 Q[2..0] = #b101;
                end
               else
                begin
                 Q[2..0] = #b011;
                end
            end
    #b101: begin
               if (up) then
                begin
                 Q[2..0] = #b110;
                end
               else
                begin
                 Q[2..0] = #b100;
                end
            end
    #b110: begin
               if (up) then
                begin
                 Q[2..0] = #b111;
                end
               else
                begin
                 Q[2..0] = #b101;
                end
            end
    #b111: begin
               if (up) then
                begin
                 Q[2..0] = #b000;
```

```
            end
           else
            begin
             Q[2..0] = #b110;
            end
        end
   end
;------------------------------------------------------------
SIMULATION

trace_on Q[2..0] up clk

setf up
clockf clk      ;Test the up counting
clockf clk
clockf clk
clockf clk
clockf clk
clockf clk
clockf clk
clockf clk
clockf clk
setf /up
clockf clk      ;Test down counting
clockf clk
clockf clk
clockf clk
clockf clk
clockf clk
clockf clk
clockf clk
clockf clk

trace_off
```

The design itself has become more complex, which indicates that the number of test vectors required is going to be larger. Only test vectors for counting up for 10 clock pulses followed by counting down for 10 clock pulses have been included, which produced the simulation listing shown below.

```
MACHXL 1.3 MACHSIM (05-15-94)
 (C) - COPYRIGHT ADVANCED MICRO DEVICES INC., 1993, 1994

MACHXL SIMULATION SELECTIVE TRACE LISTING

Title     : Three bit up-down counter   Author    : R C Seals
Pattern   : 1                           Company   : University of Greenwich
Revision  : 1                           Date      : 23/10/95
```

MACH445
Page : 1

```
        gc c  c  c  c  c  c  c  c  gc c  c  c  c  c  c  c  c
Q[2]    HHHHHLLLLLLLLLLLLHHHHHHHHHHHHHHHHHHHHHHLLLLLLLLLLLLHHHHH
Q[1]    HHHHHLLLLLLHHHHHHLLLLLLHHHHHHHHHHLLLLLLHHHHHHLLLLLLHHHHH
Q[0]    LLHHHLLLHHHLLLHHHLLLHHHLLLHHHHLLLHHHLLLHHHLLLHHHLLLHHHLL
UP      HHHHHHHHHHHHHHHHHHHHHHHHHHHHLLLLLLLLLLLLLLLLLLLLLLLLLLLL
CLK     LHHLHHLHHLHHLHHLHHLHHLHHLHHLLHHLHHLHHLHHLHHLHHLHHLHHLHHL
```

Even with this small number of test vectors, it is becoming increasingly difficult to determine if the logic design is operating correctly. The change-over from counting up to counting down occurred between vectors 10 and 11, indicated by the g above the vector and care has to be taken to determine that the correct values have been generated. This set of test vectors is not exhaustive, as the design should be tested for correct up/down operation for every output value to fully exercise each of the IF THEN ELSE statements in the CASE statement. A set of test vectors to test the first three output states is shown below.

```
SIMULATION

trace_on Q[2..0] up clk

setf up
clockf clk      ;Test the up counter for output state #b000
setf /up
clockf clk      ;Now count down for 2 clocks
clockf clk
setf up
clockf clk      ;Now count up 3 clocks to get to o/p #b001
clockf clk
clockf clk
setf /up
clockf clk      ;Now count down for 2 clocks
clockf clk
setf up
clockf clk      ;3 more up clocks to get to #b010
clockf clk
clockf clk
setf /up
clockf clk      ;Test the down count for that o/p state
clockf clk

trace_off
```

This produces the simulation listing shown below, indicating that the logic design is operating correctly for the first three output states.

MACHXL 1.3 MACHSIM (05-15-94)
(C) - COPYRIGHT ADVANCED MICRO DEVICES INC., 1993, 1994

MACHXL SIMULATION SELECTIVE TRACE LISTING

```
Title    : Three bit up-down counter   Author   : R C Seals
Pattern  : 1                           Company  : University of Greenwich
Revision : 1                           Date     : 23/10/95

MACH445
Page : 1

        gc  gc   c  gc   c   c  gc   c  gc   c   c  gc   c
Q[2]    HHHHHHHHHHHHHHHHHHHLLLLHHHHHHHHHHLLLLLLLLLLHH
Q[1]    HHHHHHHHHLLLLHHHHHHLLLLHHHHHHHHHHLLLLLLLLLLHH
Q[0]    LLHHHHLLLHHHHLLLHHHLLLLHHHLLLLHHHLLLHHHHLLLHH
UP      HHHHLLLLLLLHHHHHHHHHHLLLLLLLLLHHHHHHHHLLLLLLL
CLK     LHHLLHHLHHLLHHLHHLHHLLHHLHHLLHHLHHLHHLLHHLHHL
```

From this it can be seen that the number of test vectors required to perform a reasonable number of tests on the logic design for a 3 bit up/down binary counter is significant. Twenty vectors were needed to test the straightforward up and down counting sequences, plus another $5 \times 8 = 40$ vectors to test the changeover from up to down counting. This is a total of 60 vectors to perform some testing of the design. If a hold signal was now added and possibly a reset, preset and/or preload, the potential number of test vectors becomes significant. In these circumstances, it is usual only to test parts of the design extensively, perhaps the operation of all possible functions on output state #b010 (Note that boundary condition should not be used when only performing a limited number of tests. Boundary conditions should always be fully tested.) and then just a few on the other output states. The aim is to minimise the time and effort required for testing, but maximise the confidence in the correct operation of the design.

3.5.8 State machine testing

One type of registered logic design where testing is of considerable importance is for state machine designs. These are inherently registered, as the outputs are a combination of the present inputs and past output states. It is usual to represent state machines using diagrams such as that shown in figure 3.3(b). This state machine has one input and one output. The output remains at logic zero unless the input bit sequence of logic 0 followed by a logic 1 is detected, when an output of logic 1 is produced for one clock pulse. Three states are required. The first waits until an initial logic zero is detected when it moves to state two. At state two, if a logic 1 is detected, a move to state three is made and the output becomes a logic 1. If a logic 0 is detected, it remains at state two until a logic 1 is detected. In state three if a further logic 1 is detected, it moves back to state one to wait for another logic 0 to start the sequence again. If a logic 0 is detected, it moves to state two as this could be the beginning of another logic 0 followed by a logic 1 input sequence. The program to implement this is shown below using the CASE statement. This is a common method of implementing state machines.

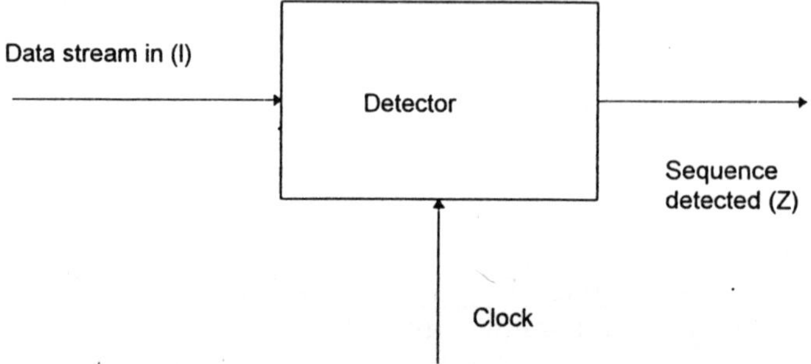

Figure 3.3(a) Sequence detector block diagram

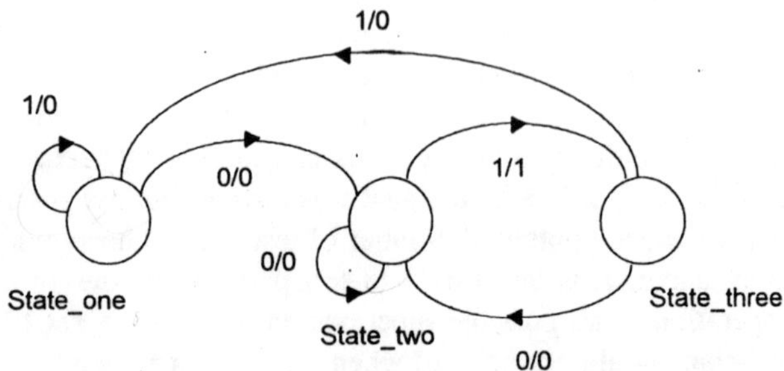

Figure 3.3(b) State machine for sequence detector

```
;---------------------------------- PIN Declarations --------------
PIN  ?        state_[1..0] registered
PIN  ?        detected
PIN  ?        clk
PIN  ?        data

string state_one '#b00'
string state_two '#b01'
string state_three '#b10'
string error_state '#b11'

;---------------------------------- Boolean Equation Segment ------
EQUATIONS
state_[1..0].clkf = clk
```

```
case (state_[1..0])
   begin
     state_one:begin                      ; This is the first state
              if (data = 0) then          ; which identifies the
               begin                      ; beginning of the
                state_[1..0] = state_two  ; identification.
                detected = 0
               end                        ; The value of the data input
              else                        ; is used to control which state
               begin                      ; to move to.
                state_[1..0] = state_one
                detected = 0
               end
             end
     state_two:begin
              if (data = 0) then
               begin
                state_[1..0] = state_two
                detected = 0
               end
              else
               begin
                state_[1..0] = state_three
                detected = 1
               end
             end
     state_three: begin
                if (data = 0) then
                 begin
                  state_[1..0] = state_two
                  detected = 0
                 end
                else
                 begin
                  state_[1..0] = state_one
                  detected = 0
                 end
               end
     error_state: begin ;Should never get here
                state_[1..0] = state_one
                detected = 0
               end
   end

;-------------------------------- Simulation Segment ------------
SIMULATION

trace_on  data state_[1..0] detected clk
```

```
setf data
clockf clk
clockf clk
clockf clk
setf /data
clockf clk
setf data
clockf clk
clockf clk
setf /data
clockf clk
clockf clk

trace_off

;-----------------------------------------------------------------
```

The design has been implemented with a four state state machine as two bits were used to identify the states. The detector itself only requires three states so the fourth state is an error state and if it is encountered, as might occur during power on, at the next clock pulse it moves to state_one. It is also worth noting that the values of detected and state_[1:0] are controlled whatever state they are in, move to, or which part of the IF THEN ELSE statement is active. This ensures a robust, reliable and self-correcting design. The test vectors shown above only test part of the possible set of state combinations that the design can move through. The outputs are left as don't cares to avoid having to identify the expected values before simulation and are checked after the simulation is complete. The simulation listing produced by these test vectors is shown below.

```
MACHXL 1.3 MACHSIM (05-15-94)
 (C) - COPYRIGHT ADVANCED MICRO DEVICES INC., 1993, 1994

MACHXL SIMULATION SELECTIVE TRACE LISTING

Title    : Three state state machine Author   : R C Seals
Pattern  : 1                         Company  : University of Greenwich
Revision : 1                         Date     : 23/10/95

MACH445
Page : 1

              gc  c  c  gc  gc  c  gc  c
 DATA         HHHHHHHHHHHLLLLHHHHHHHHLLLLLLL
 STATE_[1]    HHLLLLLLLLLLLLLLLHHHLLLLLLLLLL
 STATE_[0]    LLLLLLLLLLLLLHHHHLLLLLLLLHHHHH
 DETECTED     LLLLLLLLLLLLLLHHLLLLLLLLLLLLLL
 CLK          LHHLHHLHHLLHHLLHHLHHLLHHLHHL
```

Because the output states were not predicted, the user has to trace through the listing to determine that the design is operating as required. The sequence of test vectors is of great importance as it represents the input stream of logic values on the `data` input. The sequence used in the test vectors is given below:

1 1 1 0 1 1 0 0

which when converted into the expected state sequence list shown in table 3.5.

Table 3.5 State machine sequence listing

Value of data input	State
1	state_one
1	state_one
1	state_one
0	state_two
1	state_three
1	state_one
0	state_two
0	state_two

From an analysis of the simulation listing it can be seen that this is the sequence the design goes through, so the design seems to be correct and the test vectors have provided a reasonable level of confidence. However, although the test vectors cover all the possible correct states, they do not cover all the possible state transitions. Figures 3.4(a) to (f) illustrate how the test vectors cover the states and the transitions from state to state. The transition from `state_three` back to `state_one` was not covered, so additional test vectors to cover this are required. Only two additional ones are required to move from `state_two`, to `state_three` and then to `state_two` again and these are shown below, added to the end of the test vectors.

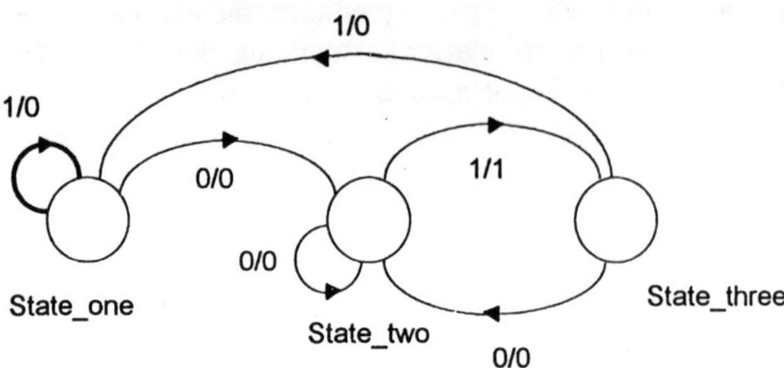

Figure 3.4(a) Testing the state machine

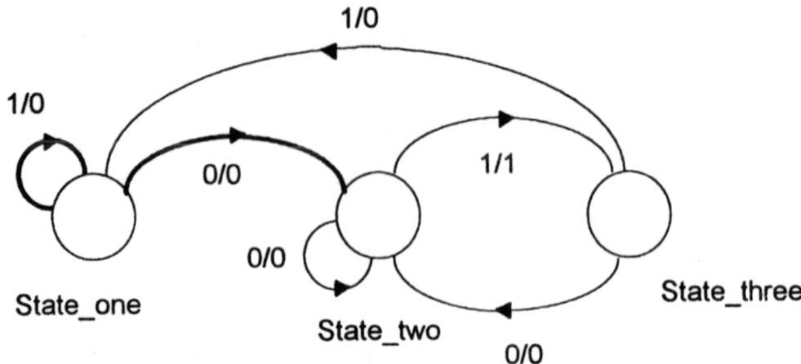

Figure 3.4(b) Testing the state machine

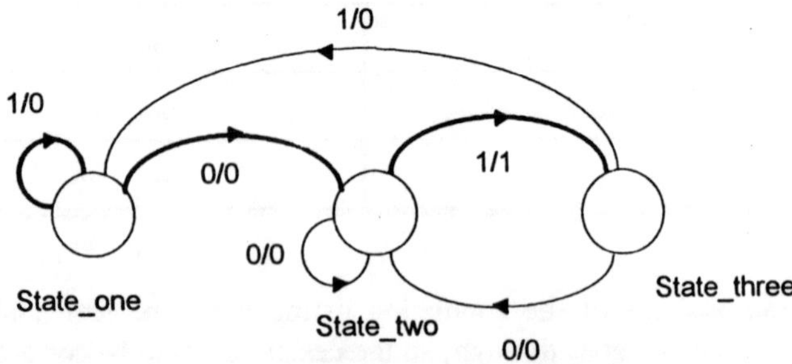

Figure 3.4(c) Testing the state machine

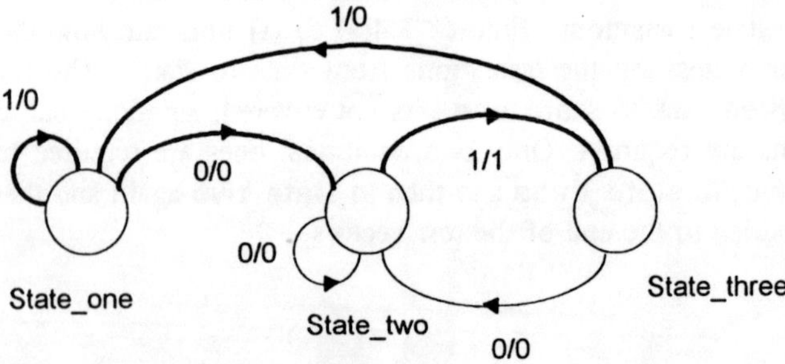

Figure 3.4(d) Testing the state machine

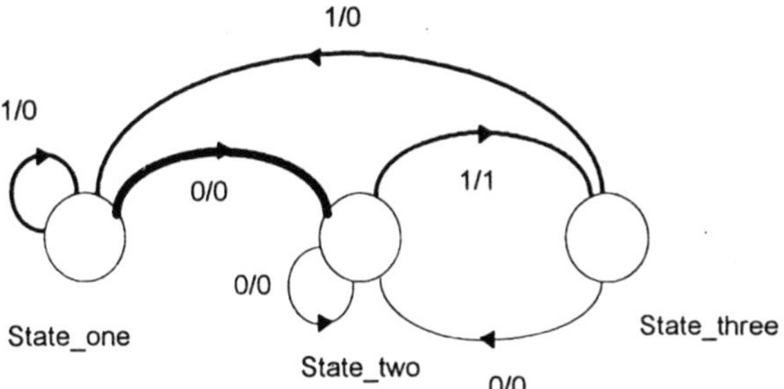

Figure 3.4(e) Testing the state machine

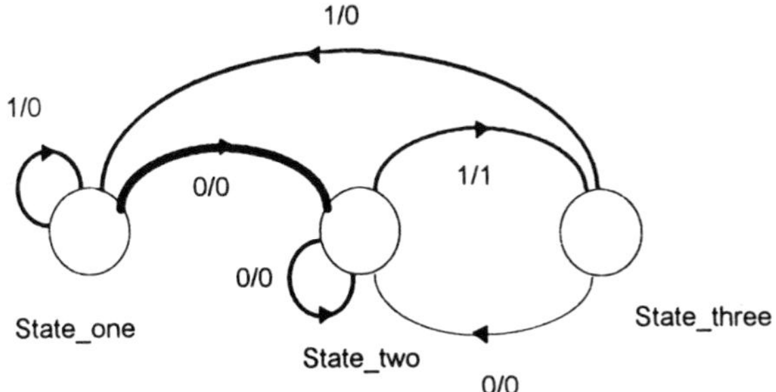

Figure 3.4(f) Testing the state machine

```
;----------------------------------- Simulation Segment ------------
SIMULATION

trace_on  data state_[1..0] detected clk

setf data
clockf clk
clockf clk
clockf clk
setf /data
clockf clk
setf data
clockf clk
clockf clk
setf /data
clockf clk
clockf clk
setf data        ;These addtional test vectors test the transition
clockf clk       ;from state_three back to state_two
setf /data
clockf clk

trace_off
;-----------------------------------------------------------------
```

Figure 3.5 shows that the transition from `state_three` to `state_two` has now been covered. Even with these test vectors not all the possible transitions or states have been covered as the `error_state` has not been tested. This can be difficult to test as being an error state, the logic should never enter that state and therefore, the test vectors cannot be used to get there. There are a number of approaches that can be used:

1) Always be very careful in designing the error states logic to obtain maximum confidence that it will work correctly, even though it is never tested. This is not a good solution, but sometimes it may be the only possible solution.

2) Carefully design the logic so that the error states can be generated by the test vectors.

3) Use the preload feature of the test vectors to force the logic into the error state and then use test vectors as normal.

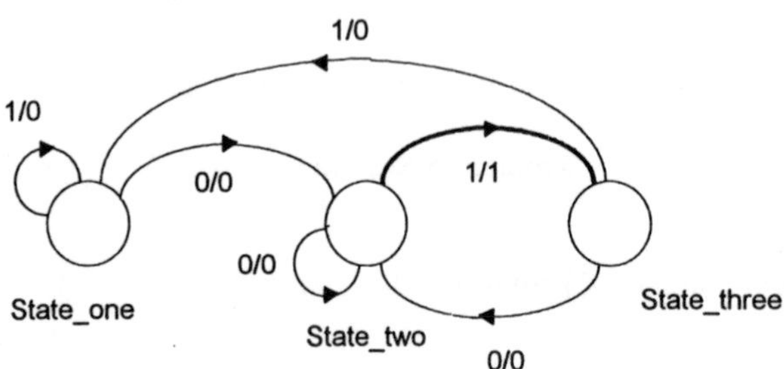

Figure 3.5(a) Testing the state machine

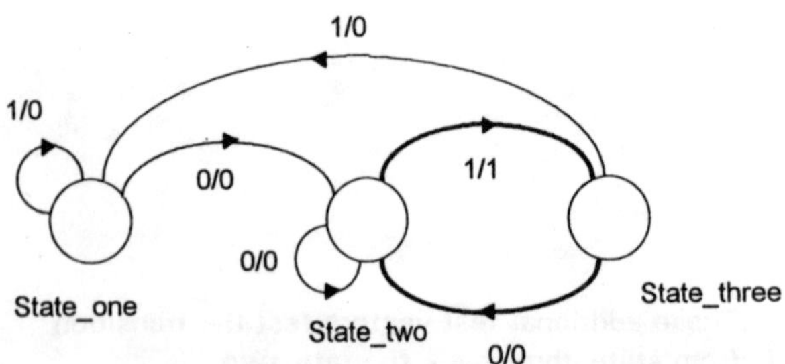

Figure 3.5(b) Testing the state machine

In this design, it is possible to generate the error state by knowing that the simulator always assumes that the initial output register values are logic 0. In the original design this is state_one, but if the definitions of the states are changed in the define section, then the power on state can be forced into the error_state. This also illustrates why variables and constant labels should always be used. The changed program has no other changes other than to the define section; even the test vectors can remain the same. The updated program is listed below.

```
;---------------------------------- PIN Declarations ---------------
PIN  ?        state_[1..0] registered
PIN  ?        detected
PIN  ?        clk
PIN  ?        data

string state_one '#b01'
string state_two '#b10'
string state_three '#b11'
string error_state '#b00'

;---------------------------------- Boolean Equation Segment ------
EQUATIONS
state_[1..0].clkf = clk

case (state_[1..0])
   begin
     state_one:begin
            if (data = 0) then
             begin
              state_[1..0] = state_two
              detected = 0
             end
            else
             begin
              state_[1..0] = state_one
              detected = 0
             end
           end
     state_two:begin
            if (data = 0) then
             begin
              state_[1..0] = state_two
              detected = 0
             end
            else
             begin
              state_[1..0] = state_three
              detected = 1
             end
           end
```

```
    state_three: begin
                if (data = 0) then
                 begin
                  state_[1..0] = state_two
                  detected = 0
                 end
                else
                 begin
                  state_[1..0] = state_one
                  detected = 0
                 end
               end
    error_state: begin ;Should never get here
                 state_[1..0] = state_one
                 detected = 0
               end
   end

;---------------------------------- Simulation Segment ------------
SIMULATION

trace_on  data state_[1..0] detected clk

setf data
clockf clk
clockf clk
clockf clk
setf /data
clockf clk
setf data
clockf clk
clockf clk
setf /data
clockf clk
clockf clk

trace_off
;-----------------------------------------------------------------
```

The simulation listing produced now shows that the error state is the first state tested and that it correctly moves to `state_one`, as shown below.

```
MACHXL 1.3 MACHSIM (05-15-94)
 (C) - COPYRIGHT ADVANCED MICRO DEVICES INC., 1993, 1994

MACHXL SIMULATION SELECTIVE TRACE LISTING
```

```
Title    : Three state state machine     Author    : R C Seals
Pattern  : 1                             Company   : University of Greenwich
Revision : 1                             Date      : 23/10/95

MACH445
Page : 1

               gc   c   c   gc   gc   c   gc   c
 DATA          HHHHHHHHHHLLLLHHHHHHHLLLLLLL
 STATE_[1]     LLLLLLLLLLLLHHHHHHHLLLLHHHHH
 STATE_[0]     HHHHHHHHHHHHLLLLHHHHHHLLLLLL
 DETECTED      LLLLLLLLLLLLLLHLLLLLLLLLLLLL
 CLK           LHHLHHLHHLLHHLLHHLHHLLHHLHHL
```

To fully test the alternative transition from error_state to state_one when the data input is a logic one, a second set of test vectors is required which are listed below.

```
;---------------------------------- Simulation Segment ------------
SIMULATION

trace_on  data state_[1..0] detected clk

setf /data
clockf clk
setf data
clockf clk
clockf clk
setf /data
clockf clk
setf data
clockf clk
clockf clk
setf /data
clockf clk
clockf clk

trace_off
;-----------------------------------------------------------------
```

These test vectors produce the simulation listing given below which is exactly the same as the previous simulation listing, showing that the transition from error_state to state_one is operating correctly.

```
MACHXL 1.3 MACHSIM (05-15-94)
 (C) - COPYRIGHT ADVANCED MICRO DEVICES INC., 1993, 1994

MACHXL SIMULATION SELECTIVE TRACE LISTING
```

```
Title    : Three state state machine Author   : R C Seals
Pattern  : 1                         Company  : University of Greenwich
Revision : 1                         Date     : 23/10/95

MACH445
Page : 1

                gc  gc  c  gc  gc  c  gc  c
 DATA           LLLLHHHHHHHLLLLHHHHHHHLLLLLLL
 STATE_[1]      LLHHHHHHHLLLLHHHHHHHLLLLHHHHH
 STATE_[0]      HHLLLLHHHHHHHLLLLHHHHHHHLLLLL
 DETECTED       LLLLHHLLLLLLLLLHHLLLLLLLLLLLL
 CLK            LHHLLHHLHHLLHHLLHHLHHLLHHLHHL
```

3.6 Problems

1. a) Deduce the truth table for the logic operation which outputs a logic 1 if 3 or more inputs of a 4 input logic function are a logic 1. Otherwise the output is to be a logic 0.
   b) Deduce the Boolean equations which will implement the logic function described in Q1(a) and implement them as a MACHXL program or other HDL with which you are familiar.
   c) Deduce the test vectors required for the program in Q1(b) and verify that the implementation gives the correct result.

2. Does the JEDEC file listed below have a checksum error?

```
PLD Programmer Codes for [p10l8]
- [ data_io] = [2213]
                PLD [p10l8] Device Map for
                Design [logic_gates]*
QF320*
QP20*
F0*
L0280 0111 0111 1111 1111 1111 *
L0300 1111 1101 1111 1111 1111 *
C04E6*
QV8*
N Vectors from File [logic_gates] for PLD [p10l8]*
X0*
V0001 X000XXXXXNXXXXXXXXXN*
V0002 X001XXXXXNXXXXXXXXXN*
V0003 X010XXXXXNXXXXXXXXXN*
V0004 X011XXXXXNXXXXXXXXXN*
V0005 X100XXXXXNXXXXXXXXXN*
V0006 X101XXXXXNXXXXXXXXXN*
V0007 X110XXXXXNXXXXXXXXXN*
```

V0008 X111XXXXXNXXXXXXXXXN*
83B8

3. Deduce the test vectors required to verify the operation of the state machine illustrated in figure 3.6.

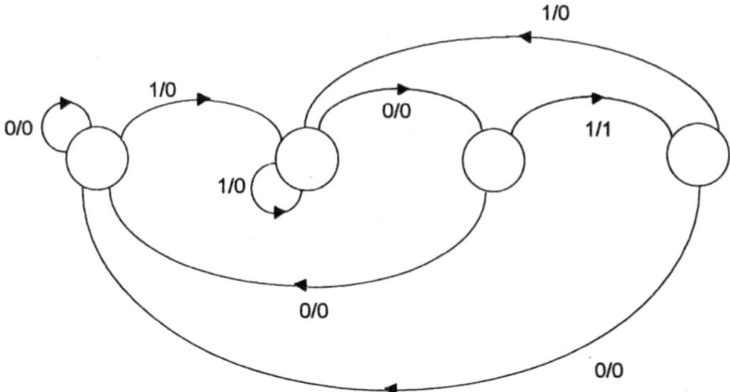

Figure 3.6 State machine for sequence detector

3.7 Further reading

Altera Data Book 1995, Altera Corporation, 2610 Orchard Parkway, San Jose, CA 95134-2020, USA.

GAL Data Book 1992, Lattice Semiconductor Corp, 55555 Northeast Moore Ct, Hillsboro, Oregon 97124, USA.

Johnson, E.L. and Karim, M.A., *Digital Design – A Pragmatic Approach*, 1987, PWS Publishers, USA.

MACH 1 and 2 Family Data Book, 1994, AMD, Inc., 901 Thompson Place, PO Box 3453, Sunnyvale, CA 94088-3453, USA.

PAL Device Data Book and Design Guide 1993, AMD, Inc., 901 Thompson Place, PO Box 3453, Sunnyvale, CA 94088-3453, USA.

PEEL Products Data Book 1994, ICT Inc., 2123 Ringwood Avenue, San Jose, CA 95131, USA.

Programmable Logic Data Book, 1994/5, Cypress Semiconductor, 3901 North First Street, San Jose, CA 95134, USA.

Stonham, T.J., *Digital Logic Techniques – Principles and Practice*, 2nd Edition, 1987, Van Nostrand Reinhold (UK).

4 Field programmable gate arrays (FPGAs)

For FPGAs, the variety of architectures is larger as each manufacturer develops concepts for particular niche markets and this, coupled with the non-deterministic nature of the timing for place and route, makes them more difficult to incorporate into designs. Due to the considerable differences in internal architecture, it is difficult to make appropriate comparisons, so a number of different architectures will be considered and their specific properties outlined. The development tools available range from low-cost PC based packages to costly high-end workstation packages and there is an encouraging move towards standardisation through two avenues, that of standard formats for intermediate stage files or through standardised design languages such as VHDL.

Because FPGAs are non-deterministic in the propagation delays of synthesised designs, extensive use is made of simulators to verify that the design and the place and route implement the specified design. Simulation can be considered to take place at two levels, that of functional simulation which confirms that the design is correct and then gate level simulation, to confirm that the design after place and route still implements the design correctly. The sequence of design and simulations is as follows. The initial design is followed by functional simulation and then place and routing. A further simulation at the gate level follows and, if all is correct, the device will be programmed. Any faults identified are corrected before proceeding to the next stage. Learning the use of FPGAs in digital system design is very much a 'hands-on' process and the quickest approach is to tackle a non-trivial design.

4.1 The basic architectures

Many of the manufacturers make programmable logic devices as well as field programmable gate arrays and the decision as to what is a PLD or an FPGA can be somewhat arbitrary. The decision has been made based on two factors, non-deterministic place and route and register-rich architectures. These do not address all those factors which can be considered to be those essential to an FPGA, but they do allow decisions to be made quickly and easily.

4.1.1 Texas Instruments and Actel

Texas Instruments and Actel both supply similar components which come in three generations with increasing gate counts, increased speed of operation and improved architectures, with fourth and fifth generation devices planned for the near future. The architectures consist of standard logic blocks called logic modules which come in two varieties, combinational logic blocks and sequential logic blocks.

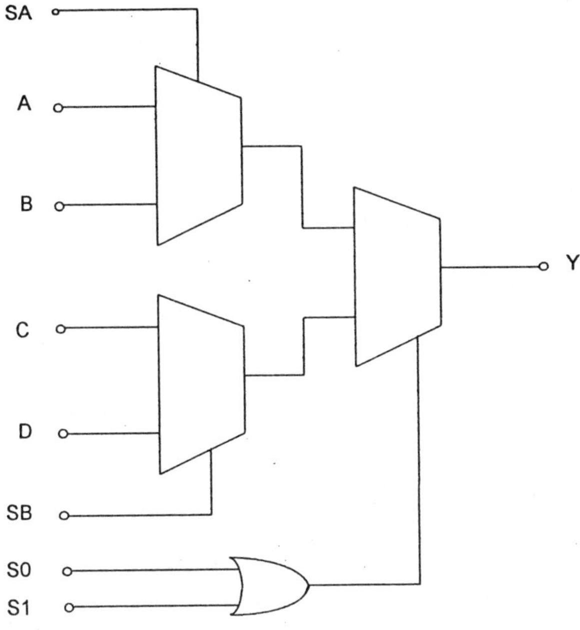

Figure 4.1 Logic function emulated by the combinational logic block

First generation devices contain only the combinational logic block. The combinational logic block has 8 inputs and one output enabling three 2-input multiplexers and one OR gate to be emulated as illustrated in figure 4.1. With this arrangement each combinational logic block can implement most simple combinational logic functions, although the efficiency of utilisation can vary. The utilisation efficiencies of several logic operations are listed in table 4.1. The NOT function, for example, is implemented by applying a permanent logic 1 to the A and S0 inputs, and a logic 0 to the B input, so that the signal X applied to the SA input will result in the complemented version of X appearing at the Y output. The implementation of the logic functions in a combinational logic block is not intuitively obvious and it is better to let the software do the placement. If a memory element such as a register is required, two combinational blocks have to be used.

Table 4.1 Utilisation efficiency

logic functions	% gates used	% inputs used
NOT	9/14	4/8
2 input AND	9/14	4/8
2 input OR	14/14	6/8

The smallest device, the Actel A1010 or Texas Instruments TPC1010A, contains 295 logic blocks arranged as a matrix array with interconnections running between the rows and columns, and I/O modules next to the physical pins. Each horizontal set of interconnections contains 22 tracks and each vertical set of interconnections contains 13, as illustrated in figure 4.2. The inputs to each logic block are taken from the two adjacent horizontal channels of 22 connectors and each output from a logic block is directly connected to one of the vertical connectors. This architecture enables good interconnections between logic blocks to be made. Connections between the horizontal and vertical connections, and the horizontal connections and inputs to the logic modules is made by antifuses, which are positioned at every cross-over point. An antifuse operates in the opposite way to an ordinary PLD fuse, in that when it is not programmed it does not make a connection, but when it is programmed it makes a low impedance connection of approximately 50 Ω. The advantage of the anti-fuse over the normal fuse is that it is physically smaller, so more fuses can be fitted into the same area that a similar number of fuses would occupy. The programming current is repeatedly pulsed until a low impedance connection through the insulator is made. The resulting connection is always low impedance and does not alter with time. In addition, because the connection does not contain any active elements as some interconnecting technologies do, there is no additional propagation delay.

4.1.2 I/O modules

The connection between the logic modules and external signals is provided by I/O modules. The I/O module can implement one of four functions: input, output, tri-state output or bi-directional buffer. The inputs and outputs are not automatically latched and if latching is required the user must design it and allocate combinational logic blocks to implement it.

4.1.3 Second generation devices

The second generation of Actel devices provides significant improvements in six parameters: an improved I/O logic blocks with latches, an increased number of combinational logic blocks, new types of sequential logic blocks, an increased numbers of I/O blocks, a 100% increase in maximum operating frequency (up to 50 MHz) and finally special purpose clock driver circuits with low skew.

These enhancements are combined with improvements in all other areas of operation. The improved I/O module blocks are now divided into two parts: pad drivers with high current output capability and I/O modules which have built in input and output latches.

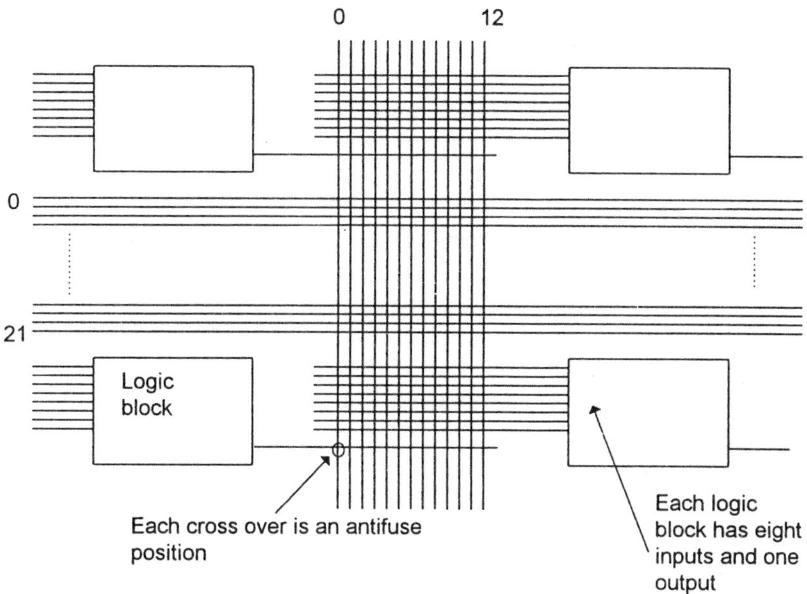

Figure 4.2 Interconnections and antifuse positions

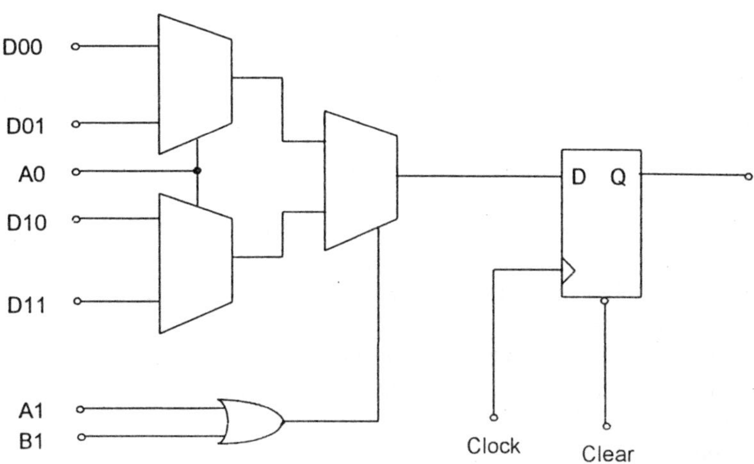

Figure 4.3 Sequential logic block

The combinational logic block has been changed slightly, so that both the two input multiplexers are controlled by the same signal. The sequential module effectively adds a D flip-flop to the Y output of the combinational logic block. The basic sequential logic block is shown in figure 4.3 and a number of variations on this are possible. The sequential logic block is also able to implement the complete combinational logic function, provided that the D type flip-flop is not used. Two identical clock driver networks are provided, which can have one of four possible clock signals, from the external clocks 1 or 2, or from the internal clocks 1 or 2. Each row of the logic block array has a separate buffer in order to minimise clock skew.

4.1.4 Third generation devices

The third generation devices offered by Actel provide improvements in four main areas: an increase in the maximum frequency operation (50% higher), an increase in the number of I/O modules, an increase in the number of combinational and sequential logic blocks and finally an increased in the number of clock networks to a maximum of four. The third generation devices effectively offer a very high performance component.

4.1.5 Cypress Semiconductor and Quick Logic

Cypress semiconductor and Quick Logic are two companies that supply an architecture which can be considered similar to Actel and Texas Instruments in many ways. Antifuses are used as the programming elements, but with a slightly different construction. The normal metal interconnect layers are separated by an insulating semiconductor layer rather than polysilicon inductors. The aim is to obtain lower on resistances and hence reduce switching times. A programming pulse applied across the via causes it to break down and form a low resistance (typically 50 Ω) conducting link. This type of antifuse has the advantage that as the pitch of the metal interconnects is reduced, the size of the antifuse is also reduced.

The devices are organised as two-dimensional arrays of blocks called logic cells as listed in table 4.2. Links are provided between the logic cells by the vertical and horizontal interconnects. The vertical interconnections contain all the inputs and outputs for the column of cells immediately to the right, which comprise a total of 24 links. This can limit input connections to some logic cells in a column and is one reason why there are 50% more columns than rows. The horizontal interconnections which contain 12 links are designed to connect links in the vertical interconnections and therefore do not have any direct connections to the logic cells, but do provide connections to most of the I/O cells. Each logic cell is identical, consisting of 6 AND gates, three multiplexers and one register, as illustrated in figure 4.4. This arrangement is able to implement any three input variable function. Some other input functions with up to 14 variables can also be implemented. The SR flip-flop can also be configured to D type, J-K type and T type flip-flops. There are five outputs from various points in the logic cell which allow independent logic functions to be placed into the same cell. For example, the register can be used independently of the rest of the logic gates, leaving some of the gates to be used separately. Placement of the design into the logic cells should be left to the software, as in general, it will be more efficient. Routing of signals between logic cells is not user controllable and is always performed by the software.

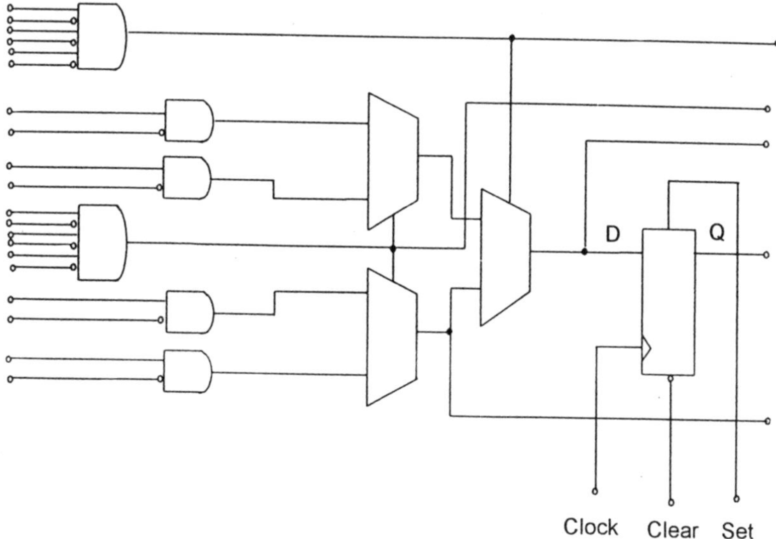

Figure 4.4 The logic cell

Table 4.2 Array dimensions

Component	Array dimensions	Array size
7C381A	8 × 12	96
7C382A	8 × 12	96
7C383A	12 × 16	192
7C384A	12 × 16	192
7C385A	16 × 24	384
7C386A	16 × 24	384
7C387A	24 × 32	768
7C388A	24 × 32	768
7c389A	32 × 36	1152

4.1.6 Modules

There are three I/O modules provided: input only, input/output and clock/input. The input only module provides both the true and complementary form of the input signal with a high fan-out capability. The input/output cell only provides true input signal capability, but active high, active low or open drain inverting buffer outputs. The clock/input modules provide three inputs, two of which are similar to the input only cell and provide a high fan-out capability true and complementary input signal useful for global register clear and set. The third signal is a global clock signal distributed to all registers on a net, with low skew and high fan-out capability. Typically, there will be two clock networks with larger devices having more.

4.1.7 ATMEL

The Atmel AT6000 FPGA offers an alternative architecture to the Texas Instruments and Cypress Semiconductor FPGAs in several areas. It has a simpler logic cell design, large numbers of logic cells, implements alternative routing mechanisms and is reconfigurable. The logic cell design is shown in figure 4.5 and is best represented by the logic symbol in figure 4.6 which illustrates the four-sided symmetrical nature of its operation. The logic cell contains two 4 input multiplexers which allow the A and B inputs (AN, AE, AS, AW and BN, BE, BS, BW) to be taken from any of the four sides. These inputs can then be combined with inputs from the local buses (LEW1, LEW2, LNS1, LNS2) in a variety of ways by the routing logic, including a D type register. There are two output multiplexers which create the four A outputs and four B outputs. Due to the symmetrical nature of the logic cells, the matrix of logic cells is arranged as a square, as listed in table 4.3.

Table 4.3 Atmel array dimensions

Component	Array dimensions	Array size
AT6002	32 × 32	1024
AT6003	40 × 40	1600
AT6005	56 × 56	3136
AT6010	80 × 80	6400

The I/O cells are arranged around the perimeter of the logic cell array. There are repeaters every eight logic cells, for both local and express bus signals to reconstitute the signals being transmitted. Local bus signals are connected to all eight logic cells in their row or column, while the express bus signals are programmable connections designed to transfer signals long distances within the array, typically between the I/O modules and selected logic cells. The repeaters are used to provide connections between local and express bus pairs in five categories; isolate local bus segments, isolate express bus segments, connect two local bus segments, connect two express bus segments and finally to implement a local/express transfer.

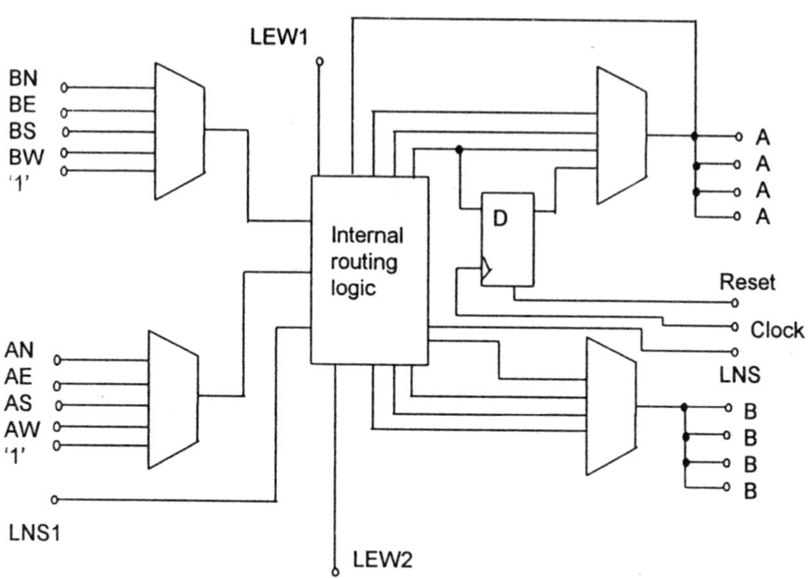

Figure 4.5 Atmel logic cell design

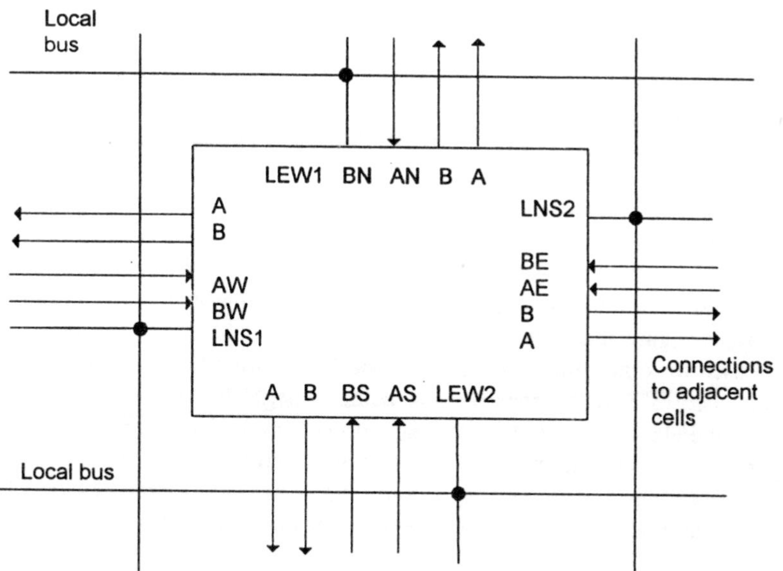

Figure 4.6 Atmel logic cell symbol

Each block of 8 × 8 cells (a total of 64 cells) is surrounded by the repeaters to provide the interconnection of short and long routes, to regenerate signals, and to provide a compromise between connectivity and the silicon required to implement the repeaters. The relatively small size of the logic cell, combined with the large number of cells and the flexible routing, provides a flexible and efficient method of implementing most logic system designs. There are limitations, as with all FPGAs, in the routing, as it relies on predefined connections. The flexibility provided by the routing cells helps to overcome this restriction, but it will still be a major bottleneck for complex designs.

4.1.8 Dynamic reconfiguration

One area that the Atmel FPGAs implement which has been until relatively recently of limited availability from other manufacturers, is the ability to re-configure part or all of the device while the logic is actually executing, which is called dynamic reconfiguration. The Atmel FPGAs are SRAM based and therefore need the programming configuration data to be transferred from non-volatile memory when power is first applied. A number of different mechanisms are available for this. To download directly from a PC parallel port (although this is most common during the development stages of a design), to transfer data from an embedded microprocessor system, or to automatically transfer configuration data from a serial or parallel EPROM or EEPROM. The third method is the most common, as it allows stand-alone designs to be implemented without any further components. Typically a serial EEPROM is used, as it has a minimum number of pin connections, a small physical size and low power consumption when powered down, which it would be for most of the time except after a power on reset.

Partial reconfiguration can be initiated after a power on reset operation configuration has occurred and can identify only those cells which need to be re-configured to implement an alternative logic operation to that originally configured. This allows the FPGA to implement certain logic designs which would initially appear to be too large. Only those designs which require specific and different logic operations at different times during system operation can make use of this facility. A typical example might a logic system which has to implement some initialisation sequence after power on but which is not required again. Reconfiguration after the logic initialisation would enable the logic cells to be reused for other functions. This approach also provides the opportunity to tune the hardware to the specific task being undertaken. An example of this might be the algorithms used in an image processing system. For certain types of operation one algorithm might be optimal, whereas for a different type of image processing a different algorithm might produce better results. Re-configuration enables both algorithms to be available in the smallest size of FPGA.

The full reconfiguration time is only a few milliseconds and partial re-configuration is approximately proportional to the amount being reprogrammed.

Some additional overhead is incurred but this is minimal. In addition, there is a compression algorithm that can be implemented, which although it is dependent on the complexity of the design, can reduce the configuration file by 80% and hence the configuration time. Again, further overhead is required to implement the compression and decompression, but this is minimal. The compression operates by knowing that after a reset, all the internal programmable points are set to a logic 0. Then only the points requiring programming to a logic 1 need to be stored and the transferred. The efficiency of the compression is dependent on the length of sequential sequences of logic 0's and logic 1's. The longer the sequences of strings, the more effective the compression algorithm is. It is not known if the development software attempts to implement designs which will maximise the efficiency of the compression algorithm, but it does convert full configuration files to partial configuration whenever it can. For example, if the total number of cells available is not used, then partial configuration will reduce the configuration time.

4.1.9 AMD

Advanced Micro Devices (AMD) were one of the pioneers in the original design and use of PLDs and have an extensive range of devices that have been introduced over a number of years. They also introduced the first widely used programming language, PALASM. However, they have never really attempted to produce FPGAs, relying instead on extending the capability of their PLDs' architecture to achieve almost the same effect. The most important devices are available in the MACH 3 and 4 series which are almost identical, differing only in the number of registers associated with each I/O pin. The latest addition to the family is the MACH 5 series. The MACH 3 series have one register per I/O pin, the MACH 4 series having three registers per I/O pin. Figure 4.7 illustrates the basic block architecture of the MACH 465, one of the larger devices, showing the two main elements: the routing resources, and the PLD block. Each PLD block effectively contains two 34V10 type PLDs which can be interconnected via the central routing resources. Based on the widely known V architecture used in PLDs, the most common of which is the 22V10, these devices have all the advantages of PLDS and some of the properties of FPGAs, although they might not be considered to be true FPGAs, due to their fixed PLD type internal architecture. The advantages are that there are large numbers of macrocells (the MACH465 has 256), input product terms (20), and input and output signals (dependent on the package size used), predictable deterministic timing and predictable global clocks with minimum skew.

They also have some properties of the FPGA, such as flexible routing, allowing any macrocell to be connected to any other macrocell, although this global interconnect ability is limited by the routing capacity to only a percentage of the available macrocells for any one design. Unfortunately, there are some disadvantages with this approach, as with any of the architectures that manufacturers have adopted, the global interconnection is more limited than for normal FPGAs; the large grain size of the logic (that is, the macrocell) means that most designs are inefficient in their utilisation of the available silicon and clocks, resets and sets are typically global, which may sometimes be a problem. However, a high level design language has been made available by AMD, called MACHXL which implements some very useful language constructs and enables a low cost development system to be implemented. There are fitters available for the majority of development systems so that VHDL programs can be implemented if required.

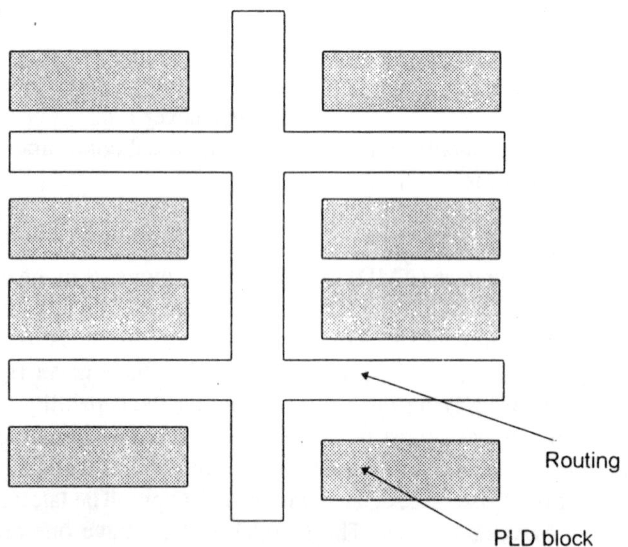

Figure 4.7 MACH 465 block architecture

Other important features of the MACH 3 and 4 series, although not all members of the families implement all these features, are that a JTAG port is built-in, in-system programming is possible by using the JTAG port from a PC and that 5 V programming of the internal EECMOS PROM containing the configuration data is possible.

4.1.10 Lattice pLSI/ispLSI 3000

Lattice is another manufacturer of PLDs that has produced a flexible and large PLD which exhibits some of the properties of an FPGA. The latest family is the 3000 series which has many similarities to the MACH 3 and 4 series. The internal architecture is basically large grain PLD, combined with deterministic timing, limited routing capacity when compared with FPGA, a JTAG port built in and in-system programming via the JTAG port, and is implemented in EEPROM CMOS. In addition, there is the capability to reconfigure the design once it has been downloaded, as for the Atmel devices, enabling the logic implemented to be optimised to the task presently being executed or implemented. Figure 4.8 illustrates the basic internal architecture showing how the interconnection has been separated into two parts, the internal global interconnection and local output routing. This is an attempt to overcome the problem that this PLD architecture suffers from, namely limited interconnection for certain types of logic system designs. The PLD blocks contain 32 macrocells, arranged into four groups of eight, based on the standard PLD registered AND-OR architecture.

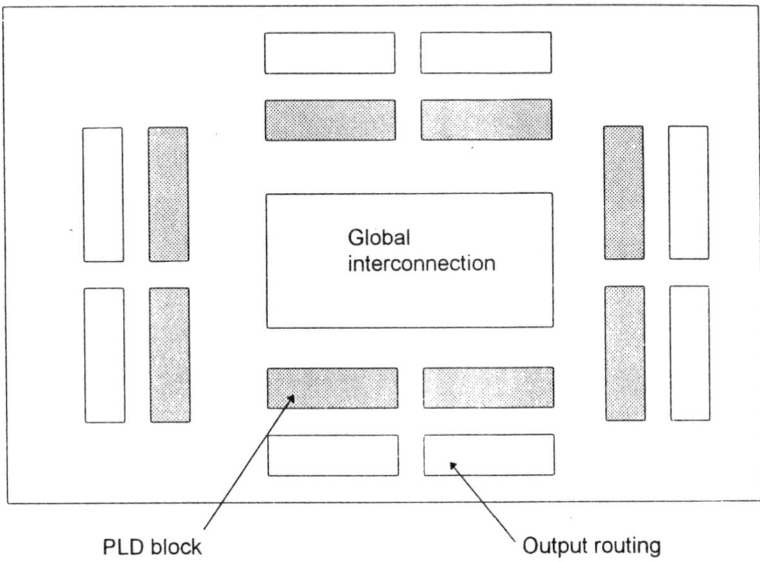

Figure 4.8 ipLSI 3256 block architecture

4.1.11 Xilinx

Xilinx is one of the major producers of large PLDs and FPGAs and manufactures four major families, two PLD and two FPGA:

1) 7200 series complex PLDs.
2) 7300 series complex PLDs.
3) XC3000 series FPGAs.
4) XC4000 series FPGAs.

4.1.12 XC7200 series complex PLDs

The XC7200 series is a relatively standard complex PLD design and is based on the concept, used by AMD and Lattice, of integrating multiple PLDs on to a single piece of silicon with global interconnections, as illustrated in figure 4.9. The PLD blocks are fairly standard and implement the usual registered AND-OR architecture and have many similarities to the standard PLD V architecture. They differ in that they have been amended to make the implementation of arithmetic logic units much easier. The macrocells contain a function block between the AND-OR array and the register which can implement two different types of operation, logic operations (using an internal look-up table) and arithmetic operations (sum and difference with fast carry in/out). Other than that, they are relatively similar to most other complex PLDs, although they are implemented using EPROM, rather than EEPROM and therefore are not in-system programmable. Nor do they implement the JTAG protocol for testing.

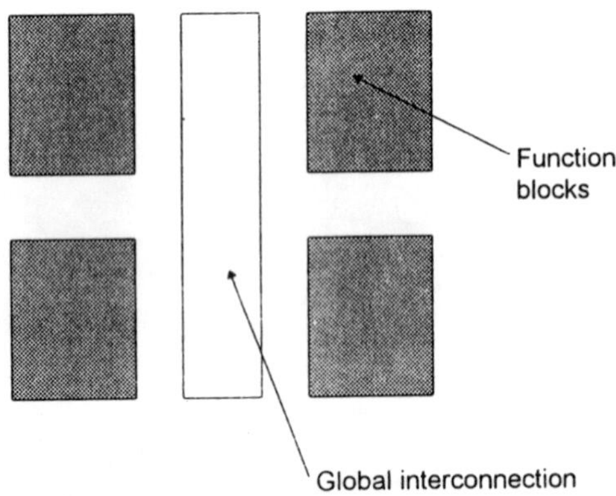

Figure 4.9 The XC7200 series basic architecture

4.1.13 XC7300 series complex PLDs

The XC7300 series illustrated in figure 4.10 has many similarities to the XC7200 series, but has the advantage of an advanced 0.8 micron CMOS EPROM implementation for smaller die size, lower power and higher clock frequencies, fast function blocks which provide high-speed logic operation, as well as the standard function which provides logic operation or arithmetic operation. Power management features can reduce power consumption by approximately 22%, swapping speed for lower power consumption, and is programmable by the user.

4.1.14 Altera

Altera is one of the main manufacturers of both PLDs and FPGAs having a more extensive range of products than Xilinx consisting of the following main families of devices:

1) Classic.
2) MAX5000.
3) MAX7000.
4) FLASHlogic.
5) MAX9000.
6) FLEX8000.
7) FLEX10000.

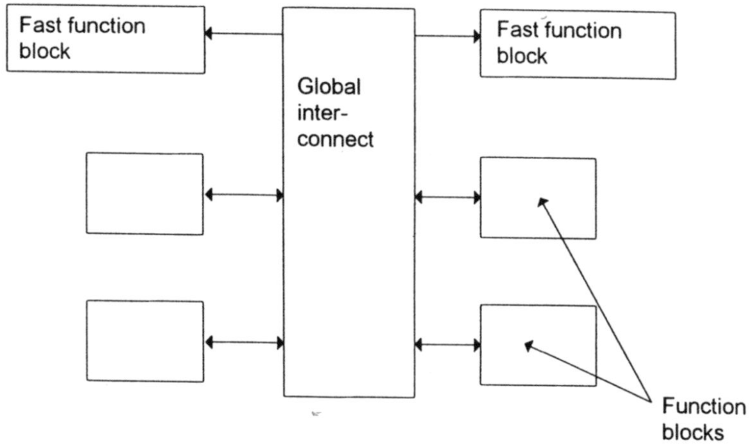

Figure 4.10 The XC7300 series basic architecture

4.1.15 Classic

Consists of small, low power and high-speed standard PLD devices of a few hundred logic gates.

4.1.16 MAX5000

Implements the standard registered AND-OR PLD architecture, but with larger numbers of macrocells and the necessary global programmable interconnection. It is similar to the Lattice and AMD complex PLDs.

4.1.17 MAX7000

A second generation version of the MAX5000 family that provides higher numbers of macrocells, improved EEPROM implementation and power management for up to 50% reduction in power by swapping speed for power. For certain devices there is the possibility of using 3 V power supply for reduced power consumption and higher operating frequencies.

4.1.18 FLASHlogic

Previously designed and manufactured by Intel, these devices are an addition to the Altera range rather than a specifically designed member of the product range. They implement a standard complex PLD architecture based on multiple 24V10 PLD blocks. They also implement the JTAG interface and in system programming as well as in system reconfiguration using SRAM and shadow EEPROM, via the JTAG port. The largest member of the family provides 160 macrocells and is compatible with Lattice and AMD complex PLDs. The major unique feature of these devices is that they have the ability to implement multiple small blocks of SRAM, 128 locations of 10 bits, instead of the logic functions. The SRAM that is used for configuring the logic functions and interconnections has been designed such that if the logic functions are not required, it can be implemented as a small block of SRAM with a very short access time. In addition, there are a number of fast 12-bit comparators available built into the logic blocks.

4.1.19 MAX9000

A third generation version of the MAX5000 or second generation version of the MAX7000, implemented in 0.65 micron CMOS EEPROM, this provides further increments in system frequencies and reduction in die size and power consumption. The number of macrocells has been increased to 560 for the largest device with a corresponding improvement in the implementation of the global interconnection and routing. Figure 4.11 illustrates the basic internal block architecture, showing reasonably sized blocks of PLDs surrounded by global interconnection and has many similarities to the Atmel approach. This is not surprising, as all the manufacturers are attempting to obtain the benefits of the largest logic module possible, but with the best interconnect strategy. Each logic block implements 16 macrocells that have the normal registered AND-OR structure. The JTAG interface is included allowing in-system programming. Power management is available, as is 3 V operation.

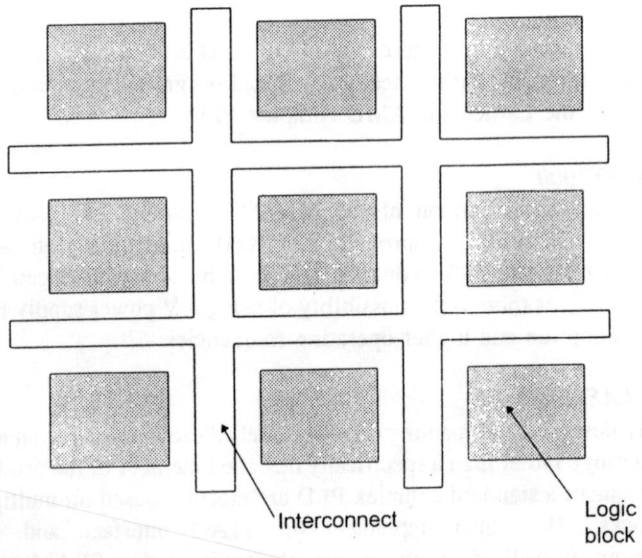

Figure 4.11 The MAX 9000 basic block architecture

4.1.20 FLEX8000

Although this family could still be considered to be a type of complex PLD, it does not implement the traditional registered AND-OR architecture, but uses a registered look-up table approach as illustrated in figure 4.12. The look-up table has four inputs and can implement any 4 variable logic function, logical or arithmetic. The fast carry in/out enables arithmetic operations to be parallelled for fast n-bit wide operations and the cascade in/out provides the ability to provide larger numbers of product terms than is available from the four input look-up table. This approach demonstrates features of both PLD and FPGA architectures. PLD features can be seen in the relatively large logic blocks (although they are no longer macrocells) and large product terms. The FPGA architectural features can be seen in the reduction in the number of registers per logic block, the global interconnect and the smaller grain size of the logic function implemented in each logic element. The largest device provides 1500 flip-flops and 32,000 usable logic gates. The JTAG port is implemented for most members of the product family and, because configuration data is maintained using SRAM cells, the device is in-system programmable and in-system re-configurable. 3 V operation and low power consumption are standard and an interesting feature is the ability to program the slew-rate on the register outputs in order to minimise noise on the power supply pins, internal interconnection signals and to reduce radiated noise where high speed operation is not required.

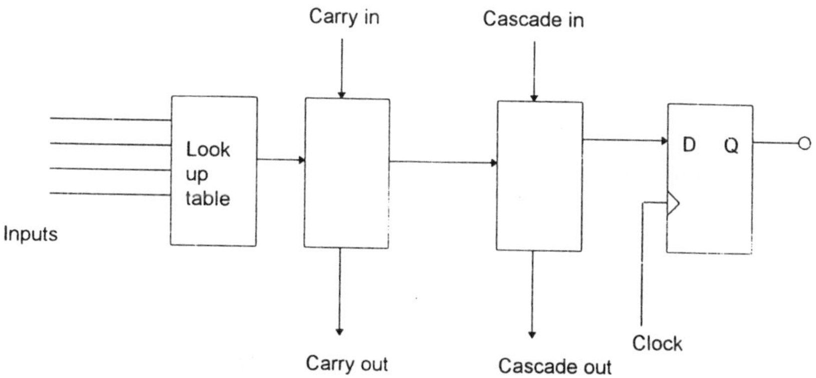

Figure 4.12 The simplified Flex 8000 look-up table logic element

4.1.21 FLEX10000

The latest generation of the FLEX series which implements all the features of the FLEX8000 series but with much larger numbers of registers, a maximum of 5,392, and logic gates, a maximum of 158,000, and higher operating frequencies due to a move to 0.5 micron CMOS. New features introduced are internal tri-state bus connection ability, very large pin counts, maximum 562 pins, multiple clock paths to reduce clock skew and an interesting feature called megafunctions. Megafunctions are the future for very large FPGAs, as they provide predesigned and optimised logical and arithmetical blocks, such as memory, digital signal processing and even complete microprocessors and microcontrollers. The FLEX10K architecture has what are called embedded array blocks, EAB, at the end of each row of logic blocks. The EAB is in reality a block of RAM which can be reconfigured to almost any required matrix. The RAM block consists of 2 Kbits of storage which can be configured as either RAM, ROM, or a look-up table. When operating as a look-up table, it is able to implement any logical or arithmetic function requiring up to 11 inputs and is up to 5 times more efficient at implementing these functions than the standard logic blocks.

4.2 Development software

As FPGAs are much more complex than PLDs, the software used during the development process is correspondingly more complex and has to perform additional functions. The designs are larger and more complex and are usually described in abstract functions using hardware description languages or schematic diagrams. In comparison, many PLD designs can be described adequately using Boolean equations.

The design development process can be considered to consist of a sequence of six steps of decreasing abstraction, as listed below:

1) Design specification.
2) Conversion of the specification into a logical consistent description suitable for entry into a CAD system.
3) Compiling the entered design.
4) Simulating the design.
5) Programming the target device.
6) System commissioning and testing.

The generation of the specification of a logic system operation is beyond the scope of this book and readers are advised to identify alternative texts if assistance is required in this area. The compilation of the entered design is covered in appendices A and B for high level language entry methods. Some description of the conversion of schematics will be given below, as will programming the target device. System commissioning and testing is beyond the scope of this book and again readers should search for alternative texts in this area.

4.2.1 CAD systems

Any CAD system used for FPGA implementation should have a number of general properties and should include a number of basic functions. Ideally, the CAD system, or development system, should have the following properties.

Architecture independent. This means that the design entry method is not specific to a particular FPGA or family of FPGAs, as this provides the widest possible target device capability, giving the user the widest choice to use the optimum device for each specific application. It also ensures that designs are portable and updatable to the newest and most appropriate target device.

Choice of execution platforms. This relates to the computer on which the development system executes and it is best if there are a number of different possibilities. If the software is restricted to only one platform, such as a PC, even if it is widely available, it may mean that potential improvements in the software may not be achievable. Typically, it is desirable for a PC based version and a widely available workstation version, such as for Sun or IBM RISC be available, with a choice of operating systems such as Windows, Windows NT and Unix.

Modular tool suite. A full suite of tools should be available from a single developer, but with the flexibility to incorporate tools from other manufacturers if necessary. This means that the software should have as open an architecture as possible with the capability to import a wide range of standard file formats at different stages in the design and to output in a wide range of file formats at different stages in the development process. An integrated tool suite where all the separate tools can be accessed from a unified menu system is preferred, with the potential to add further tools. This capacity also means that the user only has to purchase those tools required at any moment in time, which can then be added to and upgraded as required.

When considering the entry of the design into the CAD software, there are really only two techniques, schematic entry or hardware description languages. Once the design has been entered, a number of sequential steps are performed, most of which can take place without any user intervention.

Compiler netlist extractor. This tool strips away the unnecessary information contained in the compiler output file to leave only the netlist, which indicates how the various logic modules are to be connected together.

Logic synthesiser. Once the netlist has been created, the logic to implement it has to be synthesised. This is usually independent of the target device and considers only the most efficient logic circuits. However, it is possible to guide the synthesiser to use specific types of approach which, if the user is familiar with the target device, may prove to be more efficient.

Place and route, also known as a fitter. Once the logic has been synthesised, it has to be placed into the target device. This requires two processes to be completed, first the logic gates required have to be selected from those available in the target device and then all the required connections have to be made. The place and route can fail due to insufficient resources in either of these two categories. If there are insufficient gates available, there is little the designer can do except use a larger device. Sometimes, altering the design can save gates or alternative synthesis strategies can be used, but it is easier just to use a larger device. However, the routing process is more flexible and often the device will run out of routing resources before it will run out of logic gates. Typically, any design using more than 75% of the available logic gates will be difficult to route.

Simulator netlist extractor. Once the design has been placed and routed, it is simulated to ensure that it still performs the functions required and that the specific placement allows the design to operate with the timing constraints placed upon it. Before simulation takes place, a simulation netlist is created which identifies how the inputs and outputs are connected together and the timing constraints that are placed on them.

Waveform editor (test vector generation). Once the simulation netlist has been created, the test vectors need to be created and as digital systems have waveform inputs and outputs, the test vectors are created using a waveform generator.

Timing simulation. After the simulation netlist and the waveforms have been generated, the system can then be simulated to ensure that all the outputs provide the correct signals, in the correct order with the correct timing.

Timing analysis. The correct timing of the simulation signals is confirmed by the timing analysis package.

Programming of the completed design. Finally, after the designer is satisfied that the system is operating as required, it can be programmed into the target device for commissioning tests.

4.2.2 Schematic entry

Schematic entry as the name suggests creates a version of the circuit diagram on the computer display which can be converted into a netlist compatible with the place and route software. It is popular with engineers, as it is a familiar technique probably already in use for schematic entry of designs for documentation and design purposes and in many instances the same software can be used to enter the design into the FPGA development system. Once entered, the design is compiled to check for consistency and completeness and then converted into the netlist. At this point an EDIF file can be created for use as input to a variety of different development packages.

Schematic entry usually comprises three elements, a symbol editor, an HDL entry editor and a schematic entry editor. A schematic is based on the connection of symbols representing digital operations which are interconnected with wires. Although analogue elements can be incorporated into schematics, at present they cannot be incorporated into FPGAs and therefore will not be considered here. The symbols representing the digital operations have to be previously created before they can be connected together and this is achieved in two ways: by using precreated symbols supplied with the schematic editor, or through user created symbols customised to the user's requirements using the symbol editor supplied with the schematic entry editor. Because digital systems are based on a limited number of logical operations, such as AND, OR and NOT, there are standardised symbols used to represent them. These symbols are supplied with the schematic entry editor in the form of libraries and can be used immediately to enter designs. These are based on the well known 7400 series of components and most schematic entry editors are supplied with equivalent libraries. However, it is recognised that these will not always provide the most appropriate symbols for all designs and users will want to create symbols to represent their own special functions, or to include symbols for functions that were not available when the schematic entry editor was purchased. The symbol editor is a package capable of creating new symbols to the user's design that are compatible with the schematic entry editor.

Most schematic entry editors will also allow HDL programs to be represented by a symbol so that they can be incorporated into the system schematic. The symbol only needs to illustrate the HDL program as a line box drawing containing the inputs and outputs. The compiler is able to detect that it is a HDL program and invokes the HDL compiler to produce a compatible netlist during the compilation process. Once compiled, there is no significant difference in the netlist produced, whether the original symbol was a true schematic or an HDL program. This allows a mixture of true symbol entry and HDL symbol entry into the schematic so that the most appropriate method of describing the digital functions can be used.

The ability to represent complex operations with simple symbols connected by their inputs and outputs provides another useful capability, that of hierarchy. Symbols can be created that represent different levels of abstraction of the design, which helps with the design and understanding of large systems. For example, the top level hierarchical description may show only major functional blocks such as microprocessor, I/O sub-system and memory blocks. A second, less abstract level may illustrate the major blocks within the microprocessor being used and a third level may then show the individual registers and gates that make up the microprocessor. In addition, large systems can be broken down into a number of different schematics which can be worked on by different members of the design team. Provided that the interfaces between different schematics are carefully described and adhered to, the individual schematics can then be combined at a higher level, where each of the individual schematics is represented by a simple symbol. Hierarchy provides a powerful tool for controlling the creation of large complex systems created by several different designers.

4.2.3 High level language entry using HDLs

The entry of designs using hardware description languages (HDL) is covered in considerable detail later on in this book. The main process is one of describing the functions and operations to be performed by the logic using an abstract language which is independent of the target device. Although HDLs do not have to be independent of the target device it makes them more general purpose if they are. HDL compilers generally follow a two step sequence. First, the syntax is checked to confirm that the language has been used correctly and that all constructs implemented can be compiled. Second comes the conversion to a netlist format. Once the syntax has been checked, the program is converted into a netlist describing how the basic logic gates and registers will be connected together. Some optimisation of the design may be performed at this point. As described here, HDL programs can be combined with schematics to create a mixed entry method.

4.2.4 Place and route

After functional simulation the design has to be synthesised on to the target device. This is all achieved automatically by the development software. This takes place in two main steps; the placing of the logic, followed by the routing of the interconnections. Before placing occurs the logic is optimised to reduce redundant gates and registers and to maximise the effectiveness of the architecture of the target device. Typical of the algorithms used is the Espresso algorithm. Typical areas for optimisation are automatic pin placement, optimised flip-flop selection (D, T or JK types) and automatic state assignment for state machines, using Gray code, binary, one hot and so on. After optimisation has been completed, the design is fitted by a device specific tool to obtain the maximum packing of logic into the device. Once placed, the logic blocks have to be interconnected which is called routing. This is automatic and will maximise the availability of the routing connections to obtain the highest packing density of logic gates, the minimum use of routing resources and the minimum propagation delays.

Figure 4.13 illustrates the place and routing for the RISC design from chapter 8 using the Cypress CY7C381A FPGA. Compiled from a VHDL description and fitted using the WARP2 development software, running on a PC. It may be necessary for a number of attempts to be made using different placements in order to completely route the design if a high utilisation of the available logic gates is required by the design. Any design with more than 75% utilisation may prove difficult to place and route.

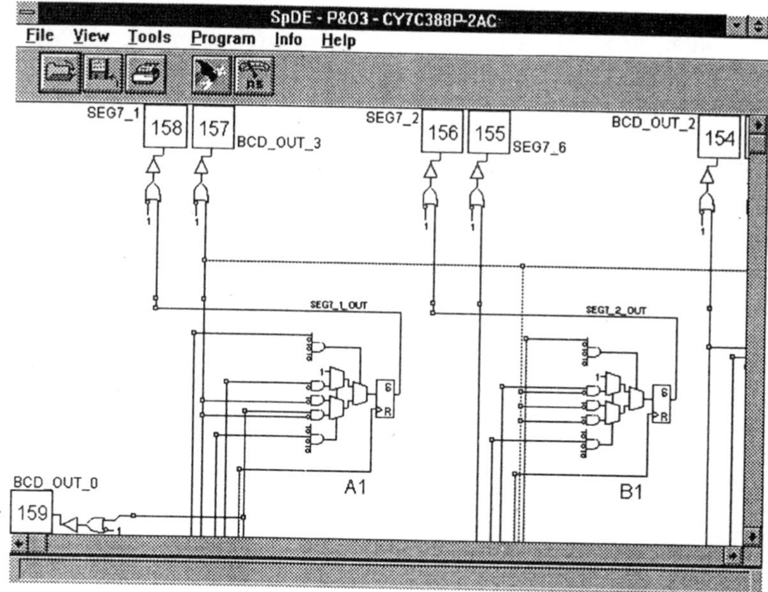

Figure 4.13 FPGA layout schematic

4.2.5 Megafunctions

Megafunctions seem to be a technique likely to be increasingly used as they provide designers with a method of improving their productivity. Megafunctions are descriptions of complex and sometimes complete functional blocks which can be efficiently implemented in the target FPGA. Typical megafunctions are RAM, ROM, arithmetic units and even complete microprocessors. All the designer has to do is to select the megafunction like any other symbol and a fully tested and efficiently implemented logic block is created. The designer then connects them together. At present, megafunctions are targeted specifically at particular FPGA architectures, so there is little possibility of transferring designs between different manufacturers. The megafunctions themselves are being created by the FPGA manufacturers and also by design companies that are then able to have their designs included in the libraries of megafunctions supplied by the FPGA manufacturers.

4.2.6 Library of parameterised models (LPM)

To improve on the success of megafunctions, standard models for components which can be implemented as megafunctions are being created. These models are designed to be independent of both manufacturers and FPGA and ASIC architectures and technologies. Typical models presently available are adders, counters, memory and so on. These models require a set of parameters to fully describe them in order to convert a general model of a component into a specific implementation, hence the name library of parameterised models (LPM). For example, an adder would require the number of bits in each numbers to be described and the technique for generating the carry bits. The models being created will be industry standards in much the same way as the 7400 series of components, except that they will be at a higher level of complexity. Each FPGA manufacturer will then provide an efficient implementation for their specific architectures so that all the designer has to do is select the LPM in the design and then select the target FPGA. Porting of designs to other FPGAs then becomes much easier. In addition, it can be envisaged that the designer may not even need to be aware that a LPM is being used but will just specify a particular operation and the development system will select the most appropriate model.

For example, an LPM model of a multiplier could be identified by the label LPM_MUL and would have a number of parameters. Typically these would be:

LPM_REPRESENTATION	What type of multiplier, such as SIGNED or UNSIGNED.
LPM_WIDTHA	How many bits in the A input to the multiplier.
LPM_WIDTHB	How many bits in the B input.
LPM_WIDTHR	How many bits in the result output by the multiplier. This can be automatically obtained from (LPM_WIDTHA + LPM_WIDTHB).

4.2.7 Behavioural retiming

A new technique being used to improve the operation of gate level synthesis is behavioural retiming. The aim behind behavioural retiming is to take a completed design which has been synthesised down to gate level, but which does not yet achieve the required speed performance and to automatically move about the registers, across combinational logic and within hierarchies. Registers can be added or deleted to achieve speed improvements and a typically improvement of 15% in operating frequency might require an increase of 5% in silicon. The process is completely automatic, requiring no intervention by the user and is obviously a potentially important tool for final tweaking. However, it does have drawbacks; some designs are not suitable and there is an increase in the gates required, so that designs which only just fit may not be amenable to this approach.

4.2.8 Formal verification

A technique that is rapidly gaining acceptance is that of formal verification, which seeks to prove mathematically that a design implements the specification correctly. It should be remembered that this technique does not necessarily identify that the specification itself is correct, although it will identify any inconsistencies. At present verification is achieved through extensive simulation and testing at each stage of the design process. For example, the initial design in a HDL will need to be functionally simulated to determine correct operation. This is then followed by place and route which requires a further simulation using the same test vectors so that discrepancies can be identified. This may then be followed by resynthesis to improve performance and to include test logic. Each time a change in gate level implementation is made, a full simulation should be performed to maintain confidence in the correctness of the design. Again, it should be noted that if the specification is incorrect, or the initial simulation is not exhaustive, then subsequent simulations may not uncover hidden faults. When formal verification is used, only the first simulation has to be checked manually. Once the functional simulation is correct then subsequent alterations to the implementation can be automatically verified and any differences identified. This approach is particularly useful when a design has to be partitioned across several FPGAs or ASICs, as the operation of the partitioned sub-design can be automatically verified against the correct part of the original complete design. The result of formal verification is a report on the differences between a 'known good' design where 'known good' is used in the sense that the designer has declared it to be good rather than through any method of deducing that it is good, and a subsequent synthesis. It is then the designer's responsibility to determine if the differences are significant and what to do about resolving them.

A variation on formal verification is the use of interactive formal verification which allows the user to query the design to identify what is causing specific effects in the design. For example, if a register is not being reset properly, a query can be created which the formal verification is able to understand. It then investigates the design, determines the area involved and then reports back to the user suggested reasons for the observed behaviour (or lack of it).

4.2.9 Intellectual property rights (IPR)

An area of increasing importance is the use of Intellectual Property Rights whereby designers, typically independent of the FPGA manufacturers and development system creators, produce designs for large digital systems which are then licensed for use by product manufacturers. The designers are able to build up expertise in specific topic areas, such as cellular telephones. Cellular telephone manufacturers are then able to buy off-the-shelf designs which are tried and tested, with efficient implementations. Agreements between development system creators and IPR holders are likely to occur in the near future, so that the designs are available to all users after payment of the appropriate fee, in much the same way that operating systems are supplied with PCs.

4.3 Programming

Once a design has been completed and converted into a binary representation suitable for storage in the FPGA, it has to be programmed into the selected device. Manufacturers have devised a number of alternative methods for achieving this, each of which has its own advantages. The main techniques are: to use special programmers for the devices, or standard PROM devices and the FPGA then transfers the data from the PROM into the FPGA whenever power is first applied, or to download the design from the computer to the FPGA directly using a special communication link and interface and then permanently storing the data in internal PROM. The advantage of using special programmers, such as are required for the antifuse devices, is that the FPGA does not have to include special logic for transferring the design, so that the existing silicon can be used for the functions of the FPGA, resulting in a more efficient solution. The disadvantage is that special programmers are required. This problem can be reduced by using special adapters on the standard programmer that most manufacturers already process.

Using standard PROM devices to hold the design is based on the idea that only existing standard programmers are required, which the designers will almost certainly already have. The drawback is that special logic has to be added to the FPGA to perform the transfer of data from the PROM to the FPGA when power is first applied. In addition, once the design has been transferred, the PROM is no longer required and is consuming power and occupying PCB for no functional purpose. These drawbacks can be reduced by the use of serial PROMs which occupy only a small amount of PCB and using CMOS technology with power down features to reduce power consumption to almost nothing when the PROM is not in use. Downloading the design over a special communication link is becoming increasingly popular as it does not require any programmers at all and because the link is usually only a simple cable, each designer can have one to test and update their designs. Although each FPGA manufacturer has a proprietary communication link, the majority are based on the JTAG connections that most large modern digital components now incorporate and can be programmed either from the printer port or the serial port of the PC. The FPGA usually stores the design internally in RAM so that if power is removed the design has to be downloaded again. However, this can be an advantage when the design is being developed. Once the design has reached a satisfactory level of performance, it can be copied from the RAM to EEPROM within the FPGA for permanent storage. Then, when power is first applied to the FPGA, it copies the design from the internal EEPROM to the internal RAM. Although this does utilise some of the silicon available for this initialisation and storage mechanism, it avoids the need for external components and special programmers. In addition, it is becoming common to design the hardware and manufacture it using unprogrammed FPGAs. The designs are simply programmed into pre-manufactured products as and when required using in-system programming. This avoids the need to stock programmed devices and means that the latest version of the FPGA design can always be used. It also enables older versions of the product to be easily reprogrammed with the most up-to-date versions of the FPGA designs, as the internal PROM is nearly always electrically erasable as well as electrically programmable.

4.3.1 Erasing

Erasing the FPGAs is a relatively simple process as there are only three main techniques for programming them: EPROM, EEPROM or SRAM based configuration. EPROM based configuration of the programmable points is no longer a preferred method and can be considered to be an old-fashioned technique. The reasons are that it requires a specialist programmer to transfer the design into the target component and in-system reconfiguration is not possible. Erasing is achieved in the traditional manner using an appropriate exposure to ultraviolet light of the specified intensity and wavelength for the required period of time, typically 20 minutes. An erased FPGA can then be reprogrammed with a new design.

EEPROM has become increasingly popular as the technology for implementing the EEPROM transistors has improved and their cost has decreased. They have the advantage of allowing in-system programming so that the target FPGA can be soldered on to the PCB before programming and, in certain circumstances, allow in-system reconfiguration. The devices can be erased by the application of the correct voltages with the correct sequencing and timing. The preferred devices have internal voltage generators to convert the normal 5 V supply to the higher voltages used for erasing and programming, typically 12 V. Other components require the availability of the 12 V on the PCB which can make the product more expensive as it may not be required for any other purpose. In addition, there may be a limit on the number of program and erase cycles that the device can undertake before it fails to program properly. Older generation technologies had cycles limited to 100 erase/programs, but the more recent generations have a considerably increased maximum number of cycles.

SRAM based configuration has the two advantages of in-system programming and also in-system reconfiguration. However, the design has to be stored somewhere in non-volatile memory which is usually a standard microprocessor compatible EPROM or EEPROM, or a specialist serial EEPROM. For SRAM based FPGA, whenever power is removed the design is lost and the device can be considered to be erased. Reconfiguration, which is equivalent to erasure followed by reprogramming, is easily and quickly achieved.

4.3.2 Programming

The programming of the target device with the completed design is generally performed in one of two ways. The first uses a special programmer where the device has to be placed into the programmer and the design information permanently transferred. If EPROM or EEPROM cells are used, then it will be possible to erase the device and reprogram with an alternative design. If fusible links or antifuse links are used, then the device cannot be erased. Because of this, fused devices are only used when products have undergone considerable testing in the real products. The second approach uses in-system programming which is increasingly popular due to the inclusion of JTAG ports in most large digital devices. These were originally included to make the testing of PCBs possible as pin spacing on ICs decreased, but have been almost universally adopted for both in-system programming and in-system reconfiguration.

Once the device has been programmed, it has to be tested. If a special programmer has been used it is sometimes possible to perform physical testing on the device while it is still in the programmer, using the same test vectors used during functional simulation. However, the majority of testing in most instances is performed with a fully configured and powered-up system operating in much the same way as the final product will. This requires considerable skill to achieve and sometimes a piece of automatic test equipment (ATE) can be used which is able to implement the same test vectors that were used during the simulation process. If the device was programmed in-system, then the only tests that can be performed are full product testing. The final method of testing is to use an FPGA emulator which replaces the device being programmed with a probe which is electrically, physically and functionally equivalent to the device being tested. The design to be executed is then downloaded into the probe, but the computer maintains the ability to monitor and control all of the internal operations at the normal speed of execution of the target device. This provides the optimum method of performing the debugging process. However, because a different emulator would be required for each different FPGA from each different manufacturer, only a limited range of emulators is available.

4.3.3 Standards

Although most manufacturers would prefer to use their own methods of representing their designs, the use of standard programming languages such as VHDL and standard programmers means that many of the stages in the production of the FPGA design have to be described in standard notations. Typical standard notations are EDIF and JEDEC or HEX. HEX is not really a standard, being simply a description of the design using hexadecimal numbering systems, but as these files are commonly used in programmers, they have a fairly standard format. If the target device is known this can be used to reverse compile the design. This approach would only really be used for an old design for which the original design process documentation has been lost but which still has to be incorporated into new products. JEDEC is more often used with PLDs than FPGAs, but some smaller FPGAs may use this format to describe how the programmable points within the FPGA should be programmed. The drawback of JEDEC is that it is not a very compact method of describing the design and larger FPGAs with several hundred thousand programmable points would require extremely large JEDEC files.

The previous two standards are concerned with the completed design just before it is programmed into the target device. EDIF is aimed at an earlier stage in the design process, typically before the design has been mapped to the target device. As most design methods are abstract and designed to be independent of the target hardware, after the compilation process the description that is created is still (almost) independent of the target and can be represented in a standard manner, such as EDIF. This is important, because the producers of the software development tools are not always the same as the component manufacturers and in order to make their software as useful as possible to the maximum number of designers, it has to be able to cope with a wide variety of target FPGAs, often from a variety of different manufacturers. The EDIF standard allows this to happen as the software developers can use the same development tools for all the different FPGAs to produce an EDIF output file and then use the design mappers from the FPGA manufacturers who are most familiar with how the FPGAs operate. The design mappers from the FPGA manufacturers all use EDIF files as their inputs, so the mappers can be used with the maximum number of different software development tools. The result is that both software tool developers and FPGA manufacturers obtain access to a larger market share with the same product. The users of the FPGAs and the software tools have the advantage that they can mix software tools, with different target devices as dictated by the design, rather than by the available properties of the tools or development system.

4.4 Exporting and importing of designs

As described previously there are a number of different stages in the design process when it is possible to transfer between different development systems. This is achieved through the use of standard file formats which are independent of both the target device and the originating development systems. Typical points at which exporting and importing of designs may occur are at schematic or HDL program level, as these can often be transferred between different competing development systems, often without any changes required. Alternatively, after compilation of the schematic or HDL, a netlist is produced and this is commonly transferred between different development systems. This technique is vital for the small manufacturer as it allows them to simply develop a front end compiler for their specific target devices and then use, under licence, the remaining stages of the development system from a larger company. After place and route, during the simulation stage, it is again common for the simulation file to be output in a format suitable for transfer between different simulators so that the most appropriate can be used for the specific target device. Finally, designs are nearly always output in some standard format to allow the designs to be programmed into the target devices using standard programmers. The increase in use of the JTAG interface for in-system programming has meant that these formats are not interchangeable, but the software will nearly always also output a format suitable for use with a standard programmer which would then be interchangeable.

4.4.1 EDIF

Electronic Data Interchange Format, or EDIF, is one of the most common approaches to the export and import of designs between different development systems. It is a text based description of the design, indicating all of the connections and how they are connected together. The design itself should be independent of the target device. Because it is a text based description, even if the design entry method was a schematic, the files produced can be very large. Part of an EDIF description is shown below.

```
(edit RISCCOMP
(edifVersion 2 0 0)
  (edifLevel 0)
  (keywordMap (keywordLEvel 0))
 (status
  (written
  (timestamp 0 0 0 0 0 0)
    (program "RISCCOMP.EXE")
  (comment "My RISC Design"))
   (comment "")
   (comment "January  25, 1996")
   (comment "")
   (comment "")
   (comment "")
  (external OrCAD_LIB
   (edifLevel 0)
   (technology
    (numberDefinition
     (scale 1 1 (unit distance))))
   (cell CLKBUF
    (cellType generic)
    (comment "From ORCAD library GATES2.LIB")
    (view NetlistView
     (viewType netlist)
     (interface
      (port PAD (direction INPUT))
      (port Y (direction OUTPUT)))))
```

The development system should be capable of both importing EDIF files from other development systems and of exporting EDIF files for use by other development systems. Although EDIF is a standard, manufacturers sometimes produce local variations that have been optimised for their particular software and users should be careful to check the EDIF version number at the beginning of the file to ensure that it is a generic version. The widely used version is EDIF

2 0 0, although version EDIF 3 0 0 also exists. The EDIF file is only a description of the design after it has been entered, either as a schematic or a HDL program and then compiled down into a netlist format. The design will not have been fitted to a target device and may or may not have been simulated. In addition, after simulation, back-annotation may have occurred with the results of static timing being included. Maintaining the correct version of the EDIF files and its derivatives at all design stages in the production process requires careful attention to version numbers and date and time stamps on the files. This is usually undertaken by the development system software.

4.4.2 PLDs to FPGAs

There are a number of objectives behind a PLD to FPGA conversion, the most important of which for most users are:

1) **To reduce physical PCB area required.** By combining several PLDs into a single FPGA much less PCB area is required due to the smaller total areas of the components, the reduction in copper tracks required for interconnection and possible reduction in power supply sizes.

2) **To reduce power consumption.** As the FPGAs are implemented in the most modern semiconductor technology in order to obtain the highest logic gate density and highest operating frequencies, the result is also to reduce the power requirements. This can then result in a reduction in the total system power requirements so that a smaller, cheaper power supply can be used. The use of low power FPGAs has also enabled much more battery powered portable equipment to be produced.

3) **To reduce cost.** The reduction in PCB area and power supply size brings an immediate reduction in the cost of the products. There may also be a reduction in the total cost of the components; however, this reduction is not usually significant as the FPGA has a more expensive development system. The major saving comes through the reduced development cycle time leading to products that are on sale quicker.

4) **To increase reliability.** The reduction in component count and reduction in soldered connections on the PCB contribute to an increase in reliability in the completed product.

5) **To produce designs that are more portable.** PLD designs are typically targeted at specific architectures, whereas FPGA designs are usually more abstract and although FPGA features may be important, it is not too difficult to port to a completely different target device.

6) **To improve the operating frequency**. It is not always possible to obtain higher operating frequencies with FPGA as the general purpose and complex nature sometimes means that propagation delays are longer. This is because PLDs have a simplified fixed architecture which can be optimised for timing purposes.

7) **To implement designs that may not otherwise be feasible**. Although not strictly a PLD to FPGA conversion advantage, it is an advantage that FPGAs have over PLDs.

The above order does not imply any priority. See chapter 7 for more detail.

4.5 Testing

For FPGAs, testing can be separated into two distinct types of tests. The first is functional testing which considers whether the final design meets the original specification by treating the device as a black box to which are applied realistic input signals and timing. The outputs are then compared with the predicted values and any differences are likely to be due to errors in the specification, errors in the implementation, or errors in the test vectors. Secondly, automatic test pattern generation (ATPG) is concerned with being able to test the internal logic of the design. Methods are used to control and monitor every node within the design. If every node is monitored, this is 100% testability. For most designs something between 95-100% is acceptable, anything less means that the design may prove unreliable.

4.5.1 Functional testing and simulation

Single device simulation using test vectors has been covered in chapter 3. When performing functional simulation on designs containing multiple FPGAs an appropriate strategy has to be followed. First, each FPGA will have a separate design file which is converted into a netlist for use by the simulator. Second, create a new design which contains the netlists from the individual devices, treating them as single components connected by the inter-FPGA wiring. Finally, load the new design into the simulator and apply the test vectors. Some development systems will enable this process to be completed within the design environment, others will require manual intervention to create the necessary files for the simulator to operate on.

4.5.2 ATPG

Automatic Test Pattern Generation is aimed at identifying a basic number of faults, typically the stuck at 0 or the stuck at 1 faults. For example, assuming that an invertor connected to an OR gate has an output which has become stuck at 1. When test patterns are applied to the inputs, the output of the OR gate will remain at a logic 1, rather than changing to the required logic level. This would be detected and the precise location identified. A 'stuck at' fault indicates that something is wrong with the device, not necessarily with the design. It is equivalent to being able to use a probe to follow the signal through a PCB from component pin to component pin to identify faulty components.

There are two main elements to design for testability; that of controllability and observability. As many of the internal nodes of an FPGA will not be directly accessible from an I/O pin, scan chains have to be inserted. Scan chains are typically automatically inserted when the design has been compiled to a netlist, after synthesis to the target device and after the design rule checker has completed. A scan chain is simply a linked list of registers which are able to serially pass an input from one end to the other. The registers of the design are used for this, with some additional signals just to facilitate the scan path. Figure 4.14 illustrates how a scan path connection is added to a simple D type flip-flop.

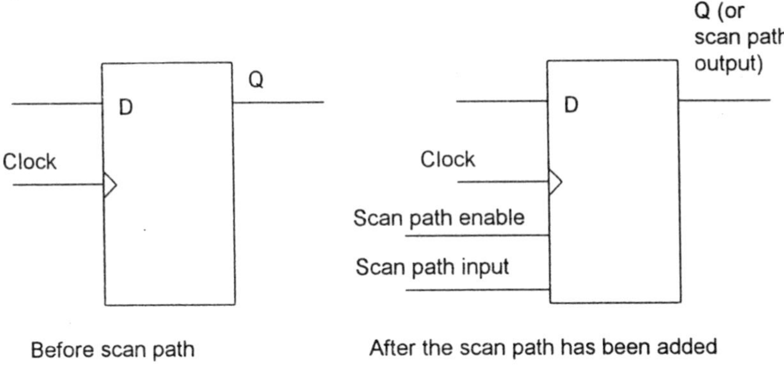

Figure 4.14 Adding a scan path to a D type flip-flop

Two additional signals are required, the scan path input and the scan path enable. The Q output of the flip-flop acts as the scan path output which will become the scan path input for the next register in the scan. When enabled, data can be passed along the path to create the required input patterns to the combinational logic and, at the same time, results can be obtained from the other end of the scan path. The process is dependent on being able to add the scan path to all registers and the use of a global clock. Guidelines for creating the scan paths are recommended, such as the following:

1) Scan chains should not include more than 64 registers. An FPGA containing 1600 registers would require 25 scan paths. Each scan path will need an input and an output and if these are not available they will have to be multiplexed with the existing functional inputs and outputs.

2) A separate pin is required for the scan path enable signal. Normally, the existing global clock can still be used.

3) If a global clock is not used, for example with multiple clocks, or gated clocks then a further signal, called scan path test mode is required, to convert the registers which use a non-global clock to use the global clock.

Although many development systems have the facility to amend the user's design so that ATPG is more efficient, there are a number of guidelines that can make this process much easier.

1) For combinational elements all of the inputs must be controllable and the outputs observable.
2) Designs should be all synchronous, using a single global clock. Gates should not be cross-coupled and there should not be any unregistered feedback loops. Gated clocks should not be used.
3) Latches should not be used as they cannot be clocked. If latches must be used, they should be forced to a transparent mode while scan chain testing is being performed.
4) Only use a single reset to all registers. Gated resets and internally generated rests should not be used.
5) Do not use internal tri-state signals as these cannot be scan chain tested.
6) Always ensure that at least some propagation delay is inserted between a register Q output to a D (or JK) input, usually via a logic gate, to avoid dynamic timing hazards. This is not really a scan chain problem but it does avoid the possibility of dynamic hazards which would cause scan chain problems.

The typical sequence for creating the test patterns is as follows:

1) The ATPG compiler creates patterns for 'stuck at 0' and 'stuck at 1' faults, often generating random input patterns and monitoring the percentage coverage continuously. When coverage stops increasing the compiler adopts a second strategy.
2) Individual nodes which have not been tested are identified and specific patterns devised to test them. If a pattern cannot be devised the node is identified as untestable and will be reported to the user. The user may decide to amend the design in order to obtain higher levels of coverage until a satisfactory value is obtained.
3) Once a satisfactory level of coverage is obtained, the compiler will merge the patterns to the minimum number possible as this will reduce the product testing time when in production.
4) Finally, patterns will be generated that test the logic of the scan chains themselves, so that the scan chains can be confirmed to be operating correctly before the testing of the device proper begins.

4.5.3 Routing and timing analysis

One aspect of testing and simulation is the calculation of the internal delays incurred as signals travel within the FPGA. When a design is entered, it undergoes functional simulation to ensure that the design is correct. For this simulation, the delays within the design are estimated by the development system, based on previous knowledge. Two factors are used to control the estimations, knowledge of the data sheets and statistical knowledge of past designs and a scaling factor applied by the development system based on how likely the design is to meet the values calculated in step 1. The delay values produced give some indication of whether the design will operate as required and will indicate where timing margins are likely to be a problem. The designer can then amend the design to avoid potential timing violations before too much effort has been expended during the place and route. Once satisfactory estimated timing values have been used in the simulation, the design is synthesised on to the target device. The synthesis process now means that more accurate timing values can be calculated as the number of logic gates and the lengths of signals are known. This timing is known as static timing and does not relate to the dynamic functional operation of the design.

Once the static timing values have been determined, these are back-annotated into the netlist produced and used for the functional simulation. A further post-routing simulation is performed using the more accurate timing values, to ensure that the system still operates as required and that timing guidelines are not violated. Any difficulties can be resolved by returning to the original design, amending as necessary and repeating the timing calculation process. It should still be remembered that these are still only simulated results and are not 100% accurate. The final programmed device may still have slight variations in signal timings. However, post routing simulations are increasingly accurate and, provided that the design does not produce any timings close to the boundary conditions of allowed timing guidelines, the real device is likely to operate close to the post routing simulation.

4.6 Problems

1) Figure 4.15 illustrates a simple logic system to which a scan chain has been added. Complete the truth table in table 4.4 which contains the scan chain input and output for this circuit, in order to detect the stuck at 1 fault.

2) Using the Actel logic block, identify how the following two input logical Boolean operators would be obtained:

a) AND b) NAND
c) OR d) NOR
e) XOR.

Table 4.4 Scan chain input and output

Clock	Scan chain input	Scan chain output
clk		
clk		
clk		
clk		

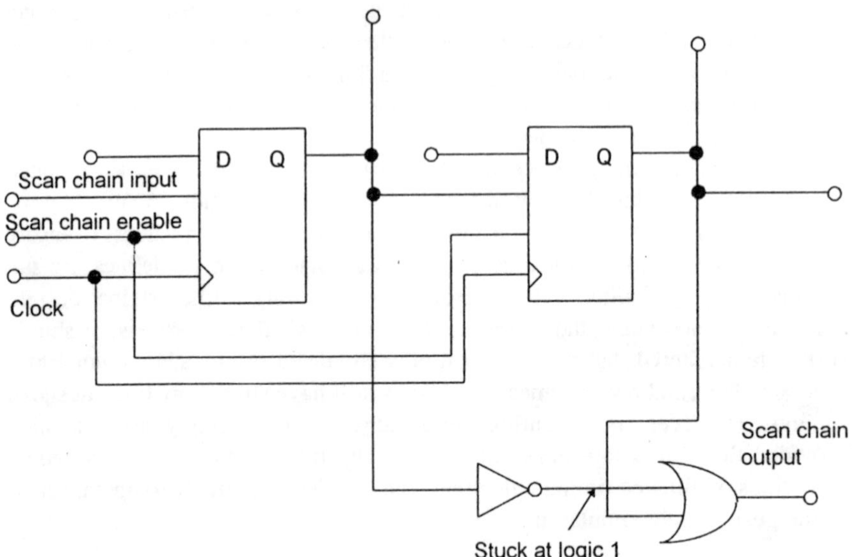

Figure 4.15 A logic system with a scan chain added

3) The PLD AND-OR architecture is shown in figure 4.16 where the fuse positions have been identified. Assuming that the device is erased, that is all programmable points are at logic 0 which is equivalent to open circuit, what is the logic function implemented by the followed compressed programming sequence?

F001 1 1,10,1,23,1,8,1,89,1,10,1,9,1,8,1,5,1,5,1,4,1,14

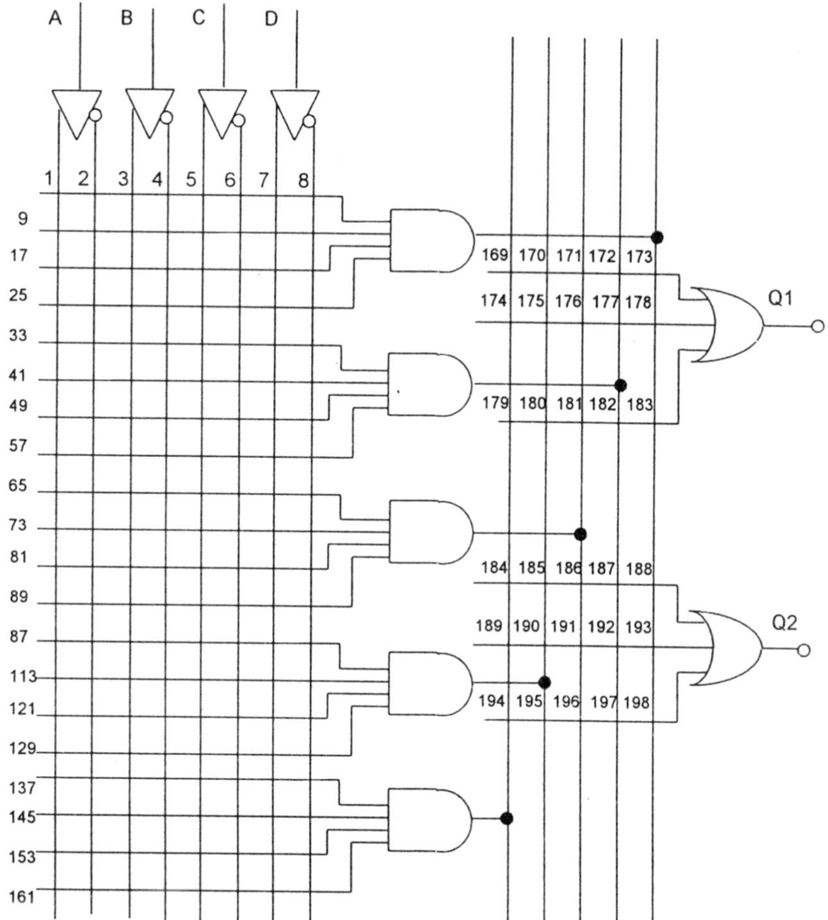

Figure 4.16 Programming points for an AND-OR architecture

The programmed device is now to be partially reconfigured using the following programming sequence.

P065 1 1,33,1,18,1,22,1,31,1,5,1,6,1,3,1,3,1,4

What is the updated logic function that will now be implemented?
Fxxx indicates the starting fuse position for a full configuration and Pxxx the starting position for a partial reconfiguration. The programming sequence then consists of the logic value of the first location to be programmed (0 or 1),

then the number of consecutive logic values of the other logic type. Then the number of consecutive logic values with the original logic value and so on. For example:

F001 1,10,1,23

indicates that it is a full configuration starting at fuse location 001 which will be programmed to a logic 1. There will only be 1 logic 1 followed by another 10 logic 0's from location 002 to location 011. Location 12 will then be another logic 1, followed by 23 more logic 0's and so on.

4.7 Further reading

Altera Data Book 1995, Altera Corporation, 2610 Orchard Parkway, San Jose, CA 95134-2020, USA.

Configurable Logic Design and Application Book, Atmel Corp., 2125 O'Nel Drive, San Jose, CA 95131, USA.

FPGA Data Book and Design Guide 1994, Actel Corp., 955E Arques Avenue, Sunnyvale, CA 94086, USA.

FPGA Data Manual, Texas Instruments, PO Box 655303, Dalllas, Texas 75265, USA.

FPGA Data 1995, Motorola, PO Box 20912, Phoenix, Arizona 85036, USA.

Lattice Data Book 1994, Lattice Semiconductor Corp. 5555 Northwest Moore Ct., Hillsboro, Oregon 97124, USA.

MACH series data book 1995, AMD Inc., 901 Thompson Place, P.O. Box 3453, Sunnyvale, California 94088-3453, USA.

Moore and Luk (Eds), *FPGAs*, Abingdon EE&CS Books, 1991, ISBN 0-9518453-0-6.

Moore and Luk (Eds), More FPGAs, Abingdon EE&CS Books, 1994, ISBN 0-9518453-1-4.

PEEL Products Data Book 1994, ICT Inc, 2123 Ringwood Ave, San Jose, CA 95131, USA.

Programmable Logic Data Book, 1994/5, Cypress Semiconductor, 3901 North First Street, San Jose, CA 95134, USA.

Programmable Logic Data Book, Xilinx 1994, 2100 Logic Drive, San Jose, CA 95124-3400, USA.

Quicklogic Data book 1994, Quicklogic Corp., 2933 Bunker Hill Lane, Santa Clara, CA 95054, USA.

5 Benchmarking

Benchmarking can be considered to be an objective comparison of selected parameters of similar and competing processes, technologies or devices. In this discussion the differences and similarities of competing programmable logic devices, field programmable gate arrays and their development systems will be considered. This is not intended to be a definitive review or explanation, since benchmarking techniques are constantly evolving as manufacturers seek to identify the best features of their products. Nor should it be considered to present a preference for any particular product or benchmarking methodology, as this can only be genuinely achieved by a prospective user who has the particular design in mind, the financial constraints designated and the timescale outlined. Instead, the discussion will attempt to identify the majority of benchmarking methods currently used and illustrate any limitations and drawbacks. Although benchmarking will be considered in some detail, it has to be remembered that once a manufacturer has been chosen, it is probable that the company will stay with that product range for a minimum of several projects as there are additional costs involved when choosing a previously unused device. Typically, these are the time spent gaining familiarity with the architecture, the cost of purchasing the development hardware and software, the time spent learning how to use the development system, and the prototyping time spent uncovering the peculiarities of the practical side of the devices, in terms of timing delays, noise rejection and so on. Because of this, it is unlikely that the full range of different manufacturers devices will be considered for each new project, with the result that benchmarking becomes an occasional task undertaken when the existing product range being used appears unable to meet the current project specification and requirements.

5.1 The need for differentiation

Manufacturers are always seeking to identify those characteristics of their own products which distinguish them in a positive way from those of their competitors. Typical quantities expressed are the capacity, the maximum speed of operation, the cost, the packaging and other environmental considerations and finally the ease of use. Parameters appear and disappear with the passage of time. Alternatively, users or purchasers are seeking to identify the most appropriate products and components for the new designs they are considering, or for improving on existing product designs to make them ever more competitive. Users are seeking to obtain the most objective viewpoint of the products available; the manufacturers are seeking to make their products the most attractive and visible to the market place. In an ideal world the two desires would be compatible, but the reality is sometimes quite different.

It is not uncommon for a manufacturer to devise a benchmark which promotes the features of its own products and which, when applied to competitors' products that do not have the same features, appears to demote them. Nor is it uncommon for manufacturers to select an apparently objective benchmark methodology and then design products specifically in order to obtain a good rating which may not then be reflected in real-life use. Therefore, benchmark methods should be designed to be as objective as possible with the requirements of the user as paramount rather than the manufacturer and which will give an accurate representation of the use of the devices and products in real-life situations. For programmable logic, there are two main areas of interest when benchmarking is applied; the components themselves and the development systems used to convert designs into programmed products.

5.2 Components

The range of programable components available from any single manufacturer is usually large, so making the selection from only one manufacturer can be difficult. When considering the offerings from all the manufacturers it becomes even more difficult. A list of the major manufacturers of FPGAs is given below, many of which also offer PLDs and there are a number of other manufacturers offering a range of PLDs only.

ACTEL	ATMEL	TEXAS INSTRUMENTS
ALTERA	CYPRESS	XILINX
AMD	LATTICE	

Typically, each manufacturer will have a number of different families of products with different architectures and technologies, say for example, four families, perhaps with four products in each family. Just for the manufacturers listed above, this will mean something like 128 different components to be considered for each new design. In reality, this global performance approach is not taken every time a new product is being designed. Instead, users will make an analysis of a number of different families, make a decision about a particular manufacturer and then establish a relationship with the manufacturer which would be expected to last a number of years. It has to be accepted that most new designs can be implemented with programmable components from any of the available manufacturers, as most of the devices have more similarities than differences. There are two main sources of benchmarking available for components; individual manufacturer specific and standardised which should be manufacturer independent. The most common quantities that are quoted to enable comparison are: gate counts, register counts, the maximum operating frequency (or minimum propagation delay) and the routing capability. In addition, individual manufacturers may quote examples of practical implementations of realistic circuits, in order to give some idea of realistic operating conditions. In has to be remembered that these figures will always be chosen to promote the most favourable opinion of the devices, but provided that they are accurate and realistic they can be most useful to the user attempting to make a decision. The two most widely quoted figures are gate count and maximum operating frequency.

Gate count would be a useful figure for use in comparison if all the architectures consisted only of logic gates. However, this is not true as most modern architectures consist of a complex mixture of logic gates, registers and other logic blocks, so that manufacturers must convert these logic blocks into gate equivalents, rather than true gate counts. This produces a figure which looks attractive for a particular application but in reality is not so good, as the logic blocks can only be used for their specific logic function. The gates are not freely available for the user to configure as required. In addition, even if the equivalent logic gates were truly user configurable, the routing capability of the architecture can be insufficient to enable all the gates to be used. Typically, for FPGAs, once more than 50% of the available equivalent gates have been allocated, the routing capability remaining becomes the biggest restriction on utilising the remaining gates. Using skilled engineers and spending more time on the design can usually increase the utilisation of equivalent gates to approximately 75% of that available, but obtaining use of the final 25% can be very difficult and time consuming. It is better to work on the assumption that you will not need more than 75% of what is available, and if you do, to use a device with more gates. Individual manufacturers and users have made claims of utilisation of over 95%, but these designs will either have taken a long time to achieve, or are particularly suited to the architecture of the programmable logic component.

The maximum operating figures quoted will be produced for a fairly standard implementations of a common logic block. Typically, a simple binary incrementing counter is chosen as this is a well known logic gate design often used in systems, with which most designers will be familiar. It is also typical of the type of logic block that will have to operate at the highest frequency within the system. Therefore, by quoting figures for the operation of a simple binary counter, users can obtain an immediate understanding of the limitation of the device as it would directly affect the system to be implemented.

The drawback of using manufacturers' own figures is that they will always promote their own devices at the expense of their competitors, this has to be expected and allowed for. The figures will be correct and consistent with the method that the manufacturer uses for counting, but may not accurately reflect the capability as required by the user. Often, they will also be different from the method used for equivalent gate counting used by other manufacturers, so that comparison is not as straightforward as it should be.

5.2.1 Manufacturers' benchmarks

When a manufacturer promotes its own benchmarks it is usually on the assumption that a user has already chosen them as the supplier and is now attempting to identify the most appropriate component from those that the manufacturer produces. This makes the benchmark much easier and perhaps more accurate as the manufacturer has an intimate understanding of the architecture and usefulness of its own devices and has almost nothing to lose by providing that information in a useful and informative manner to the user. If the user is already committed to the manufacturer's products, whatever devices are chosen, the manufacturer will gain financially. There is often no indication that any other manufacturer of programmable logic exists and even if other manufacturers are mentioned it will usually be to show how much poorer the devices are.

Typical of this type of benchmarking is the software package available from Xilinx for the selection of programmable logic called Logic Professor, although this only helps to select from the XC7000 family of components. The package operates by requesting the user to enter estimated values for a number of programmable logic related parameters, typically the number of equivalent TTL packages, the maximum clock rate required, the number of inputs, outputs and bi-directional pins required, the critical path delays for combinational circuits and the output current drive capability. This is followed by allowing the user to select the importance of the following three variables: the cost, the PCB area and the power consumption. The parameters are entered as relative values within high and low limits, in order to avoid the need for specific values such as cost, which quickly become out of date. The package then identifies the device or range of devices predicted to be the optimum selection but which still satisfies the 'must have' parameters such as speed and power consumption.

These packages are useful for gaining an understanding of the different parameters affecting the choice of PLD and FPGAs, but they do not include all possible devices, even from one manufacturer, and by necessity the user selected parameters are relative and approximate, hence the devices identified as the optimum can only be suggestions rather than definitive answers.

5.2.2 Standardised benchmarks

Although manufacturers are willing to devise their own benchmarks, users are continually looking for methods of comparison between the devices from different manufacturers, either through some widely accepted user derived objective set of benchmark testing, or through a system devised by a standardised body such as the IEEE. In recognition of this, a group of programmable logic manufacturers devised a set of manufacturer independent benchmarks, related to real-life use and then set up an independent company to maintain the benchmark suites, perform the testing and issue the results. This company is known as the Programmable Electronics Performance Corporation, which is based in the USA. These results are issued using the PREP logo which is a trademark of the Programmable Electronics Performance Corporation. The company was created in 1991 to provide reliable manufacturer independent benchmarks for the measurement and comparison of the performance of programmable logic components, and was designed to be used as an objective aid for users when choosing components for projects.

The benchmarks comprise nine functional logic blocks as listed below:

1) 8-bit data path,
2) 8-bit timer/counter,
3) small state machine (8 states),
4) large state machine (16 states),
5) 4 × 4 multiplier/accumulator,
6) 16-bit accumulator,
7) 16-bit counter,
8) 16-bit prescaled counter (cannot count immediately after loading),
9) memory map decoder.

and two main measurements are made, the number of instances of each logic block and the maximum speed of operation when implemented. For the larger programmable logic devices, all nine logic blocks must be implemented and then reported together. The implementation of the logic blocks has to be done automatically in the first instance without manual intervention, although the manufacturer may report manually assisted implementation results as additional information.These benchmarks do not use any form of gate or register counting or routing capability, since these were considered to be unsuitable for comparative assessments due to the widely varying architectures adopted by different manufacturers.

For a device to be included in the published benchmark results it had to be in production by a cut-off date, although it is possible that some manufacturers 'produced' versions of their programmable logic especially for including in the testing, without their being widely available to users. Estimated results of benchmarking or simulated results were not allowed under the PREP trademark, nor was any analysis of the figures produced. The results from all components submitted by all manufacturers were published as a totality, enabling users to make immediate comparisons. Any subsequent analysis of the PREP figures by individual manufacturers was not certified by PREP and this had to be stated whenever any PREP certified data was used.

As with all attempts to devise a totally objective method of measuring performance of products from a number of different manufacturers, individual manufacturers have criticisms and suggestions to make which result in their specific devices appearing to be the best. These criticisms have varied from misrepresentation by competing manufacturers, to advantage being taken of architectures particularly suited to the benchmarks, to uncertified analysis of the

PREP data which may be misleading and unrepresentative. However, the PREP benchmarks provide the most objective method of comparing the performance of different devices from different manufacturers that is presently available.

Typical of the uncertified analysis are the average benchmark speed and average benchmark capacity calculations. The results of all nine of the benchmarks are averaged in order to obtain a global figure of each device which attempts to represent performance with a single figure. The average benchmark speed is an average of the maximum frequency of operation of the nine benchmarks and the average benchmark capacity is an average of the number of times each benchmark logic block was able to be implemented in the device. This reduces the number of benchmark numbers down from 18 to 2 and allows easier comparison between manufacturers' devices. Manufacturers may then choose to plot a graph of average benchmark speed against average benchmark capacity with the intention of demonstrating visually the superior performance of their devices over that of their competitors, either in operating frequency (speed) or capacity, or preferably both. These types of calculations go against the spirit of the PREP benchmarks, but do provide an easy means of comparing devices. However, because they are devised by individual manufacturers they nearly always show their own devices as the best.

One drawback of the PREP benchmarks is that they do not indicate any other parameters of the logic devices which might make them particularly suited to some tasks, such as RAM blocks, JTAG connections and so on. Because of this and the disagreement of how the PREP figures were measured and subsequently manipulated, fewer devices are being submitted for PREP certification, so that manufacturers can promote the particular architecture and characteristics which may make them attractive to users. Despite this, the PREP benchmarks are still the best method of objectively comparing programmable devices that is presently available.

5.3 Additional features not otherwise benchmarked

One of the drawbacks of using the PREP benchmarks is that they do not take into account any of the special features of the architectures of the programmable devices. It is in the additional features that manufacturers seek to provide their products with a distinct feature which makes them particularly suited for certain applications, and hence users will choose them, without relying solely on benchmarking. The range of features is large but some of the more significant are described in the following.

5.3.1 RAM

Some devices feature either a specific section of the logic which has been implemented as a RAM block or allows the programmable points to be used as RAM instead of logic. This is because many logic systems need the ability to store and save data and this feature avoids the need to implement this as a separate component. This reduces the cost, the PCB area required, power consumption and perhaps most importantly, reduces the number of I/O pins, as address and data buses are not required. Using the programmable points avoids the need to dedicate part of the silicon to RAM only, so that more logic overall is available. The disadvantage is that the amount of RAM that can be implemented in this way is relatively small and when implemented as RAM, the associated logic gates cannot be accessed at all; but when only a small amount of RAM is required, this approach may be viable. The alternative of having a specific RAM block as part of the architecture is becoming increasingly popular as the total number of transistors, and hence logic gates, that can easily be implemented on a piece of silicon is increasing. This means that not only can a large number of logic gates be implemented and be made available to the user, but a large RAM is also available whenever required. The drawback is that if RAM is not required that section of the silicon is not being used, which could be considered to be inefficient. However, as the additional cost is not significant, it does not require any additional PCB area, nor does it use any I/O pins; then the only real disadvantage is that a small amount of power is consumed.

5.3.2 Reprogrammability

Regarding the reprogrammability of programmable devices, there are two main types to consider: one-time programming and reprogrammable. One-time programming, as the name suggests, can only be programmed once and if the design is not correct, the device has to be thrown away and a new one used. The advantage of this approach is that the programming elements are much smaller and hence the amount of logic that can be implemented on a specific size piece of silicon is higher.

Reprogrammability provides the user with some method of either erasing the previous programmed values using ultraviolet light, electrically erasable or RAM based programming points. Ultraviolet has the disadvantage that a special eraser is needed, but it is a well known and understood approach. Electrically erasable is becoming increasingly popular, as it avoids the need for special erasers and although special programmers are needed for some devices, modern components are beginning to require no special programming hardware. RAM based programming is the easiest to erase, simply be removing the power. The disadvantage is that every time power is reapplied there is the need to download the programming information, either from a special PROM or via a dedicated communication link. Both of these approaches, although well established, require additional components which, once the programmable logic has been reprogrammed, perform no useful purpose, but occupy PCB space, increase the cost and consume power.

A number of manufacturers have introduced devices which combine the advantages of RAM and electrically erasable programming, by implementing RAM based programmable points, but with a shadow electrically erasable memory block. During development, the logic configuration can be loaded in using the normal RAM approach and then when finalised, this information is transferred to the electrically erasable memory. Then, on subsequent power on cycles, the information is transferred from the electrically erasable block into the RAM points, thereby avoiding the need for external components and connections. It may still be necessary to use a special eraser/programmer if the information stored in the electrically erasable memory has to be changed.

5.3.3 Dynamic reprogramming

One advantage of the RAM based programming that was not mentioned above, is the ability to reprogram the logic dynamically, that is, while the device is implementing some existing logic function. This method operates on the concept that not all of the logic of a design is required all of the time. An easy to understand example is that when power is first applied, some initialisation process will take place, the logic for which is subsequently not required until power is removed and, at a later time, reapplied. Therefore, once completed, the initialisation logic can be replaced with logic required while the system is operating normally. This is called dynamic reprogramming and it allows a device to be used which contains fewer logic gates and hence less silicon and therefore has a lower cost, consumes less power and may occupy less PCB area. The disadvantage of this approach is that is requires specialist logic to implement the dynamic reprogramming and there is a time penalty associated with the reprogramming process which may be too long for the system being implemented.

5.3.4 5 V programming

For non-RAM based programming, a physical change in the structure of the programmable points is required. Traditionally, this has been achieved through the use of super voltages, that is, voltages larger than those available during normal operation. This has necessitated the use of special power supplies during the programming process. Because of this, special programmers are needed so that the devices have to be programmed before they are placed into the circuit. If changes are required they have to be removed, erased (if possible) and then reprogrammed. The use of 5 V programming eliminates the need for special power supplies and hence for special programmers and enables the devices to be programmed while *in situ*. This removes problems caused by handling during programming, such as damage to pins and electrostatic damage. It also avoids the need to stock programmed devices, so only a more limited range of the basic components need be purchased and stored, thereby reducing stock costs.

5.3.5 In-system programming

Once 5 V programming becomes available the next step is to implement in-system programming. Completed PCBs can be produced and then only programmed as required, enabling the latest version of the designs to be used.

If the devices can be electrically erased, then it is possible to change the design programmed into them after production and use, so that in-service changes to the product can be made without having to physically remove the components from the PCBs.

5.3.6 JTAG

As modern digital system increase in complexity but reduce in component count, it becomes increasingly difficult to apply external bed-of-nails testing to ensure that the PCB is constructed correctly and that the system is operating as required. To overcome this, the JTAG standard was introduced to provide an electronic method of testing the PCB. Most complex modern digital components now incorporate the JTAG interface and, for JTAG testing to be implemented, the majority of devices have to have a JTAG port. Therefore, those components with the JTAG interface are a necessity in such systems. The JTAG port has also been used for programming. A simple cable is used to connect the printer port of a PC to the device to be programmed; then, using a custom protocol, the JEDEC file is downloaded and programmed into the device. This avoids the need for special programmers and, when combined with 5 V programming and electrically erasable technologies, provides the complete programming and reprogramming environment for soldered-in devices.

5.3.7 Application specific architectures

One approach to the architecture of the programmable devices that is becoming increasingly popular is to implement logic blocks which have already been optimised for specific logic functions. RAM blocks have been mentioned, but there are also devices which include digital signal processing blocks, CPU blocks, ALU blocks and so on. The aim is to provide the exact architecture needed by the application and for specific applications, so certain devices which implement architectures dedicated to those functions will be superior to the more general purpose programmable device.

5.3.8 Low power and low voltage

As electronic systems become increasingly portable, such as mobile telephones, low power becomes a prime requirement of the electronic devices, since battery power is limited. Semiconductor technologies and architectures have been introduced which use very small currents and can operate at voltages below the standard 5 V power supplies traditionally used for digital logic. Voltages as low as 1.4 V are being used, with a widely used new standard of 3.3 V being used for a large number of modern digital devices. For portable products, low power programmable components are a necessity.

5.3.9 Programmable skew rates

Clock rates for digital systems have been steadily increasing for a number of years, driven by the high clock rates of modern microprocessors. However, fast rise and fall times for digital systems are not always advantageous, as they can generate severe electrical noise of the power rails and radiate electromagnetic interference. To overcome this problem some programmable devices have I/O pins which can have the output rise and fall times programmed to different values. This does affect the overall frequency of operation, but may be a necessary sacrifice in order to reduce electrical noise elsewhere in the system.

5.3.10 High current drive capability

Although some products require low power devices, there are other systems where a high current drive capability is an advantage. Traditionally, digital logic outputs were limited to a few milliamperes of current; if anything more was required, special driver components were used. This requires extra components and results in more PCB area, increased cost, increased current consumption and reduced reliability. Some devices now have a high output current drive capability to overcome these problems.

5.3.11 Packaging

As electronics, particularly digital electronics, becomes used in more and more applications an increasing variety of packaging options are required. These range from high temperatures to low temperatures, high humidity, low profile, small outline, low inductance and so on. The special environmental requirements list is long and variable depending on the specific application. Those programmable devices which are manufactured in the package to suit the application environment have an advantage.

5.3.12 Reliability and authorised use

Although the majority of digital systems are for ordinary domestic or industrial use, there are a few which require high levels of reliability. Typical are those required in the military and health sectors. The military require very high levels of reliability so that the weapons which use the devices do not fail during use; they have a special set of quality standards which have to be met before devices can be used. As it is expensive to meet these standards, most manufacturers only supply a limited selection of their product ranges to this standard so that in certain markets the choice of components is limited.

In the health area, although there is a need for high reliability in order to protect patients, the major problem is in avoiding expensive litigation due to faulty products. Therefore, the majority of semiconductor manufacturers specifically forbid the use of their devices in life support systems. Special permission has to be obtained and special devices used and the result of this is to make the devices very expensive. It also means that the most modern devices cannot be used as they have not undergone the extensive field testing required to be considered safe to use in the health environment.

5.3.13 Technology

Although each semiconductor technology seems the same yet different from earlier versions, there are factors to be considered. Devices made from a technology which is getting old have little room for future improvements in gate density and power consumption. However, if a newer technology is used there is usually the possibility of improvements which will enable smaller transistors to be constructed on the silicon chip. This results in higher gate densities allowing more sophisticated systems to be designed with fewer components, reduces the cost as less silicon is used, and reduces power consumption as the smaller transistors need less current to operate them. Therefore, in some sectors such as mobile telephones, where it is known that reductions in power consumption will be required in one or two year's time in order to remain competitive, choosing a device implemented in a new technology is more likely to yield those improvements with minimal change to the design of the system and, more importantly, avoiding the need for a complete redesign using a better technology.

5.3.14 Summary

The purpose and aim behind all of these concepts is to provide the user with the specific mix of the best system performance, the highest density of logic and the simplest design methodology that they are seeking. Hence, the manufacturer's products become the most attractive and they sell the most. As with any competitive market, whenever a manufacturer produces a particularly advantageous feature, other manufacturers will soon devise their own versions of the architectures that are superior in some way. Because of this, as already discussed, benchmarking needs to be undertaken periodically in order to ensure that the best performance, lowest cost and easiest and shortest development time are obtained.

5.4 Comparing development systems

Benchmarking the programmable devices only considers the performance of the components; it is also worthwhile considering the performance of the development systems themselves. While the components are the most important feature when the product under development is considered, during the development phase, the system used to create the designs is also of prime importance. Users require a system which will allow them to enter the designs in the most appropriate format and quickly enable the compilation, simulation and synthesis to be executed. Designs can be entered in a variety of formats, textual which is usually a hardware description language, graphical which is usually schematic but can be state diagrams, or block diagrams and a combination of both textual and graphical.

5.4.1 *The hardware platforms*

The development systems themselves consist of a software package and a platform to execute it on and both of these can be benchmarked. Benchmarking of the platforms will not be considered here as it is large area for discussion, but in general most software packages require the most powerful processor available, with the maximum amount of memory available, plus any hardware speedups for graphics and numeric manipulation. Packages are increasingly windows based (PC or Unix) and require large hard disks to store the program. For example the VHDL compiler and simulator produced by Cypress for the PC, called WARP 2+, occupies 55 MBytes of disk and requires 16 MBytes of RAM to execute. The Pilkington schematic capture and layout package (also PC based) occupies 100 MBytes of hard disk and also requires 16 MBytes of RAM. The Mentor graphics system executing on Sun SPARC stations occupies several hundred MBytes of hard disk and requires 64 MBytes of RAM with a graphics accelerator in order to achieve acceptable performance. The wide variety of platforms available and the rapid improvement in their performance means that benchmarking accurately is difficult. The most appropriate solution seems to be to decide how much money there is to spend on the hardware and buy the best system available, particularly large amounts of RAM as this is where the largest improvements in compilation, synthesis and simulation times can be obtained.

5.4.2 *Software*

Benchmarking the software is more realistic and dramatic improvements in performance occur only occasionally and if the same hardware platform can be used to evaluate packages from different manufacturers, then a truer comparison of the software can be obtained. At present there is no standard benchmark for development software, probably due to the wide variation of methods adopted by manufacturers for entering and simulating designs. However, where there is a standardised methodology available, such as the use of VHDL or Verilog, some comparisons can be made, see VHDL Simulators and PC based Verilog Simulators by Trivedi and Saunders. A number of criteria can be evolved and a relative weighting assigned to each by whomever is performing the evaluation. The values of the relative weightings are relatively personal choices depending on what the evaluator decides is important at that time. These may vary according to changing circumstances and any overriding company policy. For VHDL, typical criteria and weightings could be:

1)	Performance	40%
2)	Compliance	10%
3)	Debugging environment	20%
4)	Design environment	15%
5)	Technical support	5%
6)	Installation	2%
7)	Optimisation	8%

5.4.3 Performance

Performance is probably the criterion that most readily comes to mind when considering benchmarking. It is an attempt to measure how quickly the software can perform a compile and simulate for a specified design. For clarity of comparison during benchmarking it may be considered best if as many of the language features as possible are included in the design being used. However, this does tend to lead to unrealistic designs and it may be preferred to use a realistic design, preferably one that has actually been implemented for a real product, and consider the ability of the software to implement the features of the language to the compliance testing. It may be worthwhile using a range of design complexity such as simple (a few hundred gate equivalents), medium (a few thousand gate equivalents) and complex (tens or even hundreds of thousands of gate equivalents), as some software packages may have a relatively long 'get going phase' irrespective of the size of the design, followed by a relatively quick 'working phase'. This may result in some packages rating poorly for small and medium designs but excelling for the larger designs. It is wise to use examples near to the size of designs likely to be used for the actual product in order to obtain the most appropriate comparison.

5.4.4 Compliance

Compliance considers the percentage of the language definition that the software is able to cope with. It is unrealistic to expect any one package to implement the entire language specification as this is likely to be large and contain some obscure, rarely used constructs which may be difficult to compile. Software manufacturers will often decide to leave out some of the more obscure constructs for this reason or to reduce the cost of development. Failure to comply with the complete language specification should not be considered to be a terrible thing unless some specific and necessary construct that the user requires has not been implemented

As well as implementing the language specification it should be understood that there are going to be errors in the output produced. At present, there is no software design method which is guaranteed to eliminate incorrect output from software, even when the input is correct. The number faults or 'bugs' left in the software is a compromise between the cost of continuing development and the need to place the product on to the market to generate some income. Some of the bugs may be known, in which case the producer should inform the new purchaser what they are and how to get around them, with the intention that they will be 'fixed' in the next release of the software; others will have yet to be discovered. Whenever using a software package, it is worth remembering in the back of your mind that it is just possible that there may be a problem with the compiler, rather than with your use of the language.

5.4.5 Debugging environment

Assuming that a syntactically program has been obtained from the compiler implementing the language specification correctly and the user has used the language constructs correctly, then once a design has been entered and compiled there is the need to obtain some confidence in the result before committing to silicon, even if it is reprogrammable silicon. This is achieved through the use of a simulator, and it may well be that the performance of the simulator is an overriding criterion. For every design change, the compiler only has to execute once, but for every test vector the compiler has to perform a complete set of recalculations to ensure that any affected values are updated correctly. Even for simple designs containing a few hundred gate equivalents, there may be several thousand test vectors required in order to ensure a good verification.

5.4.6 Design environment

Design environment is about the ability of the software to interact and interface with other tools that may be needed during the design stage. Two have already been discussed, the compiler and the simulator. There are a number of others, such as logic emulators, hardware excelerators and importing and exporting to other CAD packages. This is a difficult area to evaluate due to the complexity of the interfacing process and users will probably have to rely on the software producer's literature to obtain some understanding of what each package can do.

5.4.7 Technical support

Most of these packages are complex and will often behave differently on different hardware platforms when configured in different ways by users. This usually ensures that most large software packages are sold with an ongoing technical support contract, usually renewable every year. This will provide telephone backup as a minimum to ensure that users can obtain help with their problems as quickly as possible. Some companies will not sell their software without a technical support contract to ensure that they do not receive a bad reputation when users cannot solve their own problems.

5.4.8 Installation

As the size of packages increases and hardware platforms increase in diversity and complexity, the ease of installation, modification and uninstallation become important. Preferred is the smart package which identifies the particular hardware platform being used and optimises the installation to obtain maximum performance. Install time is not usually a factor unless there are a large number of installations to be made, which is rare with software of this complexity and cost. Modern packages are increasingly available on CD-ROM due to the large capacity (several hundred megabytes) and low cost and long shelf life of the medium. Increasingly, documentation is also being included on the CD-ROM in electronic book form, to reduce on the physical size and cost of producing the paper versions.

5.4.9 Optimisation

Optimisation is a somewhat vague and difficult to define area for most software packages. The essential concept is that some form of assumptions have been made in some part of the packages operation which enables the software to achieve higher levels of execution speed and performance. Typically these will be about parts of the design which are rarely, if ever, changed. By assuming that they are never changed, developer pre-optimised versions of the implementations can be used instead of working from first principles, as may be defined in the language specification (see compliance).

5.4.10 Summary

As can be observed from this brief consideration of the benchmarking of software packages for standardised languages, the variety of possible criteria is large and constantly changing, with the relative importance of each being different for each user. The conclusion that can be drawn from all of this is that objective benchmarking is generally only possible where some form of standardisation exists, and even then, it is going to be fairly subjective, depending of the requirements of each user.

5.5 Trends in benchmarking

As the complexity of both the programmable logic components and the software development systems increases, each manufacturer will seek to use benchmarking as one method of presenting its products as superior to its competitors'. Users will turn to benchmarking to obtain some objective comparison of the different products. There is a great deal of common ground between these two viewpoints which will ensure that benchmarking continues to exist. However, there is a need for the user to be aware of the different methods that manufacturers have, most of which are perfectly legitimate, of manipulating the results of the benchmarks to their own advantage. An example of this are the PREP benchmarks, which are losing popularity with manufacturers as they provide less opportunity to distinguish their products from their competitors, since many of the architectural features that are being introduced have minimal effect on the benchmark results. It is completely acceptable to do this but it does prevent users from being able to compare the devices with others of a similar type and is a particular nuisance when the special architectural features may not be being used.

5.6 Case study: Device selection

In an ideal situation, each new design would be considered in isolation so that the best combination of technology, architecture, supplier and development system could be used. However, in most situations other constraints mean that a less than ideal solution has to be found. This will be considered to be the optimum, being the combination which maximises the advantages and minimises the disadvantages.

5.6.1 Constraining factors

The constraining factors for each design will vary from design to design. The factors listed below are the main ones which will affect most designs.

1) Cost.
2) Power consumption.
3) Speed of operation.
4) Cost of development system.
5) Previous experience of designer/company policy.
6) Second sourcing.

In most instances one of these factors will be given a high priority which must meet a certain criterion. For example, if speed of operation is important then all other factors may have to be 'sacrificed' to achieve it, so that the final design may be expensive, require a large power supply, use an expensive new development system, be a new product and only be available from one manufacturer. Such a design would only be manufactured if absolutely necessary due to the reliance on a single supplier.

One approach that is often used is to consider the nearest equivalent design which was used in the past and then update it to meet the new specification. While this will usually produce an acceptable design it may not be the optimum possible and over a period of time; the same approach may lead to old-fashioned solutions which are not cost effective. Periodically, a systematic appraisal of all the available factors should be made to identify whether present conditions will provide a significant improvement on the established working practices. This particularly applies to programmable logic designs as the technology is changing and improving rapidly. What was used six months ago may not be the appropriate solution now. Each manufacturer will have a range of products with different characteristics, each of which may be capable of implementing the design. When combined with products from other manufacturers, the possible number of combinations is large. Because the factors are diverse yet interrelated, it can be difficult to decide on the optimum combination. To help designers there are a number of computer packages available which enable factors to be altered interactively by the user, and quick results to be obtained. Although these packages are usually manufacturer specific they do give some indication of solution areas and optimisation. One such package available from Xilinx and discussed earlier in the chapter is called Logic Professor; it will be used to analyse a solution to a design problem.

5.6.2 Package operation

The package operates by the user entering a description of the circuit required and then determining which is the best Xilinx 7000 series device or devices to use. There are then three variables which can be altered so that 'what if' situations can be evaluated:

1) Cost.
2) Power consumption.
3) Area of PCB required.

5.6.3 Design entry

The design is entered in terms of standard logic components and standard programmable logic components. This enables the program to determine the equivalent gate count of the design. In addition, the speed of operation has to be identified in terms of the fastest input and fastest output required, and the critical path timing. The critical path within the design is the one which must occur where the logic signals enter and exit within a specific period. The critical path is described by the maximum time allowed for the signal to propagate to the output point. There are two types of critical paths, those for combinational logic which do not contain registers (as illustrated in figure 5.1), and those for sequential logic which do contain registers (see figure 5.2). The longest combinational path is the one with the most logic gates included, as it is these which introduce the biggest propagation delays. The sequential critical path is the one containing registers and is entered as a maximum frequency of operation. Once the devices have been selected it is necessary to indicate:

1) The number of inputs, their highest frequency and the average frequency.
2) The number of outputs, maximum output current required and average output current.
3) Critical path maximum propagation delay.

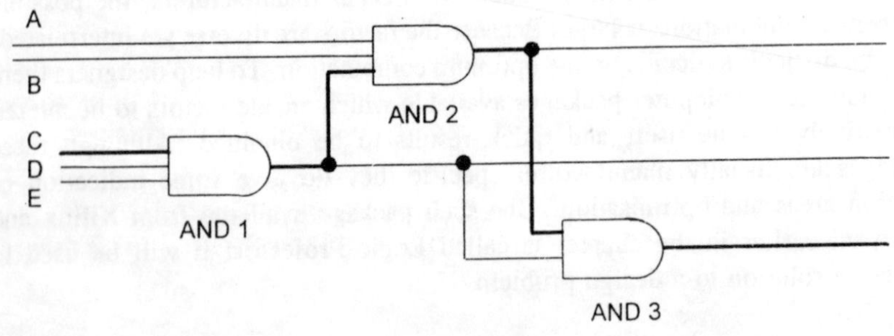

Figure 5.1 A simple combinational critical path

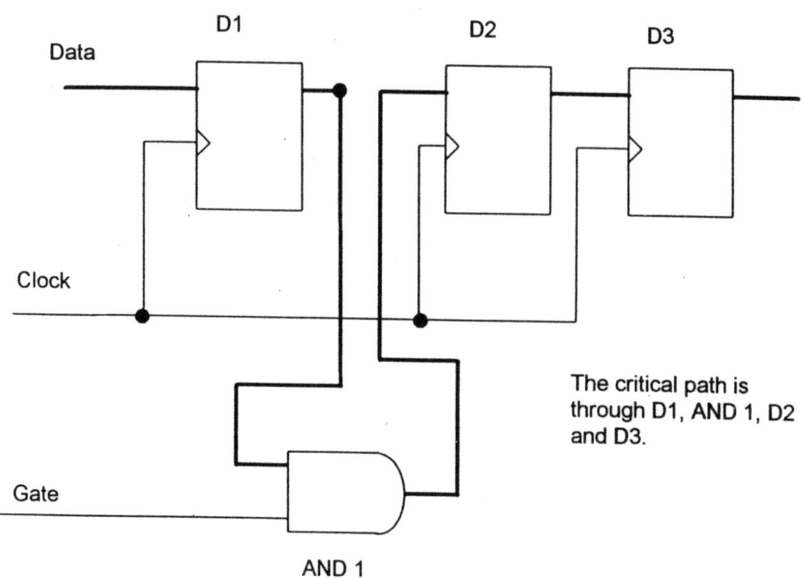

Figure 5.2 A simple registered critical path

As an example, the functional design of a 4 × 4 bit binary multiplier will be evaluated. The circuit contains the components as listed in table 5.1.

Table 5.1 List of components in the 4 × 4 binary multiplier

Logic function	Number required	TTL package equivalents	Number of TTL devices
Invertor	28	74LS04	7
2 input AND gates	72	74LS08	18
4 input AND gates	1	74LS21	1
2 input OR gates	20	74LS32	5
2 input XOR gates	20	74LS86	5

Note that in table 5.1 the quantity shown indicates the number of equivalent logic functions, not the number of packages, so that 18 invertors are required of the type found in 74LS04 package, which requires 3 packages (as there are six invertors per package). For each package type, the percentage utilisation is also entered and the type of package, surface mount or dual-in-line. The logic integration tool contains a model or description of each device which allows it to determine the equivalent gate count. For programmable logic devices the situation is a little more complicated as most modern devices have an ability to select whether or not a register is used at the output. Therefore, the equivalent functionability has to be indicated by entering the percentage of the PLD registers that are being used. Once all the necessary information has been entered, the logic integration tool can be used to indicate what the optimum implementation technology should be, using the design information entered and the constraining parameter values. For example, for the multiplier circuit the following constraints have been applied:

Cost	Low importance
Power	Low importance
Area	High importance

The recommended implementation is one XC7354 logic; see figure 5.3 with the characteristics shown in figure 5.4. By changing only the cost constraint to important with all the others remaining the same as before the recommended implementation now becomes two XC7336, as illustrated in figure 5.5.

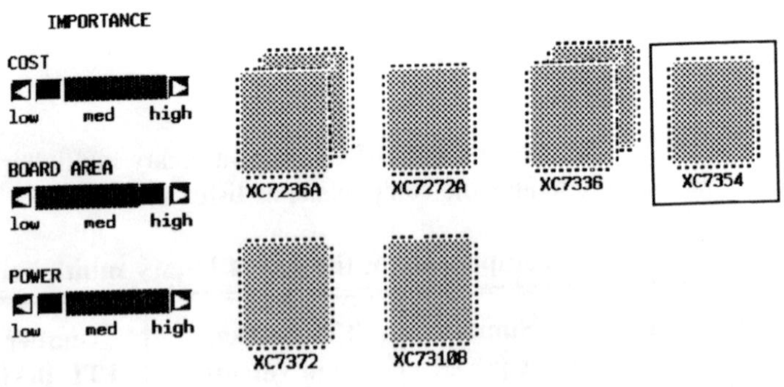

Figure 5.3 Initial device recommended

Once the implementation technology has been selected, the designer will then have to input the circuit, convert it to programming information and produce the physical devices and PCB layout for testing and verification.

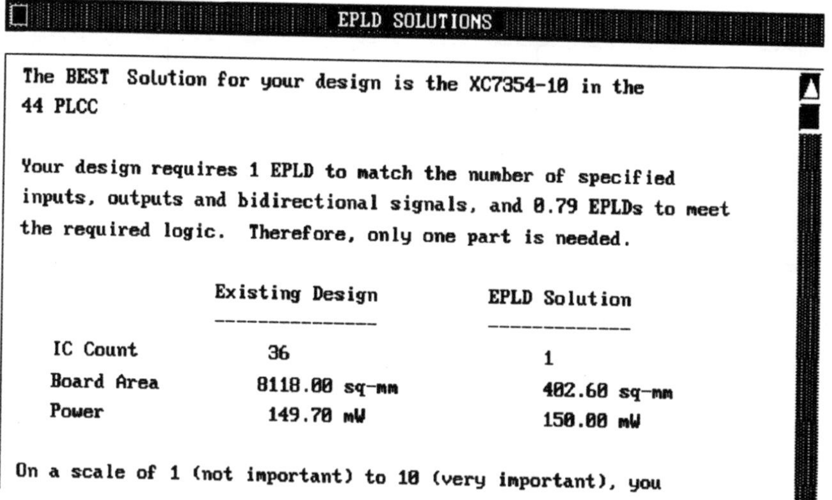

Figure 5.4 Characteristics of the initial solution

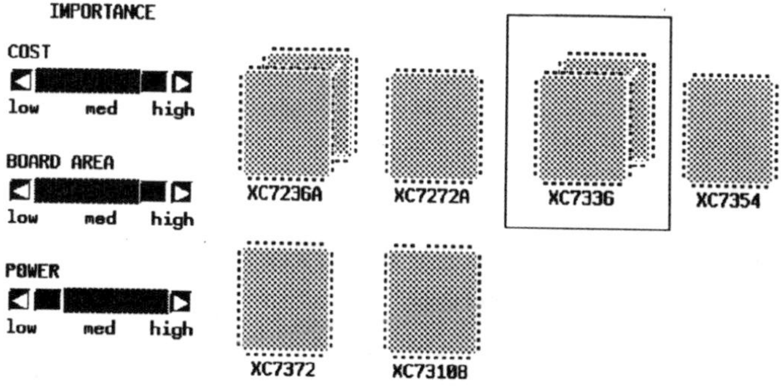

Figure 5.5 Amended recommended solution

5.7 Problems

1. The figures in table 5.2 and 5.3 give values for capacity and performance summaries of three programmable logic devices. Calculate the average benchmark speed and the average benchmark capacity and identify which is the 'best' device.

Table 5.2 Capacity summary

Benchmark number

	1	2	3	4	5	6	7	8	9
Component A	29	32	33	15	20	42	39	39	37
Component B	49	15	40	19	17	10	24	20	45
Component C	25	15	27	21	9	18	15	32	41

Table 5.3 Performance summary

Benchmark number (MHz)

	1	2	3	4	5	6	7	8	9
Component A	85	49	52	51	21	31	64	81	91
Component B	72	51	75	47	18	30	72	80	78
Component B	85	50	81	29	21	33	70	76	55

2. A 16-bit microprocessor has a 20 bit address and contains the following devices:

   a) 64 KBytes EPROM
   b) 64 KBytes RAM
   c) 32 × 8 bit I/O parts. (One component)

The address decoding is to be performed by one of the PLDs listed below. Which is the most efficient device to use.

10R8 10L8 10H6
12R6 12L6 12H4
14R4 14L4 14H4
16R4 16L6 16H4
18R2 18L2 18H2
20R1 20L1 20H2

3. Two VHDL compilers have been evaluated to determine which is the optimum for the design of medium scale digital logic systems and have obtained the ratings shown in table 5.4 on the scale 1 to 10, where 1 was extremely poor, and 10 was very good.

Table 5.4 Ratings obtained

	Company A	Company B
Performance	9	10
Compliance	10	7
Debugging environment	9	5
Design environment	6	7
Technical support	2	3
Installation	5	6
Optimisation	9	7

Using the weightings listed in section 5.4.2, calculate a benchmark figure for each product and hence identify which is the optimum solution.

5.8 Further reading

The Logic Professor, Xilinx, Inc., 2100 Logic Drive, San Jose, C 95124-3400, USA. Available in the UK from Micro Call Ltd, 17 Thame Road, Thame, Oxon, OX9 3XD.

PC-based Verilog Simulators, Y Trivedi and L Saunders, ASIC & EDA, April 1994.

Saunders, L. and Trivedi, Y., *VHDL Simulators*, ASIC & EDA, July 1994.

6 Design examples using PLDs

To illustrate the concepts of designing with a HDL for PLDs a number of examples have been implemented using MACHXL. The designs start with a simple AND function and increase in complexity to some quite sophisticated state machine designs and Reduced Instruction Set Computer (RISC) design. A specification and logic model is developed for each example, along with a complete working program and the necessary test vectors to verify correct operation.

6.1 Designing with programmable logic

There are two design objectives to keep in mind when using programmable logic devices. The first objective is to use PLDs to replace discrete ICs when redesigning existing equipment. This reduces cost, power dissipation, PCB area and increases reliability and flexibility. This approach is becoming increasingly rare as most products that will be redesigned, and which once contained discrete ICs, have already been done. The second objective, which is the more common, is to design PLDs into new generation products and services. Although there may be a variety of reasons for using PLDs, the procedure is similar in each case. A typical design sequence is illustrated below:

1) define the problem,
2) select the device,
3) write the logic equations,
4) if possible, simulate the design,
5) program the device,
6) test the programmed device in the circuit.

As with any engineering problem, it is vitally important to define the problem and produce a problem specification before any design work is done. This enables the designer, or the team of designers, to work towards a specific goal, rather than vaguely implementing bits of a solution that they think might work. It also enables a test strategy to be developed which is used to ensure that the final product executes as required. The methods of obtaining a good specification are not covered here as it can be a complex procedure and other sources of information should be used.

6.2 Programming examples

The programmable logic development package used for this purpose is fully described in Appendix A. It is the AMD MACHXL PALASM system. Each program has four parts:

1) declaration segment,
2) PIN declaration segment,
3) Boolean equation segment,
4) simulation segment.

The declaration segment is used to allocate a design name and specify the PLD that will be used. The name should be selected to have significance for the particular design. In the PIN declaration section physical PLD pins are assigned to variable names and their functions. It is not necessary to allocate a particular pin number to the variable and its function. The allowed pin types which can be used in combinations are:

input; output; registered

Any design which contains registered outputs must have a clock input to activate the registered outputs. The Boolean equation segment is used to determine the programmed logic functions to be performed. There are two types of logic entry to PLD used in given examples:

1) logic Boolean equations;
2) state machine equations.

The Boolean equations are used for the combinational logic design, such as gate, adder, multiplier. These equations have the same forms as developed in the design examples. For state machine entry to implement the state transition diagrams the CASE structure is used. The reserved word CASE is used to begin the construct, followed by the variables contained within open and close brackets. This is followed by a BEGIN END pair which enclose the possible values of the vector variable. Multiple logic equations are grouped together after each condition using a BEGIN END pair. The BEGIN END pair is always terminated by a semicolon and the semicolon after the outer BEGIN END pair terminates the Boolean Equation segment.

The simulation segment of the program allows the testing of the design prior to its programming. It enables the user to identify any errors in the logic equations or in the test vectors and starts with the reserved word TRACE_ON followed by the variables. It is important to devise such a set of test vectors to fully exercise the design without too long a simulation period.

6.3 MACHXL design examples

Six example designs implemented in MACHXL are presented in the following sections; although they have been implemented using MACHXL, the programs should easily transfer to PALASM if required and to other HDLs with a little more effort. In all cases, the designs have been made as general purpose as possible and do not use any special features of the target hardware or MACHXL.

6.4 Logic gate

The first logic function to be implemented will be one of the simplest, a single AND gate.

6.4.1 Specification

Design a logic circuit to perform the operation of a 3 input AND gate.

6.4.2 Logic model

The output equation for a 3 inputs AND gate is obtained from the truth table shown in table 6.1 and is one of the simplest. The output equation is: Z = A.B.C

Table 6.1 Truth table for a 3 input AND gate

Inputs			**Output**
A	B	C	Z
0	0	0	0
0	0	1	0
0	1	0	0
0	1	1	0
1	0	0	0
1	0	1	0
1	1	0	0
1	1	1	1

6.4.3 MACHXL program for an AND gate

```
;---------------------------------- Boolean Equation Segment ------
EQUATIONS

Z = A * B * C ;Three input AND gate

;------------------------------------ Simulation Segment ------------
SIMULATION
```

```
trace_on A B C Z

setf /A /B /C   ;Test all possible input conditions
setf /A /B  C
setf /A  B /C
setf /A  B  C
setf  A /B /C
setf  A /B  C
setf  A  B /C
setf  A  B  C

trace_off

;-----------------------------------------------------------------
```

6.4.4 Test vectors and simulation

As the logic implemented is extremely simple, the test vectors required can also be simple. As there are three inputs, there are 8 possible input combinations, so test vectors were devised for all of them and these are listed below.

```
setf /A /B /C   ;Test all possible input conditions
setf /A /B  C
setf /A  B /C
setf /A  B  C
setf  A /B /C
setf  A /B  C
setf  A  B /C
setf  A  B  C
```

These test vectors produced the simulation results given below and it can easily be seen that the logic has implemented a 3 input AND gate.

```
MACHXL 1.3 MACHSIM (05-15-94)
 (C) - COPYRIGHT ADVANCED MICRO DEVICES INC., 1993, 1994

MACHXL SIMULATION SELECTIVE TRACE LISTING


Title     : And gate           Author    : R C Seals
Pattern   : 1                 Company   : University of Greenwich
Revision  : 1                  Date      : 11/11/95

MACH435
Page : 1
```

```
    ggggggg
A   LLLLHHHH
B   LLHHLLHH
C   LHLHLHLH
Z   LLLLLLLH
```

6.5 Full adder

A common logic function required by many digital systems is that of a binary adder. This particular implementation has been designed for simplicity of the logic equations and features a ripple carry rather than any form of parallel carry or look ahead carry. If a faster carry process were required, it could easily be implemented.

6.5.1 Specification

Design a logic circuit to perform the operation of addition of two four bit binary digits using a ripple carry. No minimisation of the logic equations is required.

6.5.2 Block diagram and truth table

A full adder consists of a device with three inputs, the binary digits A, B and the carry in C and two outputs, S for sum and C_{out} for carry out. In a multi-stage adder the output C_{out} would represent the input to the next most significant stage of addition. A truth table has been used to show the inputs and the outputs. Also, from the truth table shown in table 6.2, the equations for the outputs S and C_{out} can be derived.

Table 6.2 Truth table for a full adder

Inputs			Output	
A	B	C	S	C_{out}
0	0	0	0	0
0	0	1	1	0
0	1	0	1	0
0	1	1	0	1
1	0	0	1	0
1	0	1	0	1
1	1	0	0	1
1	1	1	1	1

$$S = \overline{A}.\overline{B}.C + \overline{A}.B.\overline{C} + A.\overline{B}.\overline{C} + A.B.C$$

$$C_{out} = \bar{A}.B.C + A.\bar{B}.C + A.B.\bar{C} + A.B.C$$

In a conventional logic circuit it would be necessary to simplify ... However, using a PLD such a process is not necessary because the system ... automatically produce the optimised reduced equations.

6.5.3 *Functional block diagram*

A multi-stage adder can be designed using an appropriate number of full or half adders. The block diagrams in figure 6.1 show an adder used to add two four bit binary numbers. The numbers to be added may be represented as:

Number A: A_3 A_2 A_1 A_0
Number B: B_3 B_2 B_1 B_0

A_3, B_3: most significant bits (MSB) A_0, B_0: least significant bits (LSB)

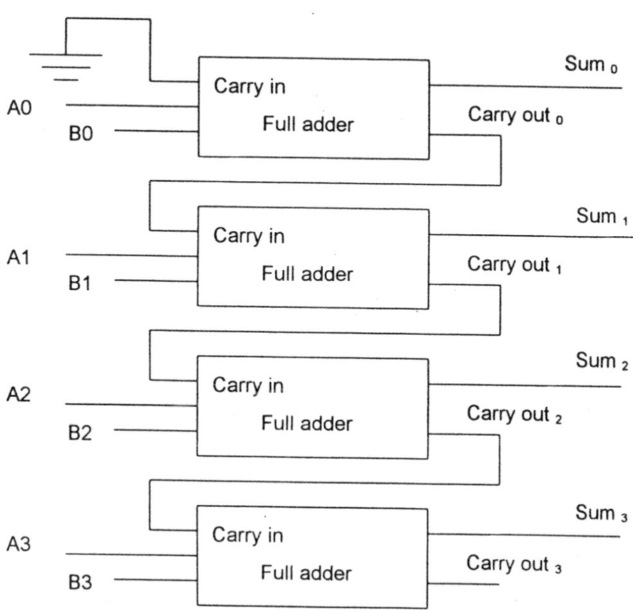

Figure 6.1 A 4-bit adder constructed from 2-bit full adders

In each stage of the block diagrams the CARRY-OUT from the previous stage becomes the CARRY-IN for the next stage as illustrated below:

$$C_{1in} = C_{out0}$$
$$C_{2in} = C_{out1}$$
$$C_{3in} = C_{out2}$$

The corresponding partial SUM of each column is represented by S_0 (LSB) S_1 S_2 S_3 and $S_4 = C_{out3}$ (MSB). The equation for each of the partial sums can be derived by construction of the truth table for each stage of the adder. For the least significant stage, where addition of A_0 and B_0 is performed, a half adder is sufficient because there is no CARRY-IN from the previous stage. Alternatively, a full adder may be used with C_{0in} permanently at logic 0. The truth table shown in table 6.3 shows the inputs and corresponding outputs for a half adder followed by the output equations.

Table 6.3 The truth table for a half adder

Inputs		Output	
A	B	S	C_{out}
0	0	0	0
0	1	1	0
1	0	1	0
1	1	0	1

$$S = \overline{A}.B + A.\overline{B}$$

$$C_{out} = A.B$$

6.5.4 MACHXL program for an adder

```
;-------------------------------- Boolean Equation Segment ------
EQUATIONS
;Least significant bit uses half adder
Sum0 = /A0*B0 + A0*/B0
Cout0 = A0*B0
;The other bits use full adders
Sum1 =  /A1*/B1*Cout0 + /A1* B1*/Cout0 + A1*/B1*/Cout0 + A1*B1*Cout0
Cout1 = /A1* B1*Cout0 +  A1*/B1*Cout0  + A1* B1*/Cout0 + A1*B1*Cout0
Sum2 =  /A2*/B2*Cout1 + /A2* B2*/Cout1 + A2*/B2*/Cout1 + A2*B2*Cout1
Cout2 = /A2* B2*Cout1 +  A2*/B2*Cout1  + A2* B2*/Cout1 + A2*B2*Cout1
Sum3 =  /A3*/B3*Cout2 + /A3* B3*/Cout2 + A3*/B3*/Cout2 + A3*B3*Cout2
Cout3 = /A3* B3*Cout2 +  A3*/B3*Cout2  + A3* B3*/Cout2 + A3*B3*Cout2

;-------------------------------- Simulation Segment -----------
SIMULATION
; There are too many possibilities to test all combinations, so only
; the boundary conditions and a few values in between will be used.
```

```
trace_on A0 A1 A2 A3 B0 B1 B2 B3 Cout0 Cout1 Cout2 Cout3 Sum0 Sum1
Sum2 Sum3

setf /A0 /A1 /A2 /A3 /B0 /B1 /B2 /B3   ;Boundary conditions
setf /A0 /A1 /A2 /A3  B0  B1  B2  B3
setf  A0  A1  A2  A3 /B0 /B1 /B2 /B3
setf  A0  A1  A2  A3  B0  B1  B2  B3
setf /A0  A1 /A2  A3  B0 /B1  B2 /B3     ;Other values
setf /A0 /A1  A2  A3  B0 /B1  B2  B3

trace_off
;--------------------------------------------------------
```

6.5.5 *Test vectors and simulation results for a 4-bit adder*

Designing the test vectors for the 4-bit adder is a little more difficult due to the large number of possible inputs. With two groups of 4-bit binary numbers, there are 256 different combinations and although it would be possible to generate all of these it would be time consuming and require a long simulation time. Only if absolute confidence in the operation of the logic was required would it be necessary to implement all 256 test vectors. Instead, a selected sub-set is used which tests all the boundary conditions with a few other values to ensure a high probability of correct operation. The set of test vectors generated is shown below.

```
setf /A0 /A1 /A2 /A3 /B0 /B1 /B2 /B3   ;Boundary conditions
setf /A0 /A1 /A2 /A3  B0  B1  B2  B3
setf  A0  A1  A2  A3 /B0 /B1 /B2 /B3
setf  A0  A1  A2  A3  B0  B1  B2  B3
setf /A0  A1 /A2  A3  B0 /B1  B2 /B3     ;Other values
setf /A0 /A1  A2  A3  B0 /B1  B2  B3
```

These test the logic when both sets of inputs are all logic zeros; when one set is all zeros and the other is all logic ones; when all the inputs are logic ones and a small number of selected general values which exercise the operation of the carry bits. The simulation results produced are shown below and it can be seen that the 4-bit adder appears to operate as required. Remember that because a full set of test vectors was not used, the reliability is not guaranteed.

```
MACHXL 1.3 MACHSIM (05-15-94)
 (C) - COPYRIGHT ADVANCED MICRO DEVICES INC., 1993, 1994

MACHXL SIMULATION SELECTIVE TRACE LISTING

Title     : Four bit adder        Author   : R C Seals
Pattern   : 1                     Company  : University of Greeenwich
```

```
Revision : 1                    Date    : 11/11/95

MACH435
Page : 1

         gggggg
A0       LLHHLL
A1       LLHHHL
A2       LLHHLH
A3       LLHHHH
B0       LHLHHH
B1       LHLHLL
B2       LHLHHH
B3       LHLHLH
COUT0    LLLHLL
COUT1    LLLHLL
COUT2    LLLHLH
COUT3    LLLHLH
SUM0     LHHLHH
SUM1     LHHHHL
SUM2     LHHHHL
SUM3     LHHHHH
```

It is a little more difficult to determine that the implementation is operating as required, but by a careful study of both the SUM and COUT values it can be seen that the correct results are produced.

6.6 Multiplier

A less commonly required logic function is that of the multiplier, as it is much more complex to implement. If possible, logic systems are designed to operate without a multiplier or to achieve the same effect using shift and add techniques. However, for smaller bit numbers a PLD implementation can be achieved. To reflect the increased complexity of the design only a 2-bit by 3-bit multiplier has been designed.

6.6.1 Specification

Design a logic circuit to perform the multiplication of two binary numbers. The numbers are given as: $A = A_2\ A_1\ A_0$ being multiplicand and $B = B_1\ B_0$ as multiplier.

6.6.2 Logic model

In the case of multiplication it would be time consuming to create the truth table in order to derive the product equations. However, it is possible to construct the circuit by inspection of the result of the multiplication. The multiplication of these two binary numbers is shown below:

Multiplicand				$A_2A_1A_0$	
Multiplier				B_1B_0	
			$A_2.B_0$	$A_1.B_0$	$A_0.B_0$
		$A_2.B_1$	$A_1.B_1$	$A_0.B_1$	
Product	P_4	P_3	P_2	P_1	P_0

For each of the columns the equations of a partial product can be derived. The least significant bit of the partial product is $P_0 = A_0.B_0$. To obtain the equation for P_1, the half adder may be used to add two binary values, $A_1.B_0$ and $A_0.B_1$. The sum equation will form the partial product P_1 and the CARRY OUT (C_1) will be used as the third input to the full adder in the next column. Using the truth table for the half adder the following equations are created:

$$P_1 = (\overline{A_1.B_0}).(A_0.B_1) + (A_1.B_0).(\overline{A_0.B_1})$$
$$C_1 = A_1.A_0.B_1.B_0$$

The third partial product P_2 is formed as the sum of the full adder. The output equations for this full adder is created as:

$$P_2 = (\overline{A_2.B_0}).(\overline{A_1.B_1}).C_1 + (\overline{A_2.B_0}).(A_1.B_1).\overline{C_1} + (A_2.B_0).(\overline{A_1.B_1}).\overline{C_1} + (A_2.B_0).(A_1.B_1).C_1$$

$$C_2 = (\overline{A_2.B_0}).(A_1.B_1).C_1 + (A_2.B_0).(\overline{A_1.B_1}).C_1 + (A_2.B_0).(A_1.B_1).\overline{C_1} + (A_2.B_0).(A_1.B_1).C_1$$

The carry out C_2 from this stage becomes the second input to the last half adder in order to obtain the equation for the most significant bit of the multiplier. The carry out (C_3) from this stage becomes the most significant bit of the product P_4. The equations for partial products P_3 and P_4 are represented as:

$$P_3 = (\overline{A_2.B_1}).C_2 + (A_2.B_1).\overline{C_2}$$
$$P_4 = A_2.B_1.C_2$$

The logic circuit using full adders, half adder and AND gates is shown in figure 6.2.

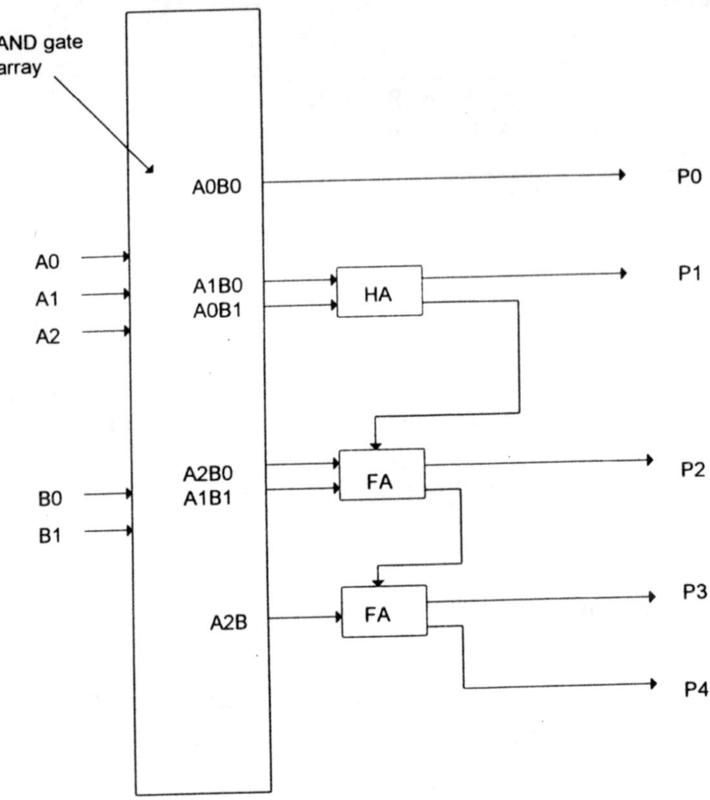

Figure 6.2 2 × 3 bit multiplier

6.6.3 MACHXL program for a multiplier

```
;---------------------------------- Boolean Equation Segment ------
EQUATIONS
P0 =  A0*B0
P1 = /(A1*B0)*(A0*B1) + (A1*B0)*/(A0*B1)
C1 =  A1*B1*B0
P2 = /(A2*B0)*/(A1*B1)*C1 + /(A2*B0)* (A1*B1)*/C1 +
(A2*B0)*/(A1*B1)*/C1 +
     (A2*B0)*/(A1*B1)*/C1 + A2*B0
C2 = /(A2*B0)* (A1*B1)* C1 + ( A2*B0)*/(A1*B1)*C1 +
(A2*B0)*(A1*B1)*/C1 +
     (A1*B1)*C1 + A2*B0
```

```
P3 = /(A2*B1)*C2 + (A2*B1)*/C2
P4 = A2*B1*C2
;---------------------------------- Simulation Segment ------------
SIMULATION
trace_on A2 A1 A0 B1 B0 P0 P1 P2 P3 P4

setf /A2  /A1  /A0  /B1  /B0
setf /A2  /A1  /A0   B1   B0
setf /A2  /A1   A0   B1   B0
setf  A2   A1   A0   B1   B0
setf  A2  /A1   A0   B1  /B0

trace_off
;-------------------------------------------------------------------
```

6.6.4 Test vectors and simulation results

As with the 4-bit adder, designing the test vectors is a complicated process due to the large numbers involved. In this particular design which only has 5 inputs, there are only a maximum of 32 possible test vectors so it would be possible to test all of them. However, to optimise the effort required, only the boundary conditions and a few other values have been used. The boundary conditions for multiplication are much the same as for addition except that care has to be taken to include the identify condition when either of the numbers is equal to a one. The test vectors devised are shown below and these produce the simulation results and from a careful study of the outputs it can be seen that the implementation is operating as required.

```
setf /A2  /A1  /A0  /B1  /B0
setf /A2  /A1  /A0   B1   B0
setf /A2  /A1   A0   B1   B0
setf  A2   A1   A0   B1   B0
setf  A2  /A1   A0   B1  /B0
```

```
MACHXL 1.3 MACHSIM (05-15-94)
 (C) - COPYRIGHT ADVANCED MICRO DEVICES INC., 1993, 1994

MACHXL SIMULATION SELECTIVE TRACE LISTING

Title    : A 2 by 3 Bit multiplier  Author    : G F Whapshott
Pattern  : 1                        Company  : University
Revision : 1                        Date     : 11/11/95

MACH435
Page : 1

     ggggg
 A2  LLLHH
```

```
A1  LLLHL
A0  LLHHH
B1  LHHHH
B0  LHHHL
P0  LLHHL
P1  LLHLH
P2  LLLHL
P3  LLLLH
P4  LLLHL
```

6.7 Sequencer

So far, all the designs have been combinational where the outputs are instantaneous combinations of the inputs. For sequential designs, registers are incorporated and clock signals used to synchronise the outputs. Typical of the design of sequential systems is the recognition of specific bit patterns in serial streams of data.

6.7.1 Specification

Design a sequential logic circuit that will detect the sequence 101 in a stream of serial data. One bit is input at every clock pulse.

6.7.2 Logic model

It has only one input, called I, having a logic value of 1 or 0. There is only one output, called Z, which has a logic value of 1 or 0. To determine the number of internal states the state transition diagrams will be used, illustrated in figure 6.3. Even this simple system requires four states and has eight possible paths through the logic. Each of the four states has been assigned a name which will be used in the implementation. Binary values are assigned to the states using a Gray code to reduce the number of changes between adjacent states and hence increase the likelihood of designing hazard-free logic. A case statement has been used to identify the present state with the value of the Z input determining which state will be moved into next. As there are two bits used to identify the state and there are four states then all possible values are used and undefined states do not have to be considered. This particular design does not implement any form of power-on reset or external reset signal and operates on the principle that, even if the power-on state is unknown, within a few data bits it will have correctly initialised. However, there is the possibility that the logic could power-on in a state which could miss the correct sequence if it was very early on in the data stream. If this potential error had to be eliminated it would be necessary to add a reset of some description to force the logic to a known state at a specified time.

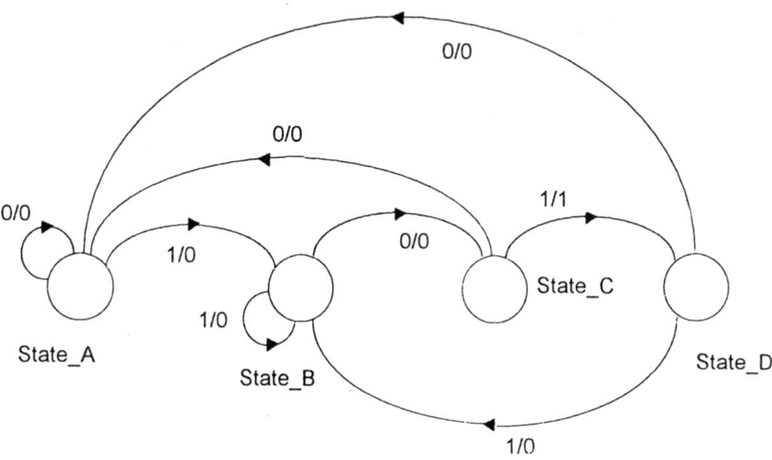

Figure 6.3 A state transition diagram for the sequence detector

6.7.3 MACHXL program for a sequencer

```
;--------------------------- PIN Declarations --------------
PIN  ?        D                                         ;
PIN  ?        Z                                         ;
PIN  ?        statem[1..0]    registered                      ;
PIN  ?        clock

; String substitutions

string state_A '#b00'
string state_B '#b01'
string state_C '#b11'
string state_D '#b10'

;------------------------- Boolean Equation Segment ------
EQUATIONS

statem[1..0].clkf = clock  ;connect clock signal to the registers

case (statem[1..0])
  begin
    state_A: begin
            if (D=0) then
              begin
                statem[1..0] := statem[1..0]
              end
            else
```

```
              begin
                statem[1..0] := state_B
              end
            Z = 0
          end
   state_B: begin
            if (D=0) then
              begin
                statem[1..0] := state_C
              end
            else
              begin
                statem[1..0] := statem[1..0]
              end
            Z = 0
          end
   state_C: begin
            if (D=0) then
              begin
                statem[1..0] := state_A
                Z = 0
              end
            else
              begin
                statem[1..0] := state_D
                Z = 1
              end
          end
   state_D: begin
            if (D=0) then
              begin
                statem[1..0] := state_A
              end
            else
              begin
                statem[1..0] := state_B
              end
            Z = 0
          end
end ;end of the case statement

;--------------------------- Simulation Segment ------------
SIMULATION

trace_on D Z statem[1..0]

setf /D
clockf
```

```
clockf          ;checks state_A operates correctly
setf D
clockf          ;should now move to state_B
clockf          ;should stay at state_D
setf /D
clockf          ;should now move to state_C
clockf          ;should now return to state_A
setf D
clockf          ;now get back to state_C
setf /D
clockf          ;back at state_C now try other exit
setf D
clockf          ;should move to state_D
clockf          ;should move to state_B
setf /D         ;now get back to state_D and try other exit
clockf
setf D
clockf
setf /D
clockf          ;should return to state_A

trace_off

;--------------------------------------------------------
```

6.7.4 Test vectors and simulation results

In this particular logic design there is only one input, but because it is a sequential system where the outputs are dependent not only on the present input but on past inputs and outputs, the design of the test vectors has to be carefully undertaken to ensure that all possible routes through the logic operation are tested. There are eight possible paths through the state machine and each one has to be tested. As each one can require from one to four clocks and data values to fully test, the number of test vectors is quite large, as illustrated below.

```
setf /D
clockf
clockf          ;checks state_A operates correctly
setf D
clockf          ;should now move to state_B
clockf          ;should stay at state_D
setf /D
clockf          ;should now move to state_C
clockf          ;should now return to state_A
setf D
clockf          ;now get back to state_C
setf /D
clockf          ;back at state_C now try other exit
```

```
setf D
clockf        ;should move to state_D
clockf        ;should move to state_B
setf /D       ;now get back to state_D and try other exit
clockf
setf D
clockf
setf /D
clockf        ;should return to state_A
```

A total of 13 clocks are required with 9 changes in the value of the data input. The simulation results produced by these test vectors are shown below and by carefully studying the logic values of `statem[1]` and `statem[0]` and converting them back into the state names, it can be seen that the logic operates as required.

```
MACHXL 1.3 MACHSIM (05-15-94)
 (C) - COPYRIGHT ADVANCED MICRO DEVICES INC., 1993, 1994

MACHXL SIMULATION SELECTIVE TRACE LISTING

Title     : Sequencer              Author    : R C Seals
Pattern   : 1                     Company   : University of Greenwich
Revision  : 1                     Date      : 11/11/95

MACH435
Page : 1

              gc  c  gc  c  gc  c  gc  gc  gc  c  gc  gc  gc
D             LLLLLLLHHHHHHHLLLLLLLHHHHLLLLHHHHHHHLLLLHHHHLLLL
Z             LLLLLLLLLLLLLLLLLLLLLLLLLLLLLHHLLLLLLLLLHHLLLLLL
STATEM[1]     LLLLLLLLLLLLLLLLHHHLLLLLLLLHHHHHHHLLLLHHHHHHHHLL
STATEM[0]     LLLLLLLLLHHHHHHHHHHLLLLHHHHHHHHLLLHHHHHHHHLLLLLL
```

6.8 Step motor controller

A design that is often used as a good case study for assessing the performance of a new HDL or PLD is the control of a step motor. A typical four-phase step motor can be made to operate in a number of different modes from full-step, to half-step, rotating clockwise or anticlockwise. More sophisticated controllers can even be made to count the number of pulses output and confirm the position of the shaft with an external optical encoder. However, for illustration purposes only the simple full-step design has been implemented.

6.8.1 Specification

Output the correct four signals, one for each phase of a four-phase step motor, operating in full-step mode. It is only necessary to rotate in one direction. No power-on or external reset capability is required.

6.8.2 Logic model

The easiest way to implement such a step motor control is through the use of a case statement. This particular implementation uses the output state as the state identifier to save on the number of registers that are needed. This introduces the problem of the possibility of undefined states occurring as the four outputs provide 16 possible combinations of which only four are actually required. The possible problem this could cause is overcome through the use of the otherwise default guard condition in the case statement which would identify any undefined states and return to a known state. In this example, the design always returns to state phase_A but it may be thought better to return to the phase which has the nearest binary value to the detected undefined state. However, if this was required, it would be necessary to define each possible combination of guard conditions so that each could be altered to the next nearest. This was not thought to be worthwhile for this simple design. Note that if clockwise and anti-clockwise and full-step and half-step operation are required, the number of undefined states is reduced. Although no power-on or external reset is provided in this design, because of the common occurrence of all registers powering up with logic zeros on the outputs, this state was explicitly defined as a guard condition. However, this could have been left out and the default otherwise part of the statement would produce exactly the same results.

6.8.3 MACHXL program for a stepper motor controller

```
;---------------------------------- PIN Declarations ---------------
PIN  ?          clk                                 ;
PIN  ?          phases[3..0]  registered                     ;

;string substitutions

string initial '#b0000'
string phase_A '#b0001'
string phase_B '#b0010'
string phase_C '#b0100'
string phase_D '#b1000'

;---------------------------------- Boolean Equation Segment ------
EQUATIONS

phases[3..0].clkf = clk
case (phases[3..0])
```

```
begin
  initial: begin
           phases[3..0] := phase_A
         end
  phase_A: begin
           phases[3..0] := phase_B
         end
  phase_B: begin
           phases[3..0] := phase_C
         end
  phase_C: begin
           phases[3..0] := phase_D
         end
  phase_D: begin
           phases[3..0] := phase_A
         end
  otherwise: begin
           phases[3..0] := phase_A
         end
end
;---------------------------------- Simulation Segment ------------
SIMULATION

trace_on clk phases[3..0]

clockf clk
clockf clk
clockf clk
clockf clk
clockf clk
clockf clk
clockf clk
clockf clk

trace_off
;----------------------------------------------------------------
```

6.8.4 Test vectors and simulation results

As this design does not contain any form of power-on reset the test vectors are simplified. All that is necessary is to provide at least 5 clocks to ensure that the four correct patterns are produced and that the sequence correctly rolls over. The test vectors devised, which are just a sequence of eight consecutive clocks, test two complete sequences. Although the logic shown here does not have an external reset it would probably be a good idea to add one to ensure that the initial sequence can be guaranteed. This would then require more test vectors. In addition, it would be a good idea to force the design into one of the undefined states to check that the logic will correctly recover from this and this could be achieved through the use of the preload test vector. The results of the straightforward test vectors are shown below.

```
MACHXL 1.3 MACHSIM (05-15-94)
 (C) - COPYRIGHT ADVANCED MICRO DEVICES INC., 1993, 1994

MACHXL SIMULATION SELECTIVE TRACE LISTING

Title     : Stepper Motor Pattern Ge Author   : R C Seals
Pattern   : 1                    Company  : University of Greenwich
Revision  : 1                    Date     : 06/05/95

MACH435
Page : 1

                  c  c  c  c  c  c  c  c
 CLK             HHLHHLHHLHHLHHLHHLHHLHHL
 PHASES[3]       HLLLLLLLLLHHHLLLLLLLLLHH
 PHASES[2]       HLLLLLLHHHLLLLLLLLLHHHLL
 PHASES[1]       HLLLHHHLLLLLLLLLHHHLLLLL
 PHASES[0]       LHHHLLLLLLLLLHHHLLLLLLLL
```

6.9 RISC design

So far, the designs have all been relatively well known ones which do not fully illustrate the power of modern HDLs. Therefore, the next design will implement a simple Reduced Instruction Set Computer capable of executing user defined programs. Although this particular design does not have the capability to execute any particularly useful programs, it could easily be extended to include more instructions with a minimum of additional effort. Designing the test vectors for this implementation is difficult, due to the very large number of possible permutations of instruction sequences, any one of which could induce a fault.

6.9.1 Specification

Implement a RISC which is capable of executing the following instructions.

jump to an absolute address
no operation
increment a register
load a value from a memory location into a register.

An 8-bit instruction length will be used with the two most significant bits being used as the opcode. The remaining bits will be used to contain the address for the JUMP instruction. The load instruction transfers data from the PROM into the register and, although the data bus is 8 bits wide, only 6 bits have been used for the register to simplify the design. The NOP instruction only has to increment the PC, so the remaining 6 bits in those instructions are not used. The INC instruction has only one register to operate on, so it too does not use any of the remaining 6 bits, only the opcode bits.

6.9.2 Logic model

For a simple design such as this only a limited Central Processing Unit (CPU) is required. This has to implement a Program Counter (PC) with a 6-bit address which is output only to the PROM containing the absolute code program, an 8-bit data bus which only has to input either instructions or data, and a single register, register A. Each instruction except for JUMP has to increment the PC, whereas JUMP has to load the PC with the 6-bit value contained in the bottom 6 bits of the instruction on the data bus. Increment operates on the single 6-bit register which has been implemented in a similar manner to the incrementing of the PC. The LOAD instruction is different in that it requires the data to be loaded to appear immediately after the LOAD instruction and therefore requires two clock pulses for the instruction, whereas all the other instructions execute in one clock pulse. In effect this is not a LOAD from anywhere in memory instruction, but an immediate load, where the immediate data is the next byte in the instruction sequence. This is perfectly acceptable to the general RISC philosophy but is rather unusual for standard microprocessor designs. It is left as an exercise for the reader to alter the design so that is can load data from anywhere in the available memory range. Hint, it will require the use of a temporary PC to maintain the instruction address while the data is being loaded and this may extend the number of clocks required for the LOAD instruction to three.

6.9.3 MACHXL program for a RISC design

```
;---------------------------------- PIN Declarations --------------
PIN  ?          addr[5..0] registered                   ;
PIN  ?          data[7..0]                            ;
PIN  ?          clk                                 ;
PIN  ?          reset                                ;
PIN  ?          load_state registered
PIN  ?          reg_A[5..0] registered

; string substitutions

string nop     '#b00'
string jump    '#b01'
string load    '#b11'
string inc     '#b10'
string first   '#b0'
string second  '#b1'
```

```
;---------------------------------- Boolean Equation Segment ------
EQUATIONS

addr[5..0].clkf = clk
load_state.clkf = clk
reg_A[5..0].clkf = clk
addr[5..0].rstf = reset
load_state.rstf = reset
reg_A[5..0].rstf = reset

case (data[7..6])
 begin
  nop : begin ;NOP - just increments the program counter
        addr[0] := /addr[0]
        addr[1] := addr[1]:+: addr[0]
        addr[2] := addr[2]:+:(addr[1] * addr[0])
        addr[3] := addr[3]:+:(addr[2]*addr[1]*addr[0])
        addr[4] := addr[4]:+:(addr[3]*addr[2]*addr[1]*addr[0])
        addr[5] := addr[5]:+:(addr[4]*addr[3]*addr[2]*addr[1]*addr[0])
        reg_A[5..0] := reg_A[5..0]
      end
  jump : begin ;JUMP - updates program counter with the specified address
         addr[5..0]  := data[5..0]
         reg_A[5..0] := reg_A[5..0]
       end
  load : begin ; load register from specified address
         case (load_state)
          begin
           first : begin
                    addr[5..0] = data[5..0]
                    load_state = second
                   end
           second : begin
                    reg_A[5..0] := data[5..0] ; load operation
                    load_state = first
                    ; now increment the program counter
                    addr[0] := /addr[0]
                    addr[1] := addr[1] :+: addr[0]
                    addr[2] := addr[2] :+: (addr[1] * addr[0])
                    addr[3] := addr[3] :+: (addr[2] * addr[1] * addr[0])
                    addr[4] := addr[4] :+: (addr[3] * addr[2] * addr[1] * addr[0])
                    addr[5] := addr[5] :+: (addr[4] * addr[3] * addr[2] * addr[1] *
                                                               addr[0])
                   end
          end ; case
      end
  inc : begin
        addr[0] := /addr[0] ; increment the program counter
        addr[1] := addr[1]:+: addr[0]
        addr[2] := addr[2]:+:(addr[1] * addr[0])
        addr[3] := addr[3]:+:(addr[2]*addr[1]*addr[0])
        addr[4] := addr[4]:+:(addr[3]*addr[2]*addr[1]*addr[0])
```

```
        addr[5] := addr[5]:+:(addr[4]*addr[3]*addr[2]*addr[1]*addr[0])
        reg_A[0] := /reg_A[0] ; increment the register contents
        reg_A[1] := reg_A[1] :+: reg_A[0]
        reg_A[2] := reg_A[2] :+: (reg_A[1]*reg_A[0])
        reg_A[3] := reg_A[3] :+: (reg_A[2]*reg_A[1]*reg_A[0])
        reg_A[4] := reg_A[4] :+: (reg_A[3]*reg_A[2]*reg_A[1]*reg_A[0])
        reg_A[5] := reg_A[5] :+: (reg_A[4] * reg_A[3] * reg_A[2] *
                                   reg_A[1] * reg_A[0])
    end
end
```

6.9.4 Test vectors and simulation results

The test vectors for the RISC design are more complex than for any other logic system so far devised as they have to represent the transfer of data from the PROM. The data transferred is equivalent to the instructions being fetched from memory although it is not possible to create conditional test vectors. Therefore, it is necessary to assume that the logic is operating correctly and that the assembly program will be executed in the correct sequence. The program chosen to test the RISC consists of two parts. After the first reset, the PROM is assumed to be full of NOPs (all the data bits set to logic zero) and this is used to test that the Program Counter incrementing logic is operating correctly. This is then followed by another reset and an assembly program which contains both NOP and JUMP instructions in the following sequence.

```
NOP
NOP
NOP
NOP
NOP
NOP
NOP
JUMP 00H
JUMP 00H
JUMP 04H
JUMP 04H
INC
INC
INC
INC
INC
```

This is an impossible sequence to generate with a real PROM, since assuming that the first NOP is at address 00H, the JUMPs to 00H should encounter NOPs, but for the purposes of these test vectors the sequence enables three of the instructions to be easily tested. The INC instruction has to increment both the program counter and the only register, register A, so that several instructions are required to ensure that it is operating as required.

```
;---------------------------------- Simulation Segment ------------
SIMULATION

trace_on  data[7..0] addr[5..0] reset load_state reg_A[5..0] clk

setf /data[7..0]
setf /reset
setf reset
setf /reset
clockf
clockf
clockf
clockf
clockf
clockf
clockf
clockf
clockf
clockf
clockf
clockf
clockf
clockf
clockf
clockf
clockf
clockf
clockf
clockf
clockf
clockf
clockf
clockf
clockf
setf   reset  ;do another reset
setf   /reset
clockf
clockf
clockf
clockf
clockf
clockf
clockf
setf data[6]
```

```
clockf
clockf
setf data[2]
clockf
clockf
setf /data[2] data[7] /data[6]
clockf
clockf
clockf
clockf
clockf

trace_off
```

The results of executing these test vectors are shown below and, as can be seen, the output from the simulator is extensive and careful study is required to verify that, in fact, the RISC design is operating as required. The test vectors for the LOAD instruction have not been included and it is left to the reader as an exercise to devise suitable values. Note, that the RISC has been designed such that the LOAD instruction has to be present for two clock pulses, so that the assembler program must always have the LOAD instruction in pairs.

```
MACHXL 1.3 MACHSIM (05-15-94)
(C) - COPYRIGHT ADVANCED MICRO DEVICES INC., 1993, 1994

MACHXL SIMULATION SELECTIVE TRACE LISTING

Title      : RISC NOP and JUMP          Author    : R C Seals
Pattern    : 1                          Company   : University of Greenwich
Revision   : 1                          Date      : 07/20/95

MACH435
Page : 1

             ggggc  c  c  c  c  c  c  c  c  c  c  c  c  c  c  c  c  c  c
 DATA[7]     LLLLLLLLLLLLLLLLLLLLLLLLLLLLLLLLLLLLLLLLLLLLLLLLLLLLLLLLLLLL
 DATA[6]     LLLLLLLLLLLLLLLLLLLLLLLLLLLLLLLLLLLLLLLLLLLLLLLLLLLLLLLLLLLL
 DATA[5]     LLLLLLLLLLLLLLLLLLLLLLLLLLLLLLLLLLLLLLLLLLLLLLLLLLLLLLLLLLLL
 DATA[4]     LLLLLLLLLLLLLLLLLLLLLLLLLLLLLLLLLLLLLLLLLLLLLLLLLLLLLLLLLLLL
 DATA[3]     LLLLLLLLLLLLLLLLLLLLLLLLLLLLLLLLLLLLLLLLLLLLLLLLLLLLLLLLLLLL
 DATA[2]     LLLLLLLLLLLLLLLLLLLLLLLLLLLLLLLLLLLLLLLLLLLLLLLLLLLLLLLLLLLL
 DATA[1]     LLLLLLLLLLLLLLLLLLLLLLLLLLLLLLLLLLLLLLLLLLLLLLLLLLLLLLLLLLLL
 DATA[0]     LLLLLLLLLLLLLLLLLLLLLLLLLLLLLLLLLLLLLLLLLLLLLLLLLLLLLLLLLLLL
 ADDR[5]     LLLLLLLLLLLLLLLLLLLLLLLLLLLLLLLLLLLLLLLLLLLLLLLLLLLLLLLLLLLL
 ADDR[4]     LLLLLLLLLLLLLLLLLLLLLLLLLLLLLLLLLLLLLLLLLLLLLLLLLLHHHHHHHHHH
 ADDR[3]     LLLLLLLLLLLLLLLLLLLLLLLLLLHHHHHHHHHHHHHHHHHHHHHHHHLLLLLLLLLL
 ADDR[2]     LLLLLLLLLLLLLLHHHHHHHHHHHHLLLLLLLLLLLLHHHHHHHHHHHHLLLLLLLLLL
 ADDR[1]     LLLLLLLLHHHHHHLLLLLLHHHHHHLLLLLLHHHHHHLLLLLLHHHHHHLLLLLLHHHH
 ADDR[0]     LLLLLHHHLLLHHHLLLHHHLLLHHHLLLHHHLLLHHHLLLHHHLLLHHHLLLHHHLLLH
 RESET       LLHLLLLLLLLLLLLLLLLLLLLLLLLLLLLLLLLLLLLLLLLLLLLLLLLLLLLLLLLL
 LOAD_STATE  LLLLLLLLLLLLLLLLLLLLLLLLLLLLLLLLLLLLLLLLLLLLLLLLLLLLLLLLLLLL
 REG_A[5]    LLLLLLLLLLLLLLLLLLLLLLLLLLLLLLLLLLLLLLLLLLLLLLLLLLLLLLLLLLLL
 REG_A[4]    LLLLLLLLLLLLLLLLLLLLLLLLLLLLLLLLLLLLLLLLLLLLLLLLLLLLLLLLLLLL
 REG_A[3]    LLLLLLLLLLLLLLLLLLLLLLLLLLLLLLLLLLLLLLLLLLLLLLLLLLLLLLLLLLLL
 REG_A[2]    LLLLLLLLLLLLLLLLLLLLLLLLLLLLLLLLLLLLLLLLLLLLLLLLLLLLLLLLLLLL
 REG_A[1]    LLLLLLLLLLLLLLLLLLLLLLLLLLLLLLLLLLLLLLLLLLLLLLLLLLLLLLLLLLLL
 REG_A[0]    LLLLLLLLLLLLLLLLLLLLLLLLLLLLLLLLLLLLLLLLLLLLLLLLLLLLLLLLLLLL
 CLK         LLLLHHLHHLHHLHHLHHLHHLHHLHHLHHLHHLHHLHHLHHLHHLHHLHHLHHLHHLHH
```

```
MACH435
Page : 2
               c  c  c  c  c  c  ggc  c  c  c  c  c  c  gc  c  gc  c  gc
 DATA[7]       LLLLLLLLLLLLLLLLLLLLLLLLLLLLLLLLLLLLLLLLLLLLLLLLLLLLLLLHHHH
 DATA[6]       LLLLLLLLLLLLLLLLLLLLLLLLLLLLLLLLLLLLLLLLLLHHHHHHHHHHHHHHLLLL
 DATA[5]       LLLLLLLLLLLLLLLLLLLLLLLLLLLLLLLLLLLLLLLLLLLLLLLLLLLLLLLLLLLL
 DATA[4]       LLLLLLLLLLLLLLLLLLLLLLLLLLLLLLLLLLLLLLLLLLLLLLLLLLLLLLLLLLLL
 DATA[3]       LLLLLLLLLLLLLLLLLLLLLLLLLLLLLLLLLLLLLLLLLLLLLLLLLLLLLLLLLLLL
 DATA[2]       LLLLLLLLLLLLLLLLLLLLLLLLLLLLLLLLLLLLLLLLLLLLLLLLLHHHHHHHLLLL
 DATA[1]       LLLLLLLLLLLLLLLLLLLLLLLLLLLLLLLLLLLLLLLLLLLLLLLLLLLLLLLLLLLL
 DATA[0]       LLLLLLLLLLLLLLLLLLLLLLLLLLLLLLLLLLLLLLLLLLLLLLLLLLLLLLLLLLLL
 ADDR[5]       LLLLLLLLLLLLLLLLLLLLLLLLLLLLLLLLLLLLLLLLLLLLLLLLLLLLLLLLLLLL
 ADDR[4]       HHHHHHHHHHHHHHHHHHHLLLLLLLLLLLLLLLLLLLLLLLLLLLLLLLLLLLLLLLLL
 ADDR[3]       LLLLLLLLLLLLLLHHHHLLLLLLLLLLLLLLLLLLLLLLLLLLLLLLLLLLLLLLLLLL
 ADDR[2]       LLHHHHHHHHHHHHLLLLLLLLLLLLLLLLLHHHHHHHHHHHHHLLLLLLLHHHHHHHHH
 ADDR[1]       HHLLLLLLHHHHHHLLLLLLLLLLLHHHHHLLLLLLLHHHHHHHLLLLLLLLLLLLLLLL
 ADDR[0]       HHLLLHHHLLLHHHLLLHHLLLHHHLLLHHHLLLHHHLLLHHHHLLLLLLLLLLLLLLHH
 RESET         LLLLLLLLLLLLLLLLLLLHLLLLLLLLLLLLLLLLLLLLLLLLLLLLLLLLLLLLLLLL
 LOAD_STATE    LLLLLLLLLLLLLLLLLLLLLLLLLLLLLLLLLLLLLLLLLLLLLLLLLLLLLLLLLLLL
 REG_A[5]      LLLLLLLLLLLLLLLLLLLLLLLLLLLLLLLLLLLLLLLLLLLLLLLLLLLLLLLLLLLL
 REG_A[4]      LLLLLLLLLLLLLLLLLLLLLLLLLLLLLLLLLLLLLLLLLLLLLLLLLLLLLLLLLLLL
 REG_A[3]      LLLLLLLLLLLLLLLLLLLLLLLLLLLLLLLLLLLLLLLLLLLLLLLLLLLLLLLLLLLL
 REG_A[2]      LLLLLLLLLLLLLLLLLLLLLLLLLLLLLLLLLLLLLLLLLLLLLLLLLLLLLLLLLLLL
 REG_A[1]      LLLLLLLLLLLLLLLLLLLLLLLLLLLLLLLLLLLLLLLLLLLLLLLLLLLLLLLLLLLL
 REG_A[0]      LLLLLLLLLLLLLLLLLLLLLLLLLLLLLLLLLLLLLLLLLLLLLLLLLLLLLLLLLLHH
 CLK           LHHLHHLHHLHHLHHLHHLLLHHLHHLHHLHHLHHLHHLHHLLHHLHHLLHHLHHLLHHL

MACH435
Page : 3
               c  c  c  c
 DATA[7]       HHHHHHHHHHHH
 DATA[6]       LLLLLLLLLLLL
 DATA[5]       LLLLLLLLLLLL
 DATA[4]       LLLLLLLLLLLL
 DATA[3]       LLLLLLLLLLLL
 DATA[2]       LLLLLLLLLLLL
 DATA[1]       LLLLLLLLLLLL
 DATA[0]       LLLLLLLLLLLL
 ADDR[5]       LLLLLLLLLLLL
 ADDR[4]       LLLLLLLLLLLL
 ADDR[3]       LLLLLLLHHHHH
 ADDR[2]       HHHHHHHLLLLL
 ADDR[1]       LHHHHHHLLLLL
 ADDR[0]       HLLLHHHLLLHH
 RESET         LLLLLLLLLLLL
 LOAD_STATE    LLLLLLLLLLLL
 REG_A[5]      LLLLLLLLLLLL
 REG_A[4]      LLLLLLLLLLLL
 REG_A[3]      LLLLLLLLLLLL
 REG_A[2]      LLLLLLLHHHHH
 REG_A[1]      LHHHHHHLLLLL
 REG_A[0]      HLLLHHHLLLHH
 CLK           HHLHHLHHLHHL
```

6.10 Problems

1. Design and implement a MACHXL program for a 3 input NOR gate.

2. Amend the step motor controller design so that it will operate in either full-step or half-step modes and will also allow a change in the direction of rotation from clockwise to anti-clockwise.

3. Implement the MACHXL program for a 4-bit binary counter. How many test vectors are required to fully test this design?

5. A data stream contains two different sequences which are to be identified:

   01101 and 10010

   Devise a suitable state machine to indicate whenever either of the streams has occurred where the data streams are not mutually exclusive. Implement the state machine as a MACHXL program and devise the required test vectors.

6. Amend the RISC design to include two additional instructions of your choice and devise a suitable set of test vectors. Would it be considered optimal to create the full set of test vectors? How many would there be?

6.11 Further reading

AMD PALCE/MACH CD-ROM Tool Collection, 1st Edition, 1995, CD-Nr. ID3001. AMD GmbH Rosenheimerstrasse 143b D-81671 Munich, Germany.

MACHXL Software User's Guide, Advanced Micro Devices Inc., PO Box 3453, Sunnyvale, CA 94088, USA.

PLDasm Software User Guide, Alterra Corporation, 2610 Orchard Parkway, San Jose, CA 95134-2020, USA.

The ProLogic Compiler User's Guide, Texas Instruments Ltd, Manton Lane, England, MK41 7PA, United Kingdom.

7 Design examples using FPGAs

A number of digital systems have been designed using VHDL and are suitable for implementation on FPGAs. Only the design of the VHDL program is given, as the simulation results are dependent on the simulator and VHDL compiler being used. The design of suitable test vectors for verifying designs was covered in the previous chapter, so only brief descriptions of the tests to be performed are be included.

7.1 A four-to-one multiplexer

A four-to-one multiplexer has four inputs and a single output. The connection between the output and one of the inputs is determined by a 2-bit binary value.

```
entity muxer is                 -- Definition of the input and output signals.
port (in1, in2, in3, in4 : in bit;
     expr : in bit_vector(1 downto 0);
     out1 : out bit);
end muxer;

architecture struct of muxer is

begin

mux :  process

begin
   case expr is                 -- Two bit vector used to select which input
     when "00" =>               -- channel is to be output.
       out1 <= in1;
     when "01" =>
       out1 <= in2;
     when "10" =>
       out1 <= in3;
     when others =>             -- Final selection also includes the error
       out1 <= in4;             -- correction code.
   end case;
end process mux;
end struct;
```

The program operates by decoding the 2-bit vector used to select the input channel using a case statement and redirecting the logic value on the input to the output; it operates almost exactly in the opposite way to the demultiplexer. The final channel will also handle any unspecified values, although these should never occur with only a 2-bit vector, but it is good programming practice always to build in error correction if possible. Only 8 test vectors are needed to test this design, as described below:

select channel 1 : input logic 0 and logic 1.
select channel 2 : input logic 0 and logic 1.
select channel 3 : input logic 0 and logic 1.
select channel 4 : input logic 0 and logic 1.

For a simple design such as this no further test vectors would be required, but a more comprehensive test would verify that it is possible to switch from any input to any other input without any problems. This would require an additional 24 tests ((4 × 3) × 2) considerably increasing the testing overhead, but without any real need unless it was to be used in a high reliability system.

7.2 A one-to-four demultiplexer

A one-to-four demultiplexer has a single input and four outputs where the output that the input logic signal will appear on is determined by the 2-bit selection signals.

```
entity demuxer is -- Definition of the input and output signals.
port (in1 : in bit;
     expr : in bit_vector(1 downto 0);
     out1, out2, out3, out4 : out bit);
end demuxer;

architecture struct of demuxer is

begin

de_mux :  process

begin
   case expr is             -- Use two bit vector to select output.
     when "00" =>           -- All other outputs set to logic zero.
       out1 <= in1;
       out2 <= '0';
       out3 <= '0';
       out4 <= '0';
     when "01" =>
       out1 <= '0';
       out2 <= in1;
       out3 <= '0';
```

```
        out4 <= '0';
      when "10" =>
        out1 <= '0';
        out2 <= '0';
        out3 <= in1;
        out4 <= '0';
      when others =>        -- This condition will also correct any
        out1 <= '0';        -- incorrect values.
        out2 <= '0';
        out3 <= '0';
        out4 <= in1;
    end case;
end process de_mux;
end struct;
```

The program operates by decoding the 2-bit vector used to select the output channel using a case statement and redirecting the logic value on the input to the selected output. The final channel will also handle any unspecified values, although these should never occur with only a 2-bit vector, but again it is good programming practice always to build in error correction if possible. Also, when an output is not being used it is set to logic zero. Only 8 test vectors are needed to test this design, as described below:

select channel 1 : output logic 0 and logic 1.
select channel 2 : output logic 0 and logic 1.
select channel 3 : output logic 0 and logic 1.
select channel 4 : output logic 0 and logic 1.

For a simple design such as this no further test vectors would be required, but a more comprehensive test would verify that it is possible to switch from any output to any other output without any problems. This would require an additional 24 tests ((4 × 3) × 2) considerably increasing the testing overhead but without any real need unless it was to be used in a high reliability system.

7.3 A 4-bit adder with 7 segment output decoder

In this design there are two 4-bit inputs which are to be added together. This will create a 5-bit binary output. The 5-bit output will then be decoded so that they can control two seven segment displays. The result will be displayed as hexadecimal rather than decimal in order to simplify the design. The maximum value that two 4-bit numbers will produce is 01FH, therefore the most significant digit of the two 7 segment displays will only ever display 0H or 1H, thus only these two values have been decoded. The least significant digit has to be able to display the full 16 values, from 0H to 0FH, and is fully decoded using a case statement. The adder has been implemented using Boolean equations based on the operation of four full adders. Deducing the bit patterns for the 7 segment displays was achieved by using a look up table as shown in table 7.1, where the segments are identified as shown in figure 7.1.

Table 7.1 Binary to 7 segment conversion

Binary	Seg a	Seg b	Seg c	Seg d	Seg e	Seg f	Seg g
0000	1	1	1	1	1	1	0
0001	1	1	0	0	0	0	0
0010	1	1	0	1	1	0	1
0011	1	1	1	1	0	0	1
0100	0	1	1	0	0	1	1
0101	1	0	1	1	0	1	1
0110	1	0	1	1	1	1	1
0111	1	1	1	0	0	0	0
1000	1	1	1	1	1	1	1
1001	1	1	1	1	0	1	1
1010	1	1	1	0	1	1	1
1011	0	0	1	1	1	1	1
1100	1	0	0	1	1	1	1
1101	0	1	1	1	1	0	1
1110	1	0	0	1	1	1	1
1111	1	0					

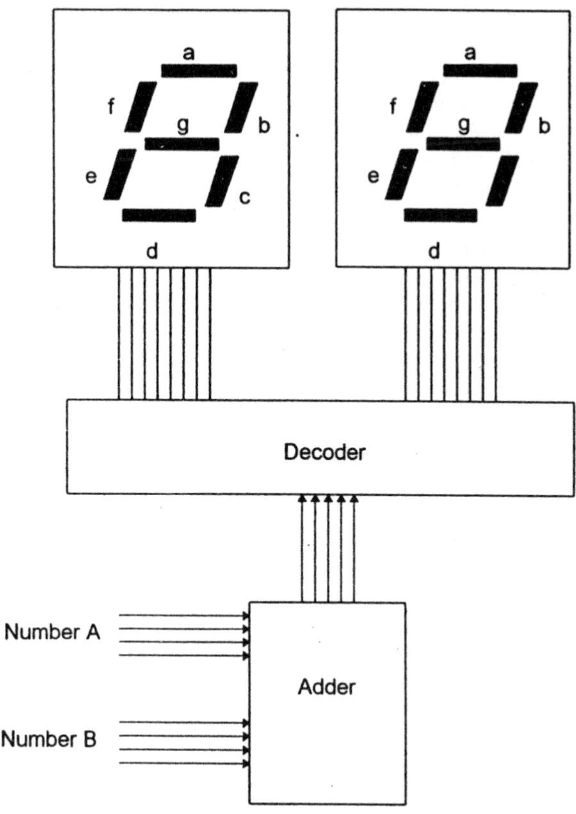

Figure 7.1 Adder and display

```
entity fourbitadd_to7seg is  -- Defines input and output connections
port (in11, in12, in13, in14 : in bit;
     in21, in22, in23, in24 : in bit;
     display1 : out bit_vector(6 downto 0);
     display2 : out bit_vector(6 downto 0));
end fourbitadd_to7seg;

architecture struct of fourbitadd_to7seg is

signal carry1, carry2, carry3, carry4 : bit;   -- Internal signals required.
signal sum : bit_vector(4 downto 0);

begin

add :  process
```

```
begin
  sum(0) <= in11 xor in21;   -- Adds least significant bits together.
  carry1 <= in11 and in21;
  sum(1) <= (not in12 and not in22 and carry1) or   -- Next bit.
         (not in12 and in22 and not carry1) or
         (in12 and not in22 and not carry1) or
         (in12 and in22 and carry1);
  carry2 <= (not in12 and in22 and carry1) or
         (in12 and not in22 and carry1) or
         (in12 and in22 and not carry1) or
         (in12 and in22 and carry1);
  sum(2) <= (not in13 and not in23 and carry2) or   -- Next bit.
         (not in13 and in23 and not carry2) or
         (in13 and not in23 and not carry2) or
         (in13 and in23 and carry2);
  carry3 <= (not in13 and in23 and carry2) or
         (in13 and not in23 and carry2) or
         (in13 and in23 and not carry2) or
         (in13 and in23 and carry2);
  sum(3) <= (not in14 and not in22 and carry1) or   -- Next bit.
         (not in14 and in22 and not carry1) or
         (in14 and not in22 and not carry1) or
         (in14 and in22 and carry1);
  sum(4) <= (not in14 and in24 and carry3) or       -- Most significant bit.
         (in14 and not in24 and carry3) or
         (in14 and in24 and not carry3) or
         (in14 and in24 and carry3);
-- Now convert the sum into 7 segment output using two case statements.
-- Result is displayed in hexadecimal.
  case sum(4) is                    -- Most significant display first.
    when '0' =>
      display2 <= "1111110";   -- Binary for zero on seven seg display
    when '1' =>
      display2 <= "1100000";   -- Binary for one on seven seg display;
    when others =>
      display2 <= "0000000";   -- Error condition, turn off display;
  end case;
  case sum(3 downto 0) is           -- Least significant display.
    when "0000" =>
      display1 <= "1111110";   -- Binary for 0 on seven seg display
    when "0001" =>
      display1 <= "1100000";   -- Binary for 1 on seven seg display;
    when "0010" =>
      display1 <= "1101101";   -- Binary for 2 on seven seg display
    when "0011" =>
      display1 <= "1111001";   -- Binary for 3 on seven seg display;
    when "0100" =>
      display1 <= "0110011";   -- Binary for 4 on seven seg display
```

```
    when "0101" =>
      display1 <= "1011011";    -- Binary for 5 on seven seg display;
    when "0110" =>
      display1 <= "1011111";    -- Binary for 6 on seven seg display
    when "0111" =>
      display1 <= "1110000";    -- Binary for 7 on seven seg display;
    when "1000" =>
      display1 <= "1111111";    -- Binary for 8 on seven seg display
    when "1001" =>
      display1 <= "1111011";    -- Binary for 9 on seven seg display;
    when "1010" =>
      display1 <= "1110111";    -- Binary for A on seven seg display
    when "1011" =>
      display1 <= "0011111";    -- Binary for B on seven seg display;
    when "1100" =>
      display1 <= "1001110";    -- Binary for C on seven seg display
    when "1101" =>
      display1 <= "0111101";    -- Binary for D on seven seg display;
    when "1110" =>
      display1 <= "1001111";    -- Binary for E on seven seg display
    when "1111" =>
      display1 <= "1000111";    -- Binary for F on seven seg display;
    when others =>
      display1 <= "0000000";    -- Error condition, turn off display;
  end case;
end process add;
end struct;
```

The test vectors for this design are also complex as there are two separate sub-functions to test, the 4 bit adder and the two binary to 7 segment decoders. Obviously, these can both be tested simultaneously using only a subset of the full test set. This is because the full set will comprise 256 different vectors, as there are two 4-bit input binary numbers which have 16 possible combinations and for proper testing it would be necessary to ensure that each of the possible 16 input patterns would work correctly after any of the other 16 possible combinations. This gives a total of 256 test vectors for comprehensive testing. This illustrates why comprehensive testing is rarely implemented, since the number of test vectors is very large for most designs. Therefore, a number of test vectors will be used which will give a reasonable level of confidence and also ensure that the majority of the design is exercised at least once.

Required tests

Ensure that all of the possible 7 segment states are tested. This will be 0 and 1 for the most significant display and 0, 1, 2, 3, 4, 5, 6, 7, 8, 9, A, B, C, D, E, F for the least significant display, to make a total of 18 test vectors. These test vectors will also be used to gain confidence in the operation of the adder. To test the adder it will be necessary to test the boundary conditions, plus a few other random values. The boundary conditions are when either input is 0000 or 1111, and there are six such conditions:

input 1	**input 2**
0000	1010
1010	0000
0000	0000
1111	1010
1010	1111
1111	1111

The value 1010 was chosen as a non-boundary condition value. Therefore, a set of 18 test vectors could have the following inputs and generate the outputs as shown.

input 1	**input2**	**result (in hexadecimal)**
The following input values test the least significant 7 segment display.		
0000	0000	00H
0001	0000	01H
0000	0010	02H
0001	0010	03H
0010	0010	04H
0101	0000	05H
0101	0001	06H
0101	0010	07H
0111	0001	08H
0010	0111	09H
0011	0111	0AH
0100	0111	0BH
0101	0111	0CH
0110	0111	0DH
0111	0111	0EH
1000	0111	0EH
The following input values test the most significant 7 segment display.		
1111	1111	1EH
1111	0000	0EH
0000	1111	0EH

The following input values ensure that the higher numbers will also add correctly.

1010	1010	14H
1110	1110	1CH

More values could be included if the designer required more confidence, but if the program produces the correct results for these test vectors there is a very good probability that it will also operate correctly for all other values.

7.4 A 4-bit counter

A simple 4-bit counter will be implemented to illustrate registered designs. Two approaches will be taken, using Boolean equations to describe the logic operations controlling each output bit, followed by a design which uses a case statement to obtain the binary increment operation.

7.4.1 A 4-bit counter using Boolean equations

The Boolean equations for a binary counter are straightforward and operate individually for each bit by detecting when all the lower significant bits are all logic 1 through the use of an exclusive or operation, as illustrated below:

count(0) = /count(0)
count(1) = count(1) xor count(0)
count(2) = count(2) xor (count(1) and count(0))
count(3) = count(3) xor (count(2) and count(1) and count(0))

The VHDL program to implement this is shown below:

```
entity fourbit_counter is
port (clk : in bit;  -- Defines input and output signals.
     cnter : buffer bit_vector(3 downto 0));
end fourbit_counter;

architecture struct of fourbit_counter is

begin

process

begin
  wait until (clk = '1');    -- Implements a registered design.
  cnter(0) <= not cnter(0);
  cnter(1) <= cnter(1) xor cnter(0);
```

```
  cnter(2) <= cnter(2) xor (cnter(1) and cnter(0));
  cnter(3) <= cnter(3) xor (cnter(2) and cnter(1) and cnter(0));
end process;
end struct;
```

7.4.2 A 4-bit counter using a case statement

When using a case statement, each of the possible count bit patterns has to have a test value, so that for a 4-bit counter this will require 16 test conditions and the program to implement this is shown below:

```
entity fourbit_counter is
port (clk : in bit;                -- Defines input and output.
     cnter : out bit_vector(3 downto 0));
end fourbit_counter;

architecture struct of fourbit_counter is

signal state1 : bit_vector(3 downto 0);

begin

process

begin
  wait until (clk = '1');      -- Waits until clock signal is logic 1.
  case state1 is               -- Case statement with 16 values.
    when "0000" =>
      cnter <= "0001";
      state1 <= "0001";
    when "0001" =>
      cnter <= "0010";
      state1 <= "0010";
    when "0010" =>
      cnter <= "0011";
      state1 <= "0011";
    when "0011" =>
      cnter <= "0100";
      state1 <= "0100";
    when "0100" =>
      cnter <= "0101";
      state1 <= "0101";
    when "0101" =>
      cnter <= "0110";
      state1 <= "0110";
    when "0110" =>
      cnter <= "0111";
      state1 <= "0111";
```

```
  when "0111" =>
    cnter <= "1000";
    state1 <= "1000";
  when "1000" =>
    cnter <= "1001";
    state1 <= "1001";
  when "1001" =>
    cnter <= "1010";
    state1 <= "1010";
  when "1010" =>
    cnter <= "1011";
    state1 <= "1011";
  when "1011" =>
    cnter <= "1100";
    state1 <= "1100";
  when "1100" =>
    cnter <= "1101";
    state1 <= "1101";
  when "1101" =>
    cnter <= "1110";
    state1 <= "1110";
  when "1110" =>
    cnter <= "1111";
    state1 <= "1111";
  when others =>          -- Rolls over and restarts the count.
    cnter <= "0000";      -- Also handles any incorrect values.
    state1 <= "0000";
 end case;
end process;
end struct;
```

7.4.3 The test vectors

Both designs will require the same test vectors as the inputs and required outputs are exactly the same, independently of how the counter is implemented. This particular counter design only has one input which is the clock, so that all that is required is enough clock pulses to ensure that the counter will correctly count through all the possible values and that it will also correctly roll-over to the beginning count after the maximum count value. Therefore the test vectors are as follows:

clock   Tests first bit changes.
clock   Tests second bit changes.
clock
clock   Tests third bit changes.
clock
clock

clock
clock Tests fourth bit changes.
clock
clock
clock
clock
clock
clock
clock
clock Tests that the counter rolls over back to zero.
clock A few extra clocks to ensure that it continues counting.
clock
clock
clock

7.5 An 8-bit counter

A more complex 8-bit binary counter will be implemented using two methods: one using the integer capabilities of VHDL and the second using the Boolean equations method.

7.5.1 An 8-bit counter using integer arithmetic

The inputs and outputs are similar to those for the 4-bit counter except that there are 8 outputs. For an 8-bit counter, the case statement method would not be used due to the large number of tests required, which is 256. Instead, an integer variable has been defined which is used to maintain the count value using the arithmetic operator addition, +, and then converted back into the bit data type using an if statement for each bit.

```
entity eightbit_counter is
port (clk : in bit;              -- Defines input and output signals.
    cnter : out bit_vector(7 downto 0));
end eightbit_counter;

architecture struct of eightbit_counter is

signal countval : integer range 0 to 255;

begin

process
```

```
begin
  wait until (clk = '1');
  countval <= countval + 1;
  if (countval mod 128 = 0) then
    cnter(7) <= '0';
  else
    cnter(7) <= '1';
  end if;
  if (countval mod 64 = 0) then
    cnter(6) <= '0';
  else
    cnter(6) <= '1';
  end if;
  if (countval mod 32 = 0) then
    cnter(5) <= '0';
  else
    cnter(5) <= '1';
  end if;
  if (countval mod 16 = 0) then
    cnter(4) <= '0';
  else
    cnter(4) <= '1';
  end if;
  if (countval mod 8 = 0) then
    cnter(3) <= '0';
  else
    cnter(3) <= '1';
  end if;
  if (countval mod 4 = 0) then
    cnter(2) <= '0';
  else
    cnter(2) <= '1';
  end if;
  if (countval mod 2 = 0) then
    cnter(1) <= '0';
  else
    cnter(1) <= '1';
  end if;
  if (countval mod 1 = 0) then
    cnter(0) <= '0';
  else
    cnter(0) <= '1';
  end if;
  end process;
end struct;
```

7.5.2 An 8-bit counter using Boolean equations

The equations required to implement the 8-bit counter are similar to those for the 4-bit counter but extended to manipulate 8 bits. The program to achieve this is given below and is the simpler of the two.

```
entity eightbit_counter is
port (clk : in bit;                          -- Defines input and output signals.
      cnter : buffer bit_vector(7 downto 0));
end eightbit_counter;

architecture struct of eightbit_counter is

begin

process

begin
  wait until (clk = '1');
  cnter(0) <= not cnter(0);
  cnter(1) <= cnter(1) xor cnter(0);
  cnter(2) <= cnter(2) xor (cnter(1) and cnter(0));
  cnter(3) <= cnter(3) xor (cnter(2) and cnter(1) and cnter(0));
  cnter(4) <= cnter(4) xor (cnter(3) and cnter(2) and cnter(1)
              and cnter(0));
  cnter(5) <= cnter(5) xor (cnter(4) and cnter(3) and cnter(2)
              and cnter(1) and cnter(0));
  cnter(6) <= cnter(6) xor (cnter(5) and cnter(4) and cnter(3)
              and cnter(2) and cnter(1) and cnter(0));
  cnter(7) <= cnter(7) xor (cnter(6) and cnter(5) and cnter(4)
              and cnter(3) and cnter(2) and cnter(1) and cnter(0));
end process;
end struct;
```

7.5.3 Test vectors for the 8-bit counter

Both example programs will use the same set of test vectors as they have the same inputs and the same expected outputs. The test vectors required are similar to the 4-bit counter except that more are needed. The 8-bit counter would require at least 256 clock pulses to verify that all the bits change as required and that roll-over to zero occurs correctly. These vectors are not shown here.

7.6 Step motor controller with position feedback

An alternative version of a step motor controller can be designed by including the ability to keep a record of the current step position within one revolution, relative to some initial starting point, as illustrated in figure 7.2. The system consists of a step motor controller using a case statement to create the four different step patterns, with a 5-bit counter used to keep track of the current step position. The design show below only contains the ability to operate in full step and in one direction only, but it could easily be extended to include bi-directional control as well as half-stepping.

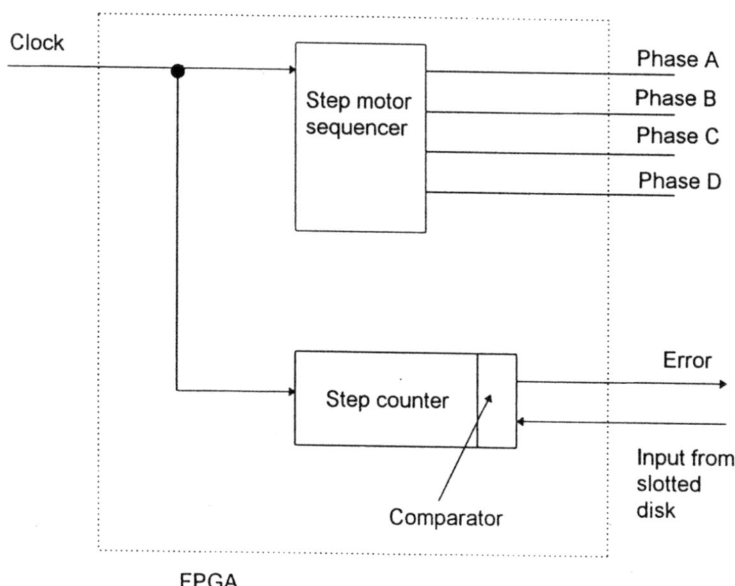

Figure 7.2 Step motor with position counter

```
entity step is
  port (rset,clk,slot : in bit;   -- Defines the input and output signals.
        a0,a1,a2,a3,a4 : buffer bit;
        error : buffer bit;
        motor_state : buffer bit_vector(0 to 3));
end step;

architecture step_design of step is
 constant s0 : bit_vector(0 to 3) := "0001";
 constant s1 : bit_vector(0 to 3) := "0010";
 constant s2 : bit_vector(0 to 3) := "0100";
 constant s3 : bit_vector(0 to 3) := "1000";

--signal motor_state : bit_vector (0 to 3);
begin

step_machine : process
begin
  wait until clk = '1';
```

```
if (rset = '0') then -- this is the step count logic
  if ((a4 = '1') and (a3 = '1')) then
   -- if count > 23, reset to zero
    a0 <= '0';
    a1 <= '0';
    a2 <= '0';
    a3 <= '0';
    a4 <= '0';
  else   -- count as normal
      a0 <=  not a0;
      a1 <= a1 xor a0;
      a2 <= a2 xor (a1 and a0);
      a3 <= a3 xor (a2 and a1 and a0);
      a4 <= a4 xor (a3 and a2 and a1 and a0);
  end if;
  if (slot = '1') then
    if ((a0 = '0') and (a1 = '0') and (a2 = '0') and
        (a3 = '0') and (a4 = '0') ) then
        -- if slot and zero count
      error <= '0';
    else
      error <= '1';
    end if;
  else
    error <= error;
  end if;
-- this is the motor step pattern generator
  case motor_state is
    when s0 =>
      motor_state <= s1;
    when s1 =>
      motor_state <= s2;
    when s2 =>
      motor_state <= s3;
    when s3 =>
      motor_state <= s0;
    when others => -- Error detection and correction.
      motor_state <= s0;
  end case;
else -- perform a reset
  a0 <= '0';
  a1 <= '0';
  a2 <= '0';
  a3 <= '0';
  a4 <= '0';
  motor_state <= s0;
  error <= '0';
end if;
```

```
end process;
end step_design;
```

Test vectors
The test vectors for this design are relatively straightforward and can be separated into three groups:

1) Testing the operation of the step pattern generator (without index detection).
2) Testing the operation of the position counter when correct.
3) Testing the operation of the position counter when incorrect.

The first group simply requires the creation of at least 24 clock pulses with the index input set to logic 0, so that no 'slots' are detected, and to check that the counter rolls over correctly. This will also have tested the operation of the index detector when it is correctly aligned as the error signal will not be activated. This is then followed by a few more clocks and then a reset to ensure that the reset returns the step pattern and position counter to their correct initial values. Finally, the slot signal can be activated which will be an incorrect position, so that the error signal should be activated. A few more clocks are required to ensure that the system recovers from an incorrect index position.

7.7 Sine wave generator

A number of interesting digital functions can easily be implemented using VHDL and the example chosen is the generation of a sine wave. The sine wave values will be generated as binary values and then passed to a digital-to-analogue convertor. Only the operation of the look-up table used to obtain the binary values is described. A case statement will be used to step through what is effectively a look-up table using a signal as the index and then output the bit vector corresponding to the index value. An 8-bit number will be used to represent the digital value of the sine wave with 24 entries in the look-up table. This will not give a particularly accurate digital representation of the sine wave, but the accuracy can be increased by having additional entries in the look-up table and increasing the number of bits used to represent the value.

7.7.1 Generating the binary sine wave values
The digital values were derived from the mathematical sine function:

$$\text{value} = \text{trunc}(128 + 127\sin(2\pi i/\text{index}))$$

where: index = 23 i = 0 ..23

which produces the 8-bit binary values shown in table 7.2.

Table 7.2 Eight bit unsigned binary values of a sine wave

Index	Integer value of sine	Binary value of sine
0	128	10000000
1	161	10010001
2	192	11000000
3	218	11011010
4	238	11101110
5	251	11111011
6	255	1111111
7	251	11111011
8	238	11101110
9	218	11011010
10	192	11000000
11	161	10010001
12	128	10000000
13	95	01011111
14	65	01000001
15	38	00100110
16	18	00010010
17	5	00000101
18	1	00000001
19	5	00000101
20	18	00010010
21	38	00100110
22	65	01000001
23	95	01011111

7.7.2 The VHDL program for a sine wave generator

The VHDL program devised is listed below.

```
entity sinewave_generator is
port (clk : in bit;   -- Defines input and output signals
      sine : out bit_vector(7 downto 0);
      index1 : buffer bit_vector(4 downto 0));
end sinewave_generator;

architecture struct of sinewave_generator is

begin

process

begin
  wait until (clk = '1');    -- Wait until the active edge of the clock.
  case index1 is
    when "00000" =>
      sine <= "10000000";
      index1 <= "00001";
    when "00001" =>
      sine <= "10010001";
      index1 <= "00010";
    when "00010" =>
      sine <= "11000000";
      index1 <= "00011";
    when "00011" =>
      sine <= "11011010";
      index1 <= "00100";
    when "00100" =>
      sine <= "11101110";
      index1 <= "00101";
    when "00101" =>
      sine <= "11111011";
      index1 <= "00110";
    when "00110" =>
      sine <= "11111111";
      index1 <= "00111";
    when "00111" =>
      sine <= "11111011";
      index1 <= "01000";
    when "01000" =>
      sine <= "11101110";
      index1 <= "01001";
    when "01001" =>
      sine <= "11011010";
      index1 <= "01010";
    when "01010" =>
```

```
      sine <= "11000000";
      index1 <= "01011";
    when "01011" =>
      sine <= "10010001";
      index1 <= "01100";
    when "01100" =>
      sine <= "10000000";
      index1 <= "01101";
    when "01101" =>
      sine <= "01011111";
      index1 <= "01110";
    when "01110" =>
      sine <= "01000001";
      index1 <= "01111";
    when "01111" =>
      sine <= "00100110";
      index1 <= "10000";
    when "10000" =>
      sine <= "00010010";
      index1 <= "10001";
    when "10001" =>
      sine <= "00000101";
      index1 <= "10010";
    when "10010" =>
      sine <= "00000001";
      index1 <= "10011";
    when "10011" =>
      sine <= "00000101";
      index1 <= "10100";
    when "10100" =>
      sine <= "00010010";
      index1 <= "10101";
    when "10101" =>
      sine <= "00100110";
      index1 <= "10110";
    when "10110" =>
      sine <= "01000001";
      index1 <= "10111";
    when "10111" =>
      sine <= "01011111";
      index1 <= "11000";
    when others =>      -- Final value and error correction.
      sine <= "10000000";
      index1 <= "00000";
  end case;
end process;
end struct;
```

7.7.3 The test vectors

The test vectors for this design are fairly simple, consisting only of at least 24 clock pulses to ensure that the correct values are output and that the index rolls over correctly to the beginning of the look-up table once the maximum value has been reached. The test vectors are not shown here.

7.8 An 8-bit RISC design

An 8-bit Reduced Instruction Set Computer (RISC) has been designed which has two instructions:

NOP no operation which just increments the program counter.
JUMP jumps to the absolute address specified in the instruction.

The NOP instruction is identified from the two most significant bits of the instruction, as is the JUMP instruction. The remaining 6 bits of the NOP instruction are ignored, and for the JUMP instruction the remaining 6 bits form the absolute address to jump to. This limits the RISC to a maximum memory space of 64 bytes for this design. A block diagram of the RISC connected to an EPROM is shown in figure 7.3 and indicates the signals to be defined. The RISC requires the following:

An 8-bit input only data bus.
A 6-bit output only address bus, driven by the program counter.
A clock input.
A reset (this is optional during the simulation stage, but would be required when implemented).

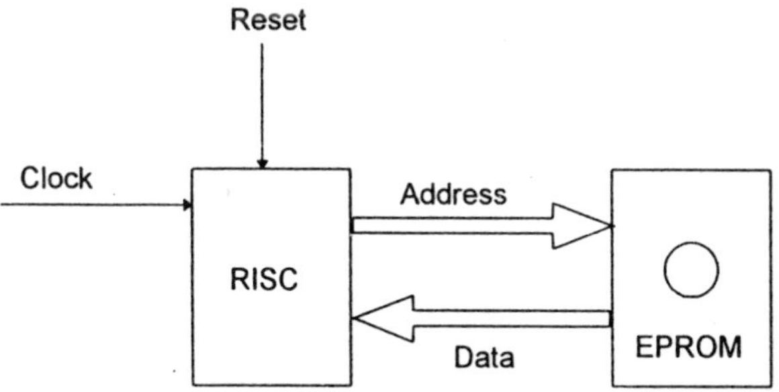

Figure 7.3 A simple RISC

A simple case statement is used to distinguish between the two instructions when the NOP has to increment the 6-bit program counter which has been implemented using Boolean equations and the JUMP instruction only has to transfer the value on the bottom 6 bits of the data bus to the 6-bit address bus.

```
entity risc is
  port (rset,clk : in bit;          -- Defines input and output connections.
  instruction : in bit_vector(7 downto 0);
  a0,a1,a2,a3,a4,a5 : buffer bit);
end risc;

architecture risc_design of risc is

begin

risc_machine : process
begin
  wait until clk = '1';          -- Makes this a clocked design.
  if (rset = '0') then           -- Test for reset first.
    case (instruction(7 downto 6)) is        -- Decode instruction opcode
      when "00" => -- NOP so inc PC   -- This is no operation.
        a0 <= not a0;            -- Increments the program counter.
        a1 <= a1 xor a0;
        a2 <= a2 xor (a1 and a0);
        a3 <= a3 xor (a2 and a1 and a0);
        a4 <= a4 xor (a3 and a2 and a1 and a0);
        a5 <= a5 xor (a4 and a3 and a2 and a1 and a0);
      when "10" =>               -- JUMP to address given in the instruction.
        a0 <= instruction(0);
        a1 <= instruction(1);
        a2 <= instruction(2);
        a3 <= instruction(3);
        a4 <= instruction(4);
        a5 <= instruction(5);
      when others =>         -- All other instructions cause a reset at present.
        a0 <= '0';
        a1 <= '0';
        a2 <= '0';
        a3 <= '0';
        a4 <= '0';
        a5 <= '0';
    end case;
  else                           -- perform a reset
    a0 <= '0';
    a1 <= '0';
    a2 <= '0';
    a3 <= '0';
    a4 <= '0';
    a5 <= '0';
  end if;
end process;
end risc_design;
```

The test vectors for this design are fairly simple as the device only has two instructions and, provided that they are executed a few times, the design can be considered to be correct. A suitable RISC assembly language program is given below:

```
NOP
NOP
JUMP  08H ;This will jump forward to address 08H
NOP
NOP
NOP
NOP
NOP
NOP        ;This is address 08H
NOP
NOP
JUMP  0H   ;Now jump back to the beginning to repeat the program.
```

It may be thought worthwhile to ensure that the program counter will correctly increment from 00H to 03FH and a total of 64 NOPs would be required to achieve this.

7.9 Problems

1. Design and implement a VHDL program for a 3 input NOR gate.

2. Implement the VHDL program for a 4-bit Gray code counter. How many test vectors are required to fully test this design?

3. A data stream contains two different sequences which are to be identified

   01101 and 10010

   Devise a suitable state machine to indicate whenever either of the streams has occurred where the data streams are not mutually exclusive. Implement the state machine as a VHDL program and devise the required test vectors.

4. Amend the RISC design outlined earlier to include two additional instructions and devise a suitable set of test vectors. Would it be considered optimal to create the full set of test vectors? (How many would there be?)

5. Implement the VHDL program for a 4-bit up/down counter which has the capability to pre-load a specified start value which is not '0000'. Is it

reasonable to devise a complete and full set of test vectors for this design? If not what would constitute a suitable set of test vectors?

6. Amend the sine wave generator example given in section 7.7 so that the frequency of the output sine wave is selected from one of 4 binary weighted values. The same input clock frequency to the design, the clk signal, must be used for all of them.

7.10 Further reading

MasterClass. The multimedia VHDL Tutorial (CD-ROM), Esperan Multimedia Products Ltd, Unit 1, Hilldrop Lane, Ramsbury, Wilts SN8 2RB, UK.
E-mail address info@esperan.com

Moore, W. and Luk, W., Editors, *FPGAs*, Abingdon EE&CS Books, 1991, ISBN 0-9518453-0-6.

Moore, W. and Luk, W., Editors, *More FPGAs*, Abingdon EE&CS Books, 1994, ISBN 0-9518453-1-4.

WARP2 VHDL Compiler for PLDs and CPLDS, version 4.0. Cypress Semiconductor, 3901 North First Street, San Jose, CA 95134, USA.

8 Migration

If a design is to remain in production over a period of time it will often require updating, both to improve its functionality and correct any errors, but also to take advantage of advances in technology. Such advances are being achieved in two ways:

1) Improvements in the underlying semiconductor technology which leads to:

   a) Reduced power consumption.
   b) Increased speed of operation.
   c) Reduced silicon die size.
   d) Reduced cost.
   e) Increased functionality.

2) Alternative architectures.

The result of these continuing and continuous improvements is that a design using state of the art components only one or two years ago is now out of date and uncompetitive and requires updating to newer components and technologies. This process of updating is known as migration, and a number of major migrations have occurred in the past:

1) Discrete transistors to integrated circuits.
2) Standard digital components to programmable logic devices.
3) Programmable logic devices to field programmable gate array devices.
4) Field programmable devices to application specific integrated circuit devices.

Past experience would indicate that before too long there will be a need to migrate from application integrated circuits to some alternative.

The improvements in technologies having been occurring at approximately the same rate for over forty years, with the density of transistors used to build the digital circuits doubling every 18 months. This is known as 'Moore's Law' although it is really only an observation, but past experience supports this idea so that the device with 20,000 logic gates being used in a design today will be replaced by a device with 33,000 gates in 12 months' time, at the same or lower price. This improvement creates two effects, one is that devices are only available for production for a limited period of time, one or two years for some devices, before they are replaced with something 'better', and secondly that the improvements in gate densities and technologies enable different architectures to be used in designs to lead to a greater improvement in products. Because devices are only available for limited periods before they become obsolete it is important to design products so that they can be ported to different manufacturers' devices and to newer versions from the same manufacturer. This requires the designer to avoid, if at all possible, any architectural or design language specific features which would be difficult to transfer, hence the importance of a standardised design language such as VHDL. VHDL has two important features which make it vital for modern designs:

1) It is standardised and is therefore independent of any individual manufacturer. This creates a large pool of experienced designers and tools which can be utilised on successive projects and subsequent generations of products.

2) It is independent of any particular device and technology, so it can be used to design for PLDs, FPGAs and ASICs without any significant alteration in the programs. The synthesis of the program on to a specific device is accomplished by the compiler and optimiser and, provided that the device manufacturers and tool developers continue to offer this synthesis ability for their latest devices, designers will be able to transfer to the latest devices with the minimum redesign costs. Some redesign costs are inevitable, due to differences in propagation delays and internal architectures which will result in differences in timing and potentially in in-system operation, so an appropriate set of test vectors and accurate simulation are vital to ensure as smooth a transfer as possible.

8.1 Migration from discrete logic to PLDs

There are a number of reasons for transferring from discrete logic to programmable devices:

1) To reduce costs through a reduced number of components, PCB area and power supply requirements, which also leads to increased reliability.
2) To achieve an increase in the speed of operation of the system.
3) To reduce the time to market.

Typically, discrete logic devices contain only a few gates, for example a 74LS00 contains only 4 NAND gates in a 14-pin dual-in-line package (DIL), where as a simple PLD such as the 22V10 contains over 200 logic gate equivalents in a 24-pin DIL package. However, it needs to be remembered that although the number of equivalent logic gates has been increased, they can only be used in a limited number of ways, so instead of achieving the 50 to 1 improvement in device packages that might be expected from a simple comparison of gate numbers, the actual improvement is probably only about 10 to 1. This is still a major improvement and brings additional benefits in extra features that the PLD architectures contain. Typical gate densities of the three implementation approaches are:

TTL 5 gates cm^{-2}
PLD 150 gates cm^{-2}
FPGA 5000 gates cm^{-2}

Migration from TTL to PLDs effectively requires the design to be re-entered, as the TTL version will only exist as a circuit diagram or schematic. Some PLD compilers will accept input from schematic capture packages, but for the majority of PLDs some form of hardware description language is used. The migration process is therefore one of describing the operation of the TTL circuit in terms of Boolean equations or state diagrams and then compiling these descriptions for the target device.

8.1.1 Hardware description languages

It is generally thought to be an advantage of using PLDs that designs are implemented using hardware description languages rather than schematics, as the increasingly abstract textual descriptions can be used, rather than the more labour intensive pictorial schematics. This facilitates the porting of the design to alternative technologies and target devices. These languages were originally designed to enter directly the Boolean equations that were created to describe the logic to be implemented. For the discrete TTL logic these equations would be first minimised manually to obtain the minimum production cost. This is not necessarily the same as the minimum component count as many designs used only one type of logic gate, typically the NAND gate, and all logic functions were implemented using these gates. Because only one type of gate was used, they could be purchased in bulk to obtain a lower device cost and this also minimised storage and handling costs which minimised production costs. As this design technique relied on manual input, mistakes were difficult to avoid and all products had to be prototyped and extensively debugged to ensure accurate operation.

The use of HDLs reduced the need to be a human expert in logic minimisation as the compilers were supplied with built-in optimisers which were much more effective than the average designer, enabling a shorter design time to be achieved with the same efficient solutions in fewer components. Because the PLD architecture was so flexible there was no need to select a specific type of logic gate for implementation and designs only needed to create the original Boolean equations. Minimisation for the target architecture was performed automatically and without manual intervention, thereby reducing design and prototpying periods.

8.1.2 Simulation

A major improvement that HDLs brought with them was the simulator. Because the early PLDs were one-time programmable, it was important to verify the designs before they were programmed, to avoid wasteful trial and error development. The simulators took the output from the compiler, usually in the form a standardised JEDEC file used for programming, and with some knowledge about the architecture of the PLD and a set of test vectors describing the inputs and expected outputs, the operation of the design could be verified. Although these simulators were functional, that is, they simulated the operation of ideal logic functions within the PLD rather than at transistor level, they provided a large degree of confidence in the designs before programming. They also provided an environment where designers could try out ideas without having to resort to expensive and time consuming prototyping techniques.

8.1.3 A typical design flow

As an example consider the migration of a simple video digitiser, which is first implemented in discrete logic and then in PLDs. The video digitiser is shown in block form in figure 8.1 and is designed simply to provide the line and position along the line of the first pixel to be detected, which is above the threshold brightness manually selected.

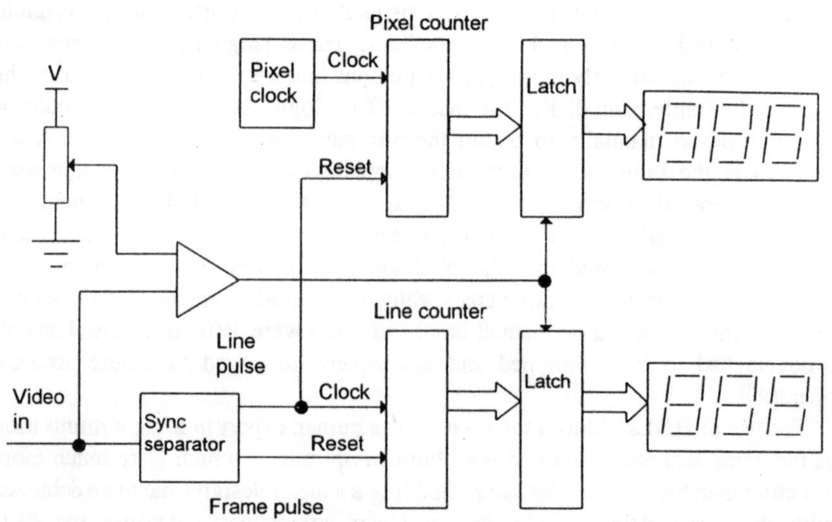

Figure 8.1 A simple video digitiser

The system consists of a small amount of analogue electronics to process the incoming video signal to extract the frame and line synchronisation signals and perform a comparison of the video voltage with the selected threshold. The output from the comparator is used to latch the line and pixel count into latches for display on the 7 segment displays, in hexadecimal. The frame signal extracted from the video signal resets all the counters and clears the latches and the line synchronisation pulse increments the line counter. The pixel counter is reset by the line synchronisation pulse and incremented by an independent crystal-controlled oscillator. A single frame is used with no interlacing so that the maximum line count is 312 and, to simplify the display decoding, BCD counters are used, so three are required. To maintain the aspect ratio of the original image of 3:4, the pixel frequency is selected to give 416 counts per video line. Again, BCD counters are used to simplify the display logic, so another three 4-bit BCD counters are included. Four bit latches are provided on the output of the counters and hexadecimal to 7 segment LED decoders used to create the display logic. The TTL parts used are listed in table 8.1.

Table 8.1 TTL parts list

Function	**TTL part**	**Number**	**Total power (mW)**	**Total PCB area (mm^2)**	**Total pins**	**Total cost (£)**
BCD counter	74LS160	6	558	930	96	4.26
4 bit latches	74LS374	3	405	581	60	2.94
Hex to 7 segment	74LS48	6	750	930	96	7.44
Totals		15	1713	2441	198	16.64

The same design, but now implemented using PLDs, specifically the 22V10, required the parts listed in table 8.2. A slight restriction was placed on the design in order to minimise the number of components. The pixel count was restricted to a maximum count of 399, instead of the original 416, so that it could be fitted into a single PLD. The latches were implemented using a 22V10 for each counter output. Although this was not particularly efficient it did mean that only one type of component was used. The hexadecimal to 7 segment decoders were implemented as two time multiplexed digits per 22V10. Each 22V10 has two 4-bit BCD hexadecimal inputs, plus the multiplexing clock, a 7-bit 7 segment output connected to both displays in parallel and a further output which selects the active display via a transistor.

Table 8.2 PLD parts list

Function	PLD part	Number	Total power (mW)	PCB area (mm^2)	Total pins	Cost (£)
BCD counter	22V10	2	700	464	48	11.96
4 bit latches	22V10	2	700	464	48	11.96
Hex to 7 segment	22V10	3	1050	696	72	17.64
Totals	-	7	2450	1624	168	41.16

Each of the different functions would require a separate design file, so that three HDL programs would be required. Each would need to be simulated individually, as only the more sophisticated PLD development systems would be able to provide a simulation for the complete design. From the tables 8.1 and 8.2 it can be seen that the component count has been reduced and that only one type of component is now used which would result in a reduction in stock costs during production and PCB layout costs during prototyping. The PCB area required has been reduced by 33% and the number of pins, which makes it more reliable, by 15%. The major problem with moving to the PLDs has been the 43% increase in power required. However, this could be overcome by using a lower power version of the 22V10, although this would be more expensive. The biggest problem with moving from discrete TTL to PLDs seems to be the cost which has actually increased by 233%. This is not quite as bad as it first seems, as these prices are for one-offs, whereas in production, bulk purchasing would reduce the cost significantly. The savings would be made in the need to purchase one type of PLD ONLY, rather than three types of TTL, so that large quantities of the PLD would be required and hence lower prices obtained. However, it should still be remembered that it is likely that the PLD parts would still probably cost more than the TTL parts; however, when the overall cost of the product is considered, the PLD product will be cheaper.

8.2 Migration from PLDs to FPGA devices

The second major wave of migrations occurred when Field Programmable Gate Arrays (FPGAs) were developed. These devices offered significantly more gate equivalents on a single device than the PLDs, but also provided a much more flexible architecture, enabling more functionality to be created than the increase in gate densities might first have indicated. Typically, the first FPGAs were a few thousand gate equivalents, whereas the existing larger PLDs had a few hundred gates. They provided between 5 and 10 times the functionality rather than 1 or 2 times improvement that might have been expected, when compared with the comparison of discrete logic with PLDs. Continuing improvements in FPGAs now mean that devices with 30,000 to 50,000 gate equivalents are available at compatible prices with the first 2000 gate devices. Because of this, the functionality is much higher and products provide more capability for less cost, less PCB area, less power and so on.

8.2.1 HDLs and VHDL

Migrating from PLDs to FPGAs does not require the same major difference in design methods, as PLDs are developed using HDLs, and FPGAs can also be designed using HDLs, some of which are the same. For example, PALASM (a HDL from AMD) can be used, in a variety of slightly varying dialects, to program the simplest PLDs and some of the more complex MACH series FPGAs. However, the existing HDLs are not going to be able to be used for a further migrations, say to ASICs, as they do not have the abstract design capabilities that are required. Because of this, and the deficiencies in the existing HDLs, and the fact that they were manufacturer specific and targeted to their own architectures, the standardised language VHDL was developed and this is the major vehicle for migration. The requirement now is to transfer from HDL to VHDL which is a more significant task.

8.2.2 Combining several PLD designs into a single FPGA design

There are a number of different migrations possible from PLDs to other devices; these are:

1) PLD to complex PLD.
2) PLD to mask programmed PLD.
3) PLD to FPGA.

Each of the migrations has slightly different requirements and processes but the underlying feature of all of them is the desire to obtain further benefits in the product being created through higher levels of integration. It should also be understood that as well as the benefits of higher levels of integration and reduced costs, there is considerable opportunity for higher levels of functionality, so that the migrations can be separated into two levels:

1) Signal for signal, timing for timing transfer.
2) Higher levels of operating performance, such as frequency and complexity but also more functionality than that provided by the original PLD design.

As the devices were originally designed using a HDL, it is often quite simple to combine the separate HDL files into a single entity which can then be fitted into a single complex PLD (cPLD).

8.2.3 Migrating a several PLD design to a single cPLD

The same design that was migrated from TTL to PLD will now be migrated to cPLD to demonstrate the simplicity of the progress. The approach taken will be to take the HDL programs for the PLDs written in PALASM and combine them into a single program written in MACHXL which is compatible with PALASM, for the MACH series of complex PLDs. There are three different programs to be converted; the two BCD counters, the latches and the BCD to seven segment decoders. However, due to the extra resources of the cPLD, the restrictions imposed on the PLDs can be removed and the pixel counter will be extended to 416 again. The multiplexed seven segment displays will still be used in order to maintain a low pin count. The PALASM program for the line counter is shown in listing 8.1 (the pixel counter is almost identical but has a maximum value of 416 instead of 312), the latches in listing 8.2 and the BCD to seven segment decoders in listing 8.3. The combined files are shown in listing 8.4 which have been amended to take advantage of the extra sophistication of the MACHXL language. This has enabled the CASE statement to be used to simplify the 6 digit time multiplexed seven segment display implementation.

Listing 8.1 PALASM program for line counter

```
;---------------------------------- PIN Declarations --------------
PIN  ?          frame                                  ;
PIN  ?          line_clk                               ;
PIN  ?          line_cnt[9..0] registered              ;
;
;string substitutions
;
string zero9 '#b0000000000'
string zero4 '#b0000'
string max_line '#b1100010010' ; 312 in BCD
string nine '9'

;----------------------------------- Boolean Equation Segment ------
EQUATIONS
line_cnt[9..0].clkf = line_clk

if (frame) then
  begin
    line_cnt[9..0] := zero9
  end
else
  begin
```

```
    if (line_cnt[9..0] = max_line) then
      begin
        line_cnt[9..0] := zero9
      end
    else
      begin
        if (line_cnt[3..0] = nine) then
          begin
            line_cnt[3..0] := zero4
            if (line_cnt[7..4] = nine) then
              begin
                line_cnt[7..4] := zero4
                line_cnt[3..0] := line_cnt[3..0]
                line_cnt[8] := /line_cnt[8]
                line_cnt[9] := line_cnt[9] :+: line_cnt[8]
              end
            else
              begin
                line_cnt[4] := /line_cnt[4]
                line_cnt[5] := line_cnt[5] :+: line_cnt[4]
                line_cnt[6] := line_cnt[6] :+: (line_cnt[5] * line_cnt[4])
                line_cnt[7] := line_cnt[7] :+: (line_cnt[6] * line_cnt[5] *
                        line_cnt[4])
                line_cnt[9..8] := line_cnt[9..8]
              end
          end
        else
          begin
            line_cnt[0] := /line_cnt[0]
            line_cnt[1] := line_cnt[1] :+: line_cnt[0]
            line_cnt[2] := line_cnt[2] :+: (line_cnt[1] * line_cnt[0])
            line_cnt[3] := line_cnt[3] :+: (line_cnt[2] * line_cnt[1] * line_cnt[0])
            line_cnt[9..4] := line_cnt[9..4]
          end
      end
  end
;----------------------------------------------------------
```

Listing 8.2 PALASM program for latches

```
;--------------------------------- PIN Declarations --------------
PIN  ?        comp_clk                                ;
PIN  ?        line_cnt[7..0]                          ;
PIN  ?        line_BCD_out[7..0]                      ;
;string substitutions
;
```

```
;---------------------------------- Boolean Equation Segment ------
EQUATIONS
line_BCD_out[7..0].clkf = comp_clk
line_BCD_out[7..0] := line_cnt[7..0]
;-----------------------------------------------------------------
```

Listing 8.3 PALASM program for BCD to seven segment decoders

```
;---------------------------------- PIN Declarations --------------
PIN  ?         comp_clk                                  ;
PIN  ?         seg7[6..0]                                ;
PIN  ?         line_BCD_out[7..0]
PIN  ?         select                 registered
PIN  ?         d_clk
;
;string substitutions
;
string zero       '#b0000'  ; BCD binary zero to 9
string one        '#b0001'
string two        '#b0010'
string three      '#b0011'
string four       '#b0100'
string five       '#b0101'
string six        '#b0110'
string seven      '#b0111'
string eight      '#b1000'
string nine       '#b1001'
string seg7_zero  '#b0111111'    ; seven segment 0 to 9
string seg7_one   '#b0000110'
string seg7_two   '#b1011011'
string seg7_three '#b1001111'
string seg7_four  '#b1100110'
string seg7_five  '#b1101101'
string seg7_six   '#b1111101'
string seg7_seven '#b0000111'
string seg7_eight '#b1111111'
string seg7_nine  '#b1110111'

;-------------------------- Boolean Equation Segment ------
EQUATIONS
select.clkf = d_clk

select := /select
if (select = 0) then ;output low for bits of BCD as 7 seg
  begin
```

```
    if (line_BCD_out[3..0] = zero) then
      begin seg7[6..0] = seg7_zero end
    if (line_BCD_out[3..0] = one) then
      begin seg7[6..0] = seg7_one end
    if (line_BCD_out[3..0] = two) then
      begin seg7[6..0] = seg7_two end
    if (line_BCD_out[3..0] = three) then
      begin seg7[6..0] = seg7_three end
    if (line_BCD_out[3..0] = four) then
      begin seg7[6..0] = seg7_four end
    if (line_BCD_out[3..0] = five) then
      begin seg7[6..0] = seg7_five end
    if (line_BCD_out[3..0] = six) then
      begin seg7[6..0] = seg7_six end
    if (line_BCD_out[3..0] = seven) then
      begin seg7[6..0] = seg7_seven end
    if (line_BCD_out[3..0] = eight) then
      begin seg7[6..0] = seg7_eight end
    if (line_BCD_out[3..0] = nine) then
      begin seg7[6..0] = seg7_nine end
  end
else   ; output high 4 bits of BCD as 7 seg
  begin
    if (line_BCD_out[7..4] = zero) then
      begin seg7[6..0] = seg7_zero end
    if (line_BCD_out[7..4] = one) then
      begin seg7[6..0] = seg7_one end
    if (line_BCD_out[7..4] = two) then
      begin seg7[6..0] = seg7_two end
    if (line_BCD_out[7..4] = three) then
      begin seg7[6..0] = seg7_three end
    if (line_BCD_out[7..4] = four) then
      begin seg7[6..0] = seg7_four end
    if (line_BCD_out[7..4] = five) then
      begin seg7[6..0] = seg7_five end
    if (line_BCD_out[7..4] = six) then
      begin seg7[6..0] = seg7_six end
    if (line_BCD_out[7..4] = seven) then
      begin seg7[6..0] = seg7_seven end
    if (line_BCD_out[7..4] = eight) then
      begin seg7[6..0] = seg7_eight end
    if (line_BCD_out[7..4] = nine) then
      begin seg7[6..0] = seg7_nine end
  end
;------------------------------------------------------
```

Listing 8.4 MACHXL program for complete simple video digitiser

```
;-------------------------- PIN Declarations ---------------
PIN  ?          seg7[6..0]                    ;
PIN  ?          digit[2..0]        ; Selects which digit is active
PIN  ?          BCD_out[6..0]      ; Temporary store for BCD
PIN  ?          line_BCD_out[9..0]
PIN  ?          pix_BCD_out[10..0]
PIN  ?          frame                                  ;
PIN  ?          line_clk                               ;
PIN  ?          pix_clk                                ;
PIN  ?          comp_clk                               ;
PIN  ?          line_cnt[9..0] registered              ;
PIN  ?          pix_cnt[10..0] registered              ;
;
;string substitutions
;
string zero       '#b0000'  ; BCD binary zero to 9
string one        '#b0001'
string two        '#b0010'
string three      '#b0011'
string four       '#b0100'
string five       '#b0101'
string six        '#b0110'
string seven      '#b0111'
string eight      '#b1000'
string nine       '#b1001'
string seg7_zero  '#b0111111'    ; seven segment 0 to 9
string seg7_one   '#b0000110'
string seg7_two   '#b1011011'
string seg7_three '#b1001111'
string seg7_four  '#b1100110'
string seg7_five  '#b1101101'
string seg7_six   '#b1111101'
string seg7_seven '#b0000111'
string seg7_eight '#b1111111'
string seg7_nine  '#b1110111'
string zero10 '#b00000000000'
string zero9 '#b0000000000'
string zero4 '#b0000'
string all_off '#b0000000'
string max_pix '#b10000010110' ; 416 in BCD
string max_line '#b1100010010' ; 312 in BCD
string first  '#b000'   ; Used to identify which multiplexed 7 seg digit
string second '#b001'
string third  '#b010'
string fourth '#b011'
string fifth  '#b100'
string sixth  '#b101'
```

```
;---------------------- Boolean Equation Segment ------
EQUATIONS

pix_cnt[10..0].clkf = pix_clk
line_cnt[9..0].clkf = line_clk
line_BCD_out[9..0].clkf = comp_clk
pix_BCD_out[10..0].clkf = comp_clk
digit[2..0].clkf = line_clk
;
; This is the pixel counter
;
if (line_clk) then
  begin
    pix_cnt[10..0] := zero10
  end
else
  begin
    if (pix_cnt[10..0] = max_pix) then
      begin
        pix_cnt[10..0] := zero10
      end
    else
      begin
        if (pix_cnt[3..0] = nine) then
          begin
            pix_cnt[3..0] := zero4
            if (pix_cnt[7..4] = nine) then
              begin
                pix_cnt[7..4] := zero4
                pix_cnt[3..0] := pix_cnt[3..0]
                pix_cnt[8] := /pix_cnt[8]
                pix_cnt[9] := pix_cnt[9] :+: pix_cnt[8]
                pix_cnt[10] := pix_cnt[10] :+: (pix_cnt[9] * pix_cnt[8])
              end
            else
              begin
                pix_cnt[4] := /pix_cnt[4]
                pix_cnt[5] := pix_cnt[5] :+: pix_cnt[4]
                pix_cnt[6] := pix_cnt[6] :+: (pix_cnt[5] * pix_cnt[4])
                pix_cnt[7] := pix_cnt[7] :+: (pix_cnt[6] * pix_cnt[5] * pix_cnt[4])
                pix_cnt[10..8] := pix_cnt[10..8]
              end
          end
        else
          begin
            pix_cnt[0] := /pix_cnt[0]
            pix_cnt[1] := pix_cnt[1] :+: pix_cnt[0]
            pix_cnt[2] := pix_cnt[2] :+: (pix_cnt[1] * pix_cnt[0])
```

```
          pix_cnt[3] := pix_cnt[3] :+: (pix_cnt[2] * pix_cnt[1] * pix_cnt[0])
          pix_cnt[10..4] := pix_cnt[10..4]
        end
      end
  end
;
; This is the line counter
;

if (frame) then
  begin
    line_cnt[9..0] := zero9
  end
else
  begin
    if (line_cnt[9..0] = max_line) then
      begin
        line_cnt[9..0] := zero9
      end
    else
      begin
        if (line_cnt[3..0] = nine) then
          begin
            line_cnt[3..0] := zero4
            if (line_cnt[7..4] = nine) then
              begin
                line_cnt[7..4] := zero4
                line_cnt[3..0] := line_cnt[3..0]
                line_cnt[8] := /line_cnt[8]
                line_cnt[9] := line_cnt[9] :+: line_cnt[8]
              end
            else
              begin
                line_cnt[4] := /line_cnt[4]
                line_cnt[5] := line_cnt[5] :+: line_cnt[4]
                line_cnt[6] := line_cnt[6] :+: (line_cnt[5] * line_cnt[4])
                line_cnt[7] := line_cnt[7] :+: (line_cnt[6] * line_cnt[5] *
                        line_cnt[4])
                line_cnt[9..8] := line_cnt[9..8]
              end
          end
        else
          begin
            line_cnt[0] := /line_cnt[0]
            line_cnt[1] := line_cnt[1] :+: line_cnt[0]
            line_cnt[2] := line_cnt[2] :+: (line_cnt[1] * line_cnt[0])
            line_cnt[3] := line_cnt[3] :+: (line_cnt[2] * line_cnt[1] * line_cnt[0])
            line_cnt[9..4] := line_cnt[9..4]
```

```
        end
      end
    end
;
; Latch
;

line_BCD_out[9..0] := line_cnt[9..0]
pix_BCD_out[10..0] := pix_cnt[10..0]

;
; Dual three digit seven segment display
; This version is time multiplexed using the line sync pulse
; and a 6 bit shift register to select the digit
;
case (digit[2..0])
  begin
    first  : begin
               BCD_out[3..0] := line_BCD_out[3..0]
               digit[2..0] := second
             end
    second : begin
               BCD_out[3..0] := line_BCD_out[7..4]
               digit[2..0] := third
             end
    third  : begin
               BCD_out[1..0] := line_BCD_out[9..8]
               BCD_out[3..2] := #b00
               digit[2..0] := fourth
             end
    fourth : begin
               BCD_out[3..0] := pix_BCD_out[3..0]
               digit[2..0] := fifth
             end
    fifth  : begin
               BCD_out[3..0] := pix_BCD_out[7..4]
               digit[2..0] := sixth
             end
    sixth  : begin
               BCD_out[2..0] := pix_BCD_out[10..8]
               BCD_out[3] := #b0
               digit[2..0] := first
             end
    otherwise : begin
                  BCD_out[3..0] := line_BCD_out[3..0]
                  digit[2..0] := first
                end
  end ; case
```

```
;
; Now convert 4 bits BCD to 7 segment
;
 case (BCD_out[3..0])
  begin
   zero   : begin  seg7[6..0] = seg7_zero  end
   one    : begin  seg7[6..0] = seg7_one   end
   two    : begin  seg7[6..0] = seg7_two   end
   three  : begin  seg7[6..0] = seg7_three end
   four   : begin  seg7[6..0] = seg7_four  end
   five   : begin  seg7[6..0] = seg7_five  end
   six    : begin  seg7[6..0] = seg7_six   end
   seven  : begin  seg7[6..0] = seg7_seven end
   eight  : begin  seg7[6..0] = seg7_eight end
   nine   : begin  seg7[6..0] = seg7_nine  end
   otherwise: begin seg7[6..0] = all_off  end
  end ;case
```

In all programs the test vectors have not been included to simplify the programs, but would obviously be required before programming the target device. Table 8.3 lists the parameters of the MACH device from which it can be seen that there is a considerable reduction in power consumption over the TTL and PLD implementation; the number of components has been reduced, as has the PCB area and the number of pins required. All these factors will lead to a cheaper and more reliable product. The only drawback is that the MACH445 is more expensive than either of the components for the TTL or PLD versions. However, as discussed for the TTL to PLD migration, there will be cost savings to be made in the reductions in power consumption, PCB area, lower stocking levels and in-bulk purchasing that will probably make the complex PLD solution the most cost effective. It is worth noting that the migration time from the PLD solution to the complex PLD solution took approximately two hours, which included the optimisation of the program and identification of the most appropriate member of the MACH family, plus the writing of the extra test vectors required for simulation. The time taken to create the individual PALASM programs approached one hour per function and there were four functions: pixel counter, line counter, latch and BCD to seven segment decoder, totalling 4 hours. Because the programs were written in very similar HDLs, it was a relatively simple task to concatenate all the programs, rationalise and simplify the test vectors.

Table 8.3 cPLD parts list

Function	PLD part	Number	Power (mW)	PCB area (mm^2)	Total pins	Cost ($)
Complete system	MAC H445	1	1275	289	100	49.58

8.2.4 Migrating to a mask programmed PLD

Once a design has been prototyped using the PLD, there are potential benefits to be obtained in terms of cost, in moving to a mask programmed device. This occurs when the cost of producing the mask, the non recurring engineering (NRE) costs become less than the total savings obtained through the cheaper mask programmed devices. Typically, this value is somewhere between 1000 and 10,000 devices, depending on the specific technology and manufacturer used. The process itself removes all the programmable cells from the PLD, replacing them with a standard semiconductor process, usually CMOS, which implements the same architecture of the programmed device. All that is needed is the netlist created by the original PLD development software which is passed to the manufacturer of the masked PLDs, after which the process is mainly out of the hands of the designer. All the designer is required to do is verify that the prototyped masked PLD operates as required in the product. The masked device is then pin, function and timing compatible, although there will be some changes in the electrical characteristics, typically, a reduction in power consumption.

Figure 8.2 illustrates a typical timing sequence of a product which will be entering mass production and for which it has been decided to use masked PLDs. The development stage takes the required amount of time, based on the product complexity and is then followed by a period of initial production using PLDs. During this initial period, the masked PLD version is prototyped to ensure that it correctly implements the functions and that it operates as required in the product and on average this takes 5 weeks. Once the masked PLD has been confirmed, it enters mass production which takes approximately 7 weeks. At this point production with the PLD can cease and the masked PLD can be used, with its lower cost. This fits in with the cost cycle of a new product, which when first introduced can be high as customers will want it, but as demand falls, it is possible to continue reducing the product price through reduced production costs, thereby maintaining the same levels of revenue. The opportunity to switch between PLDs and masked PLDs also means that wide fluctuations in product sales can be accommodated. A base line production quantity has to be decided which can be implemented using the masked PLDs. If demand increases, the programmed PLDs can be used to meet demand and this can be accompanied by an increase in cost to cover the extra expense of the programmed PLDs.

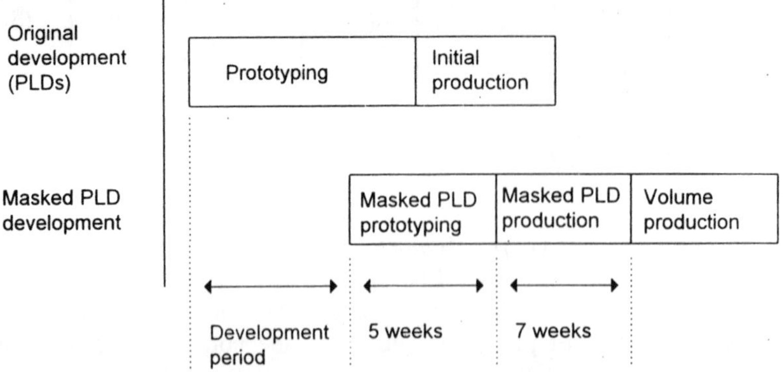

Figure 8.2 Timing sequence for creation of mask programmed PLDs

8.2.5 Migrating PLDs to FPGAs

The same problem of implementing the position and orientation sensor will be used to demonstrate the migration from PLDs to FPGAs, by writing the complete program in VHDL for an FPGA and then comparing with the PLD solutions; one for 22V10s and one for MACH445 written in PALASM. The VHDL program is shown in listing 8.5 and it can be seen that it is almost a direct equivalent to the MACHXL program for the MACH445. This demonstrates the advantages of using high level hardware description languages, even if they are different, because there are usually equivalent constructs in most HDLs. No attempt has been made to obtain the most efficient implementation; instead the quickest migration period was aimed for. This particular example took approximately four hours to complete, which included designing the waveform test vectors for the VHDL program.

Listing 8.5 Position and orientation sensor in VHDL

```
------------------------ PIN Declarations --------------
entity position_and_orientation_sensor is
  port(
       frame, line_clk, pix_clk, comp_clk : bit;
       seg7          : buffer bit_vector(6 downto 0);
       digit        : buffer bit_vector(2 downto 0);
       BCD_out        : buffer bit_vector(3 downto 0);
       line_BCD_out : buffer bit_vector(9 downto 0);
```

```
      pix_BCD_out  : buffer bit_vector(10 downto 0);
      line_cnt     : buffer bit_vector(9 downto 0);
      pix_cnt      : buffer bit_vector(10 downto 0));
end position_and_orientation_sensor;

architecture implementation of position_and_orientation_sensor  is


--
-- constant substitutions
--
constant zero       : bit_vector(3 downto 0) := "0000";  -- BCD binary zero
to 9
constant one        : bit_vector(3 downto 0) := "0001";
constant two        : bit_vector(3 downto 0) := "0010";
constant three      : bit_vector(3 downto 0) := "0011";
constant four       : bit_vector(3 downto 0) := "0100";
constant five       : bit_vector(3 downto 0) := "0101";
constant six        : bit_vector(3 downto 0) := "0110";
constant seven      : bit_vector(3 downto 0) := "0111";
constant eight      : bit_vector(3 downto 0) := "1000";
constant nine       : bit_vector(3 downto 0) := "1001";
constant seg7_zero  : bit_vector(6 downto 0) := "0111111";    -- seven
segment 0 to 9
constant seg7_one   : bit_vector(6 downto 0) := "0000110";
constant seg7_two   : bit_vector(6 downto 0) := "1011011";
constant seg7_three : bit_vector(6 downto 0) := "1001111";
constant seg7_four  : bit_vector(6 downto 0) := "1100110";
constant seg7_five  : bit_vector(6 downto 0) := "1101101";
constant seg7_six   : bit_vector(6 downto 0) := "1111101";
constant seg7_seven : bit_vector(6 downto 0) := "0000111";
constant seg7_eight : bit_vector(6 downto 0) := "1111111";
constant seg7_nine  : bit_vector(6 downto 0) := "1110111";
constant zero10     : bit_vector(10 downto 0) := "00000000000";
constant zero9      : bit_vector(9 downto 0) := "0000000000";
constant zero4      : bit_vector(3 downto 0) := "0000";
constant all_off    : bit_vector(6 downto 0) := "0000000";
constant max_pix    : bit_vector(10 downto 0) := "10000010110"; -- 416
in BCD
constant max_line   : bit_vector(9 downto 0) := "1100010010";  -- 312 in
BCD
constant first      : bit_vector(2 downto 0) := "000"; --Used to identify
which multiplexed 7 seg digit
constant second     : bit_vector(2 downto 0) := "001";
constant third      : bit_vector(2 downto 0) := "010";
constant fourth     : bit_vector(2 downto 0) := "011";
constant fifth      : bit_vector(2 downto 0) := "100";
constant sixth      : bit_vector(2 downto 0) := "101";
```

```
-------------------------- Boolean Equation Segment ------
-- EQUATIONS

--pix_cnt(10 to 0).clkf = pix_clk;
--line_cnt(9 to 0).clkf = line_clk;
--line_BCD_out(9 to 0).clkf = comp_clk;
--pix_BCD_out(10 to 0).clkf = comp_clk;
--digit(2 to 0).clkf = line_clk;

begin

pix_count : process

-- This is the pixel counter

begin
  wait until pix_clk = '1';
  if line_clk = '1' then
    pix_cnt(10 downto 0) <= zero10;
  else
    if (pix_cnt(10 downto 0) = max_pix) then
      pix_cnt(10 downto 0) <= zero10;
    else
      if (pix_cnt(3 downto 0) = nine) then
        pix_cnt(3 downto 0) <= zero4;
        if (pix_cnt(7 downto 4) = nine) then
          pix_cnt(7 downto 4) <= zero4;
          pix_cnt(3 downto 0) <= pix_cnt(3 downto 0);
          pix_cnt(8) <= not pix_cnt(8);
          pix_cnt(9) <= pix_cnt(9) xor pix_cnt(8);
          pix_cnt(10)<= pix_cnt(10) xor (pix_cnt(9) and pix_cnt(8));
        else
          pix_cnt(4) <= not pix_cnt(4);
          pix_cnt(5) <= pix_cnt(5) xor pix_cnt(4) ;
          pix_cnt(6) <= pix_cnt(6) xor (pix_cnt(5) and pix_cnt(4)) ;
          pix_cnt(7) <= pix_cnt(7) xor (pix_cnt(6) and pix_cnt(5) and
                pix_cnt(4)) ;
          pix_cnt(10 downto 8) <= pix_cnt(10 downto 8);
        end if;
      else
        pix_cnt(0) <= not pix_cnt(0);
        pix_cnt(1) <= pix_cnt(1) xor pix_cnt(0);
        pix_cnt(2) <= pix_cnt(2) xor (pix_cnt(1) and pix_cnt(0));
        pix_cnt(3) <= pix_cnt(3) xor (pix_cnt(2) and pix_cnt(1) and
pix_cnt(0));
        pix_cnt(10 downto 4) <= pix_cnt(10 downto 4);
      end if;
    end if;
```

```
  end if;
end process pix_count;

line_count : process
-- This is the line counter

begin
  wait until line_clk = '1';
  if frame = '1' then
    line_cnt(9 downto 0) <= zero9;
  else
    if (line_cnt(9 downto 0) = max_line) then
      line_cnt(9 downto 0) <= zero9;
    else
      if (line_cnt(3 downto 0) = nine) then
        line_cnt(3 downto 0) <= zero4;
        if (line_cnt(7 downto 4) = nine) then
          line_cnt(7 downto 4) <= zero4;
          line_cnt(3 downto 0) <= line_cnt(3 downto 0);
          line_cnt(8) <=  not line_cnt(8);
          line_cnt(9) <= line_cnt(9) xor line_cnt(8);
        else
          line_cnt(4) <=  not line_cnt(4);
          line_cnt(5) <= line_cnt(5) xor line_cnt(4) ;
          line_cnt(6) <= line_cnt(6) xor (line_cnt(5) and line_cnt(4)) ;
          line_cnt(7) <= line_cnt(7) xor (line_cnt(6) and line_cnt(5) and
                line_cnt(4)) ;
          line_cnt(9 downto 8) <= line_cnt(9 downto 8);
        end if;
      else
        line_cnt(0) <=  not line_cnt(0);
        line_cnt(1) <= line_cnt(1) xor line_cnt(0);
        line_cnt(2) <= line_cnt(2) xor (line_cnt(1) and line_cnt(0));
        line_cnt(3) <= line_cnt(3) xor (line_cnt(2) and line_cnt(1) and
                line_cnt(0));
        line_cnt(9 downto 4) <= line_cnt(9 downto 4);
      end if;
    end if;
  end if;
end process line_count;

latch_values : process
-- Latch

begin
  wait until comp_clk = '1';
  line_BCD_out(9 downto 0) <= line_cnt(9 downto 0);
  pix_BCD_out(10 downto 0) <= pix_cnt(10 downto 0);
```

```
end process latch_values;

seg7_display : process

--
-- Dual three digit seven segment display
-- This version is time multiplexed using the line sync pulse
-- and a 3 bit shift binary counter used to select the digit
--
begin
  wait until line_clk = '1';
  case digit(2 downto 0) is
    when first  =>
      BCD_out(3 downto 0) <= line_BCD_out(3 downto 0);
      digit(2 downto 0) <= second ;
    when second  =>
      BCD_out(3 downto 0) <= line_BCD_out(7 downto 4);
      digit(2 downto 0) <= third  ;
    when third  =>
      BCD_out(1 downto 0) <= line_BCD_out(9 downto 8);
      BCD_out(3 downto 2) <= "00";
      digit(2 downto 0) <= fourth ;
    when fourth  =>
      BCD_out(3 downto 0) <= pix_BCD_out(3 downto 0);
      digit(2 downto 0) <= fifth  ;
    when fifth  =>
      BCD_out(3 downto 0) <= pix_BCD_out(7 downto 4);
      digit(2 downto 0) <= sixth  ;
    when sixth  =>
      BCD_out(2 downto 0) <= pix_BCD_out(10 downto 8);
      BCD_out(3) <= '0';
      digit(2 downto 0) <= first  ;
    when others  =>
      BCD_out(3 downto 0) <= line_BCD_out(3 downto 0);
      digit(2 downto 0) <= first  ;
  end case;
--
-- Now convert 4 bits BCD to 7 segment
--
  case BCD_out(3 downto 0) is
    when zero  => seg7(6 downto 0) <= seg7_zero;
    when one   => seg7(6 downto 0) <= seg7_one;
    when two   => seg7(6 downto 0) <= seg7_two;
    when three => seg7(6 downto 0) <= seg7_three;
    when four  => seg7(6 downto 0) <= seg7_four;
    when five  => seg7(6 downto 0) <= seg7_five;
    when six   => seg7(6 downto 0) <= seg7_six;
    when seven => seg7(6 downto 0) <= seg7_seven;
```

```
    when eight  => seg7(6 downto 0) <= seg7_eight;
    when nine   => seg7(6 downto 0) <= seg7_nine;
    when others  => seg7(6 downto 0) <= all_off;
  end case;

end process seg7_display;

end implementation;
```

A comparison of the relative cost, PCB area and approximate logic gate equivalents for each of the three solutions is shown in table 8.4.

Table 8.4 Comparison of the three solutions to the position and orientation sensor

Solution	Relative cost	PCB area (mm^2)	Logic gates
PLDs	1	625	1400
cPLD	2	310	4000
FPGA	3	390	1000

Using only these three simple parameters to compare the various implementations, it can be seen that the PLD solution is at present the cheapest, but occupies the most PCB area. The cPLD and FPGA solution provide almost equal implementations, although the FPGA is 50% more expensive. However, this is a relatively simple design for a FPGA, but a complex design for PLDs and cPLDS, so the FPGA would also be capable of much more complex solutions with no additional cost. The cost of the PLD and cPLD solutions would be scalable with complexity. It is interesting to note that the number of equivalent logic gates is much larger for the cPLD, due to the restricted architecture which requires a larger device to be used to obtain the required number of pins and automatic interconnection. The PLD and FPGA solutions have almost the same number of logic gates; the PLDs because the routing is implemented on the PCB, and the FPGA because a much smaller cell size is used, with much better internal interconnection than the cPLD. For this example, migrating to the cPLD or FPGA would not provide a significant advantage, but would be relatively easy to achieve.

8.3 Migration to application specific integrated circuits (ASICs)

There are two main ASIC implementation technologies:

1) Gate array. 2) Full-custom.

The gate array only requires a final metallisation layer to be added, hence reducing the NRE fabrication costs, with the basic circuit element already being fully implemented. Typically, the circuit element could be a 2 or 3 input NAND gate. Full custom design allows each transistor used in the design to be optimised for size, number of emitters and so on, so that the smallest silicon area is used, power is reduced and speed maximised. The drawback is that this can take longer to lay out, and the simulation process is more complicated, plus all the semiconductor process masks are required rather than just the final metallisation, so NRE costs are increased. Therefore, each design has to consider the specific requirements of the final product in terms of the cost, speed and power consumption, before the decision to migrate to ASIC is made, let alone which ASIC implementation technology to use.

The advantages of using FPGAs are the speed of prototyping, simulation and physical testing, combined with the low non recurring engineering (NRE) costs. NRE costs in this instance are those costs, usually one-off, which are specific to each new design, which for FPGAs are small. The NRE costs for Application Specific Integrated Circuits (ASICs) are high due to the production of the masks used in semiconductor production, typically in the region £5000 to £15000. Any change to a mask layout incurs this cost, so each new design requires this payment and each successive amendment requires similar payments. Due to this, the aim with ASIC design is to get it right first time and this has led to the development of sophisticated design and simulation software tools. This has benefitted FPGA designs as they have many similarities and can also be used to design FPGAs. The disadvantage of FPGAs is the relatively high unit costs, typically 5 to 20 times more expensive than the equivalent ASIC. Therefore, depending on the number of products to be made, there is a cross-over point at which it becomes worthwhile to move to an ASIC. In fact, many designs which might appear cheaper when implemented as ASICs often are not, due to other factors, such as the need for a PCB redesign (although this should be avoidable) and the need to incorporate changes in the design at regular intervals, each of which would require another NRE cost for the ASIC. Even when a design is going to be implemented as an ASIC it is often beneficial to prototype using FPGAs for two main reasons:

1) The entire hardware system can be tested at a much earlier stage in the design, before ASIC NRE costs are incurred.
2) Any products which interact with software can develop the software with working hardware, again without ASIC NRE costs.

Therefore, there is a considerable demand for migration from FPGA to ASIC during a product's lifetime, and in fact, there is considerable demand at present to move from PLDs to FPGAs. There is only limited demand to migrate from discrete logic to PLDs, as most new designs use PLDs as a minimum, often starting with FPGAs.

8.3.1 The migration process

The migration process is required if a design is to be initially prototyped using FPGA and then converted to ASIC. These designs can be split into two categories:

1) Those FPGAs not designed with migration to ASIC in mind.
2) Those FPGAs designed with migration to ASIC as a target.

As a general principle, all designs should incorporate those features which make migration to ASICs easier, as they produce better designs overall. Provided that the guidelines are implemented at the beginning of the design stage, the extra time, money and FPGA resources required are minimal. The main FPGA design method at present uses schematic capture to input designs and these CAD descriptions can usually be imported into ASIC development systems with minimal changes. The subsequent aim is to automate as much of the following processes as possible so that migration costs are minimised.

8.3.2 Schematic based migration

The schematic migration process has to maintain equivalence between the FPGA and ASIC implementations in two main categories:

1) Functionality. 2) Timing.

Maintaining functionality is not too difficult, provided that the migration design guidelines are followed and that the development system used has accurate descriptions of both the original FPGA component libraries and the target ASIC equivalents. However, maintaining timing equivalence is more difficult, as the semiconductor implementation technologies are usually different in two main areas:

1) The semiconductor processes used, with the ASIC implementation being inherently faster.
2) FPGAs have a macro architecture with inherent routing delays, whereas ASICs have neither (although they do introduce timing delays of their own).

The aim of the migration process is to lay out the ASIC implementation so that it executes with equivalent functionality and compatible timing to the FPGA.

Although the FPGA to ASIC migration aims to maintain timing relationships, because the ASIC implementation is inherently faster, there may be the desire to take advantage of this so that the ASIC implementation has a higher operating frequency. It may be that only the ASIC implementation is capable of operating at the required frequencies and the FPGA implementation may only be to test functionality.

8.3.3 HDL based migration

The alternative design methodology involves the use of VHDL (very high speed integrated circuit hardware description language) which uses a high level language abstract description of the digital design to be implemented. The VHDL descriptions can be written to include timing information which simplifies the migration process. VHDL is increasingly used as it is an IEEE standard so that any design written in VHDL for an FPGA can easily be recompiled for an ASIC, without any changes (theoretically at least!). Because VHDL has become accepted as a design standard, it is becoming increasing popular as a design technique as designs can be transferred between development systems and implementation technologies (FPGA and ASIC, different manufacturers, and so on), whereas schematic capture systems tend to be proprietary with each one being manufacturer dependent and incompatible with others.

8.3.4 Automated migration

Automated migration is the process of converting a design for one type of implementation, usually FPGA, so that it can be used with another type of implementation, usually ASIC. The aim is to automate this process and use a special computer program. The process operates by taking the original design and converting it to an equivalent design for a different target device. Typically, this is achieved by taking the FPGA netlist converted if necessary, into a standard netlist format and then converting into an ASIC netlist format. It will usually be necessary at this stage to provide the conversion mechanism with some additional information about pin, I/O selection (tri-state, output only and so on) and the required final timing characteristics. This process is speeded up considerably if both the FPGA and ASIC netlists are one of the standard representations. There must also be an equivalent model library for the ASIC as for the FPGA. The basic logic gates are no problem, as all implementations have suitable equivalent models, but flipflops have to have a scan cell equivalent to support automatic scan chain insertion and the use of automatic test pattern generation (ATPG). ATPG should be supportable as additional test vectors will be required for critical paths and for ensuring compatible output timing. I/O cells are normally no problem as ASIC I/O cells are actually better than FPGA ones. Once the conversion has been completed, the migration software will perform a validation process to ensure that the two implementations are equivalent. Note that if there is a fault in the FPGA implementation, the fault will be faithfully translated to the ASIC implementation. Finally, the new ASIC implementation will require post-layout simulation with back annotation, so that correct operation with an inherently faster technology is confirmed. A detailed list of the steps in the migration process is given below. Steps 1 to 5 are the conversion of the design conceptually from FPGA to ASIC and steps 6 to 8 are the actual implementation as an ASIC.

Migration flow

1) Convert FPGA netlist to ASIC netlist format.
2) Reduce and optimise the logic.
3) Insert scan chain to enable testing.
4) Simulation and verify timings.
5) Generate test vectors to ensure high fault coverage.
6) Layout of transistors which form the logic.
7) Simulation to verify timings and operation of physical layout.
8) Manufacture of ASICs.

Typically, steps 1 to 5 will take between 3 and 5 days in total and steps 6 to 8 a further 2 to 6 weeks, depending on the fabrication process used. This compares favourably with the 2 to 6 months that would be required for the design to be implemented directly in ASIC. It should be remembered, however, that timescales are constantly being reduced although migration times will probably not be able to be reduced significantly, but that designing for implementation in ASIC will be. This will make migration a less attractive process.

8.4 Good design practice for successful migration

Good design practice if migration is thought to be possible in the future, is much the same as good design style for FPGAs and can be summarised by the following list of statements:

1) Always endeavour to use synchronous design techniques and synchronous circuits as they are more reliable and easier to migrate. Timing differences in implementation between FPGA and ASICS mean that synchronous designs will nearly always migrate automatically, whereas asynchronous designs will nearly always require redesign. Redesign negates the advantages of automated migration.
2) Gated clock signals should not be used. It may not be possible to insert a scan chain through a gated clock. Without a scan path high levels of fault coverage cannot be obtained.
3) Always use the same clock edge for all registers and latches as this ensures that signals propagate correctly through the entire circuit.

4) Clock signals should not be divided, as each branch may result in different timing characteristics which can be difficult to reproduce by the migration process.
5) All registers should use the same clock signal. If buffering is required, ensure that all registers receive a clock which has been through the same number of buffers, otherwise small timing differences may affect synchronisation.
6) Never use routing delays to obtain correct operation of a circuit, always redesign for correct synchronous operation. Rerouting after migration may result in a change in timing, as an increase in voltage results in gates operating faster and an increase in temperature, results in gates operating more slowly. During manufacture different devices in different batches may also have different timing characteristics.
7) Use a spread of timing specifications for the model library during simulation to ensure the robustness of the synchronous designs.
8) The clock should not be used as the data input signal to a register.
9) Use a top-down design method such as VHDL, when only the libraries need to be switched when migrating from FPGA to ASIC. Note however, that this does not guarantee to eliminate all problems.
10) Asynchronous signals used for register control, such as reset and set, should not be controlled from internal nodes as this make them uncontrollable during testing. The preferred solution is to connect them directly to external pins.
11) Asynchronous paths within the design should be avoided.
12) Feedback signals should not be gated, as this can make testing extremely difficult.

8.5 Design for testability before and after migration

When creating a new design it should always be remembered that if the product is successful and continues to sell, at some point in its life cycle at least one, if not more, migrations will take place and each migration will require extensive testing to ensure that the developed product is still operating as required. To make the simulation easier, it is preferred that the design is implemented both from the viewpoint of obtaining the desired functionality and from its capability to be tested. If the guidelines of design for migration are followed, they will also make the testing process after migration much easier. In addition, the following are a number of guidelines which will further improve the testability of a design and hence its migration capability:

1) Aim to achieve the maximum minimisation in the logic, provided that glitches and hazards are eliminated. A glitch is an unwanted pulse with a short time period which is always present and a hazard is a short unwanted logic state which occurs under specific logic conditions.

2) Hazards and glitches may be eliminated through the use of Gray coding so that only one output at a time is changing rather than through the use of redundancy.
3) Attempt to avoid reconvergence, which is when a logic function is implemented using the same inputs but with different logic gates in different places and then recombined, so that testing one implementation will be affected by the other.
4) Do not assume that registers or latches will power up in a known state. Always ensure that a reset or known state initialisation is possible.
5) If at all possible do not leave unused states within a state machine; either incorporate unused states somewhere, even if they are unnecessary, or provide a design which will eventually return to a valid state after a number of clock pulses. The preferred solution is to return the state machine to a known state after one clock pulse.
6) Try to limit the complexity of state machines by using multiple smaller state machines, as this enables each smaller state machine to be more fully tested, rather than very large state machines which can be very time consuming to test.

If the above guidelines are followed, they will improve the testability of the logic to ensure that it is functioning. What these guidelines do not indicate are the tests required to confirm the functionality of the design, that is, what it is created to do, which should be added to those created through the guidelines, although there is probably going to be overlap between the two types of testing. Functional testing is covered at a number of other places within this book, particularly in the design chapters (6 and 7).

8.6 Simulation, test vectors and testing

To ensure that the design operates as required, extensive simulation is used, which simulates at the semiconductor level so that functionality and timing can be accurately predicted. The inputs to the simulator are test vectors which describe the inputs and predict the expected outputs. The simulator takes the inputs, calculates the simulated outputs based on the logic design implemented and then compares with the predicted outputs. Any differences then indicate that the design does not implement the required functionality and the design will need to be analysed to identify the fault. With ASICs, it is much more important to get the design correct and automatic test pattern generators (ATPG) can be used to ensure maximum test coverage. The ideal would be to obtain 100% testability, but with complex designs this is not always possible; nevertheless, coverage of 95% to 100% should be aimed for. One of the reasons for not being able to attain 100% testability is hidden nodes. These are parts of the design which are not connected to, or accessible from, a physical I/O pin. Figure 8.3 illustrates difficulty, with register A O/P not being accessible except indirectly via register B. It is usual to incorporate extra circuitry to enable inaccessible nodes to be accessed for testing purposes and this is called a scan path.

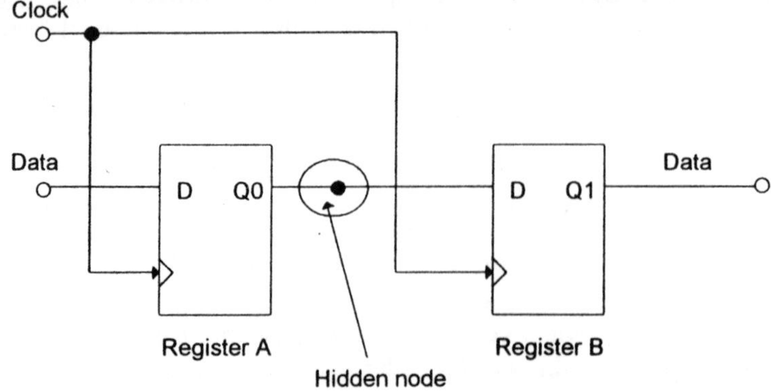

Figure 8.3 Hidden nodes

8.7 Problems

1. A three bit ripple counter is shown in figure 8.4. Redesign this as a three bit synchronous counter suitable for use in an FPGA or ASIC design.

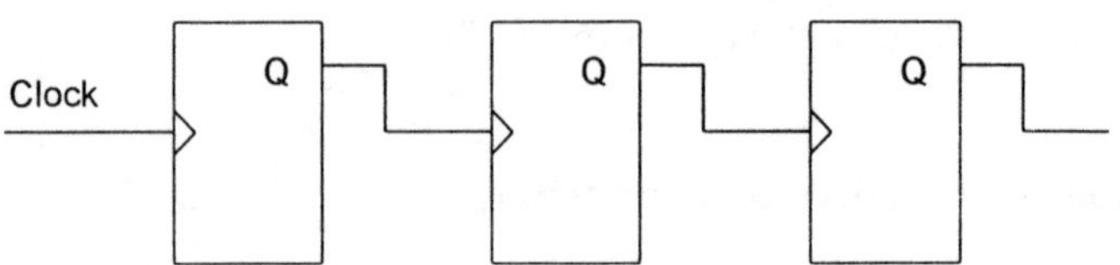

Figure 8.9 A three bit ripple counter

2. Design a system capable of implementing a four digit (0000 to 9999) BCD counter using TTL logic gates. Then migrate this design to a PLD of your choice and subsequently to an FPGA. Try to use the same migration process both times, either schematic or HDL based and only use the minimum size of target devices required. Compare the PCB area, the current consumption and approximate gate counts of the three implementations.

3. For the three designs in Q2, determine the actual costs of manufacture for the following quantities:

a) 100; b) 1000; c) 10,000

and identify which is the best implementation in each case.

8.8 Further reading

'Encore! Gate Arrays', data sheet, Orbit Semiconductor Inc., 1215 Bordeaux Drive, Sunnyvale, CA 94089, USA.

'EPF8050M: ASIC Prototyping Vehicle', data sheet, Altera Corporation, 2610 Orchard Parkway, San Jose, CA 95134-2020, USA.

Hardwire Data Book, Xilinx, 2100 Logic Drive, San Jose, CA 95124-3400, USA.

Heins K., 'FPGA design for ASIC conversion', *Electronic Product Design*, February 1995, pp29-30.

Informations- und Nachrichtentechnik: 'A Guide to Testability with PLDs' (in English), Testability guide 02/92, iNT GmbH, Bunsenstrasse 6, D-8033 Martinsried, Germany.

Janai M., 'Technologies for economic production of ASICs', *Solid State Technology*, March 1993.

'Netlist to Gate Array in a Day', Chip Express, 2903 Bunker Hill Lane, Suite 105, Santa Clara, CA 95054, USE, Email: Chip Express@luna.portal.com.

Stalkamp R.A., 'Designing for gate array conversion', *Electronic Product Design*, October 1994, pp 43-48.

Sutlieff C., 'Testing time for ASICs', *IEE Review*, January 1991, pp 27-31.

TI data books, FPGA Data manual and FPGA Applications handbook, 1994 editions or later.

'Xilinx to ASIC retargeting', Sagantec Netherlands BV, PO Box 2102, 5600 cc Eindhoven, The Netherlands.

Appendix A MACHXL

A.1 MACHXL user's handbook

MACHXL is an integrated environment for creating designs for AMD MACH 3 and 4 series programmable logic components. These are high density electrically erasable CMOS programmable logic devices, based on the macrocell concept. MACHXL cannot be used to develop designs for the MACH 1 and 2 series, nor can it be used to develop designs for simple PLDs such as the 22V10. However, the programming language used by MACHXL is a superset of PALASM which is a standard language used by AMD for programming all their PLD products. By obtaining the appropriate PALASM compiler and avoiding MACH specific constructs, the entire range of products can be programmed. The MACHXL software development product is low cost and enables all the design principles and applications that are used as examples in this book to be implemented.

MACHXL enables the user to edit, compile, simulate and program a range of cPLDs from the same user interface. The use of the interface is relatively self explanatory and the user should be able to deduce the actions required. Detailed information can be obtained from the full user manual. Although PALASM and its superset MACHXL are high level languages, they should not be confused with the majority of high level languages designed to execute on a personal computer. HLLs for programmable logic are hardware description languages (HDLs) and effectively each statement executes in parallel with all other statements. Execution does not begin at the top of the program listing, then sequentially executing each statement in turn until the end of the listing is reached. This must be remembered when writing HDL programs and any timing requirements of the design have to be explicitly implemented. The MACHXL package consists of five different programs which are executed sequentially once the source text file has been created. These are:

1. **Parser** Checks the syntax of the statements in the source text file (file extension .PDS) and if error free creates an intermediate file with a .TRE extension. A listing file is always created.

2. **Boolean post processor** Takes the intermediate file and converts complex statements such as CASE and IF THEN ELSE into equivalent Boolean equations.

3. **STATE syntax expander** If the state machine constructs have been used (not recommended for new MACHXL designs) this program converts them into Boolean equations. The Boolean post processor will then be executed a second time.

4. **Logic minimiser** Uses the file outputs from the Boolean post processor and reduces them to their minimum form, to maximise the efficiency of their implementation on to the architecture of the selected devices.

5. **Fitter** Fitting is a complex process which takes the output from the minimiser, allocates logic equations to logic hardware, determines the logic programming and routing required and creates the JEDEC file used for programming.

Designs can fail at any of the five stages, although the most common problems are the use of incorrect syntax in the source file which will be identified by the parser, and insufficient hardware resources being available during the fitting stage.

A.1.1 PALASM syntax

Where the name PALASM is used, the explanation applies equally to PALASM and MACHXL programs. If MACHXL is used, it only applies to MACHXL programs and should not be used in PALASM programs. Unlike most high level languages, PALASM does not use statement terminators, so the user must be alert to the differences. PALASM uses the beginning of the next valid statement as the terminator for the previous one and this can cause some confusion until the user becomes familiar with this concept.

A.1.2 Comments

The beginning of a comment is indicated by a semicolon and is terminated by the return key. Therefore, comments do not automatically extend over several lines and operate in a similar way to comments in assembly language programs.

Example

```
pin  11   value1 ;This is the comment for the statement at the
                 ;beginning of the line and continues over
                 ;three lines.
```

A.1.3 Program file structure

The PALASM program file structure is standardised for all designs and consists of three sections:

1. Declaration section containing nine fields which describe the design.

2. Design sections. There are two possible types of design sections:

   a) state machines; b) equations.

   At least one section must be present and may contain multiple instances of these constructs.

3. Simulation section.

A.1.4 The declaration section

The declaration section consists of a number of different fields the first six of which are identified by reserved words as illustrated below:

title	The title of the design goes here
pattern	The revision number of the PCB goes here.
revision	Version number of the software.
author	Designer's name goes here.
company	Company name goes here.
date	Date of version goes here.

These six fields effectively act as comments and should be used to keep track of revision numbers and PCB to be used for production amd maintenance purposes. They have no effect on the PLD design. The seventh field is optional and is used to describe any special functions the PLD may have, such as a security fuse, or a turbo bit. It is identified by the reserved word OPTIONS. The eighth field is required and is hardware specific, describing the target PLD and the allocation of signal names to pin numbers. It is identified by the reserved word CHIP, followed by a design name (user selectable) and then the target cPLD. Available target identifiers are:

MACH435
MACH445
MACH465
MACH335

Following this, each of the pins to be used is identified on a separate line using the reserved word PIN, followed by the signal name and then the pin type. If physical connection to a pin is not required and an internal macro cell can be used, the reserved word NODE can be used instead. Available pin types are listed below and can be used in combination. The sequence used in combinations is not important.

```
3volt          ; 3 volt drive level
5volt          ; 5 volt drive level
cmos_level     ; CMOS voltage levels
combinational  ; combinational output
registered     ; registered output
latched        ; latched output
pinfbk         ; pin feedback
cmbfbk         ; combinational feedback
regfbk         ; registered feedback
group          ; sequence of signals grouped together
high           ; active high outputs
low            ; active low outputs
open_drain     ; open drain output for different voltage or current levels
delayclk       ; delayed clock signal
ttl_level      ; TTL voltage levels.
```

An example of the use of the CHIP reserved word is given below.

Example

```
CHIP   decoder_design   MACH445 ;This selects device
                                ;Now the pin definitions follow
pin  2 value1
pin  3 value2
pin  4 input_6
```

The ninth and final field is also optional and is a string substitution function. If a sequence of characters is to be used repeatedly within a program, or some simplification of statements is required to aid understanding, then the string reserved word can be used. This is followed by the name of the string and the text to be substituted in single quotation marks. If any constants are required within the logic description, for example, to describe the output LED patterns for a seven segment display, it is good programming practice to replace them with a constant name during the logic description. This is achieved through the use of a string substitution section which associates constant names with constant values. During the compilation process, constant names are replaced with the corresponding constant values. The single quotation marks are not included. The use of a string substitution section improves the readability of the programming listing and is considered to be good programming practice.

```
string state1          '#b0001'
string state2          '#b0010'
string last_state      '#b00'
string enable_1        'value1 * input_6'
```

Once the program header has been completed, the logic specification or description can be entered. A complete example of a declaration section is given below:

```
title      dram controller
pattern    pcb_revision_A_1996
revision   first
author     R C Seals
Company    University of Greenwich
Date       13th July 1996

options    turbo = on
           security = off

chip       d_controller     mach445

;Pin definition section

pin  6     clk2
pin  7     pclk
pin  8     ads
pin  9     clk2mio
pin  10    pa2
pin  12    iready
pin  13    ras0p
pin  14    sel1
pin  15    ras1p
pin  16    refin

;strings substituted

string     qads    '(ads * pclk * /iready)'
string     ras0n   '((ras0p + ras1) * /sel1)'
```

A.1.5 Key punctuation

Below is a list of the key punctuation symbols with some simple examples of how they can be used.

```
()    ;groups logic      A = B*(C + D)
;     ;Anything after the semicolon is treated as a comment until the
      ;next return.
..    ;Double full stop indicates a range of values.
?     ;Floating PIN or NODE assignment to avoid specifying the pin
      ;number before fitting.
```

A.1.6 Number bases

Three number bases are used, which are identified by the preceding single character:

```
binary       #b101     (binary representation of 5)
decimal      #d5
hexadecimal  #h5
```

The hash symbol, #, is used to distinguish the numbers from user specified signal names.

A.1.7 User specified signal names

As well as the predefined keywords and key punctuation symbols, the user is able to specify signal names. Signal names are associated with either inputs or outputs and are used to hold logic values which may vary during the operation of the logic function implemented. The variable names can contain up to 14 alphanumeric characters plus the underscore character. Upper and lower case letters are treated identically. The space character cannot be used in signal names, nor can any other punctuation character.

A.1.8 Examples of valid variable names

```
state
upper_level
data
val_1
val_2
val270
```

A.1.9 Examples of invalid variable names

```
numb 11
numb-11
data>count
```

A.1.10 Examples of 'bad' design names

Although the following are syntactically correct signal names, they are regarded as bad programming style, because they do not convey any information about the significance of the signal within the design.

```
Burt
Jons_work
rubbish1
```

A.1.11 Examples of 'good' design names

```
4_bit_adder
address_decoder
state_machine
```

A.1.12 Pin vector definitions

It is not necessary to give separate variable names to each pin. Groups of pins with a common functions, such as a data bus, can be defined as a one dimensional vector.

Example

```
PIN  13:16  /state[3:0] registered
```

This allocates a group of 4 outputs to 4 successive pins, and is equivalent to:

```
PIN  13 /state[3] registered
PIN  14 /state[2] registered
PIN  15 /state[1] registered
PIN  16 /state[0] registered
```

Not all the pins on the PLD chosen have to be defined. Individual vector states can be accessed as indicated above, or as groups.

Example

```
drive = motor * fuel * state[3]
state[3:2] = state[1:0]
```

Vector notation is supported for combinational and registered designs and is particularly useful for signals grouped and used as a bus system. Vectors can be defined in two ways:

1) during the pin definition,
2) using the reserved word VECTOR to group existing signals.

An example of defining a vector during the pin definitions is given below.

```
pin data[7..0]          ; this is an 8-bit vector
```

Below is an example of defining a vector using the VECTOR reserved word

```
vector addr := [A3, A2, A1, A0]  ; this is a 4-bit vector
```

Using the vector notation is a shorthand way of manipulating multiple signals.

```
addr[3..0] := data[3..0]
```

which is the same as:

```
addr[3] := data[3]
addr[2] := data[2]
addr[1] := data[1]
addr[0] := data[0]
```

Similarly:

```
addr[3..0] := data[7..4] * opcode[1..4]
```

is the same as:

```
addr[3] := data[7] * opcode[1]
addr[2] := data[6] * opcode[2]
addr[1] := data[5] * opcode[3]
addr[0] := data[4] * opcode[4]
```

A.2 Logic specification

The logic specification is a description of the logic function to be implemented by the PLD and consists of assignments, logic equations and high level language constructs such as IF THEN ELSE.

A.2.1 Basic assignments

Assignments are identified by the equals character and can be made to variables or vectors, but they must have previously been defined. The normal meaning of the equals symbol is used, with the variable on the left hand side of the equals sign becoming equivalent to the right hand side. If the equals sign on its own is used, the assignment is to be implemented using combinational logic, that is, without registers and clock signals. If the equals sign is preceded by a colon, sequential logic is used, that is registered logic. The right hand side can be a signal variable, a constant name or a number. For combinational variables the changes happen instantaneously. If a registered output is being used, then the output is updated at the next rising edge clock pulse.

The following assignment operators can be used:

=	assignment for combinational outputs
:=	assignment for registered outputs
*=	assignment for latched outputs

Note that registered outputs are clocked on the rising edge of the clock pulse when they take on the new value. Latched outputs become newly valid on the rising edge of the clock pulse, remain changeable throughout the clock pulse, and are latched to a stable value on the falling edge of the clock pulse.

Example

```
C = A * (D + E)*/D
state[0] = A
state[1] = C*state[3]
```

Multiple vectors can also be simultaneously assigned, as illustrated in the example below:

Example

```
state[3:0] = vector[0.3]* vect[3.0]
```

which is equivalent to:

```
state[3] = vector[0] * vect[3]
state[2] = vector[1] * vect[2]
state[1] = vector[2] * vect[2]
state[0] = vector[3] * vect[0]
```

Vectors can also be assigned a number up to the maximum value representable by the number of bits, N, in the vector, such that the maximum number is 2^N-1. Variables can also be assigned numbers, but it can only be 0 or 1.

Example

```
C = 0    ; If a number base is not defined
B =1     ; It is treated as decimal

vector[3:0] = 6;
```

This is equivalent to:

```
vector[3:0] = #b0110
```

or

```
vector[3] = #b0
vector[2] = #b1
vector[1] = #b1
vector[0] = #b0
```

A.2.2 Logic equations

Almost any Boolean statement can be implemented, the main limitations are those of the number of inputs in the AND gates in the AND-OR array which limits the number of variables that can be ANDed. For the 22V10 this is 22, with each variable being available as its true or complement form. The number of inputs to the OR gate in the AND-OR array limits the number of product terms in any one equation. The implementation of other logic functions such as exclusive OR is achieved through basic AND and OR. The logic operations available in MACHXL are:

```
*    AND
+    OR
:+:  Exclusive OR
/    NOT
```

Normal precedence of logic operations is applied, but to ensure that the correct logic is implemented, open and close brackets can be used to group operations. Brackets can be nested to any level.

Examples of logic equations

```
A =   C * D
B =   A*(Q1:+:Q2) + /F + /F*(D0:+:/state)
```

The following basic Boolean operators are implemented for both combinational and registered designs and, in addition to those listed previously. Any Boolean equations have to be placed into the equations part of the design file, which is identified by the EQUATIONS reserved word. The equations section is assumed to continue until another section's reserved word is identified. It is possible in assignments to group variables together using the open and close brackets.

```
Z   =   A*B               ;  AND operation
Z   =   /(A*B)            ;  NAND operation
Z   =   A+B               ;  OR operation
Z   =   /(A+B)            ;  NOR operation
Z   =   A:+:B             ;  Exclusive OR operation
Z   =   (A*B)+(/A*/B)     ;  Two product terms
```

The same process can be performed with other language constructs using the BEGIN and END reserved words. An example is:

```
if (A = C * D) then
  begin
    B = A*(Q1:+:Q2) + /F + /F*(D0:+:/state)  ;These 5 statements
    vector[3] = #b0                          ;have been grouped
    vector[2] = #b1                          ;together.
    vector[1] = #b1
    vector[0] = #b0
  end
else
  begin
    B = #b0
  end
```

BEGIN and END act as group delimiters; they can be nested to any level and can be used in any program statement apart from assignment to effectively turn several statements into a pseudo single statement. It is important to remember that BEGINs and ENDs are always in pairs and, although they can be nested, there must always be the same number of BEGINs as there are ENDs.

Table A.1 Signal extensions

Signal extension	Explanation
.ACLK	Asynchronous clock to register
.CLKF	Synchronous clock (preferred)
.ALE	Asynchronous Latch Enable
.LE	Synchronous Latch Enable
.TRST	Output buffer enable
.RSTF	Reset
.SETF	Preset
.D	Data input to D type flip-flop
.T	Data input to Toggle flip-flop
.J	J input to JK flip-flop
.K	K input to JK flip-flop
.R	R input to SR flip-flop
.S	S input to SR flip-flop
.FB	Feedback from I/O pin

A.2.3 Signal extensions

Each output can have a variety of parameters controlled by using a signal extension. A full stop is used to separate the signal name from the signal extension.

```
signal_name.signal_extension
```

All the valid signal extensions are given in table A.1.

Examples

```
count.d          :=  value    ; D type flip-flop with
count.clkf        =  clk      ; synchronous clock
counter.t        :=  value    ; T type flip-flop with
counter.clkf      =  clk      ; synchronous clock
register_A.j     :=  1        ; JK flip-flop set up as
register_A.k     :=  1        ; a toggle
register_A.clkf   =  clk
```

A.3 High level language constructs

A number of other high level constructs are put together in the design file by the user, to describe the logic function to be implemented.

A.3.1 Structured statements

MACHXL supports two high level language constructs which can be used to combine the simpler logic equations and to provide some flexibility in the execution of the logic implemented. The two constructs are:

IF THEN with an optional ELSE

and

CASE

A.3.2 IF THEN ELSE

The IF THEN ELSE statement enables a conditional response to be made. That is, the response is dependent on the test condition, called the logic condition. The logic condition used to control the test must be contained within the open and close brackets and must be resolvable at all times. The statement can be used in two forms; the first is without the ELSE when the test is performed to decide whether to execute the logic equation or not:

```
IF (logic condition) THEN
   begin
      statement
   end
```

The second is with the ELSE in place, which is when one of two logic equations must be executed:

```
IF (logic condition) THEN
   begin
      statement 1
   end
ELSE
   begin
      statement2
   end
```

A complete example is given below.

Example

```
IF (drive) THEN
  begin
    drive = 0
```

```
  end
ELSE
  begin
    drive = 1
  end
```

Note that in this example the logic condition is simply a variable name. This is assumed to be:

```
IF (drive = 1) THEN
  begin
    drive = 0
  end
ELSE
  begin
    drive = 1
  end
```

Vectors can be used within the logic condition brackets as illustrated below.

Example

```
IF (vector[3..0]) THEN
  begin
    logic statement
  end
```

which is equivalent to ANDing all the vectors together as in:

```
IF (vector[3] * vector[2] * vector[1] * vector[0]) THEN
```

Specific vector values can also be checked for, as in the following:

```
IF (vector[3..0] = 6) THEN
  begin
    logic statement
  end
```

Conditions can be nested and the only restriction is that it must eventually evaluate to a boolean true or false:

```
IF ((vector[3..0] = 6) + (drive = 0)) THEN
  begin
    logic statement
  end
```

IF THEN ELSE statements can be nested, but care should be taken to ensure that the ELSE applies to the correct IF.

A.3.3 CASE construct

The CASE construct only operates on vectors, and matches the vector variable value against specific numerical values to select a statement to be executed. The reserved word CASE is used to begin the construct, followed by the vector variable contained within open and close brackets. This is followed by a BEGIN END pair which enclose the possible values that the vector variable can take. The possible values are called the guard conditions and identify which of the possible logic equations is actually executed. Each state possible is separated from the logic equation to be executed by a colon.

A.3.4 Example of syntax

```
CASE (vector[n..0])
     BEGIN
          value_0: begin statement_1 end
          value_1: begin statement_2 end
            .
            .
            .
          value_N: begin statement_N end
     END
```

The BEGIN and END surrounding each sequence of statements are compulsory. The number of values is determined by the size of the vector. A 2-bit vector has four values, a 3-bit vector has eight, and so on. A 1-bit vector is a special version of the case statement and is equivalent to an IF THEN ELSE statement.

Example

```
CASE (state[1..0])
     BEGIN
          0: begin vector[3] = 0 end
          1: begin vector[2] = 0 end
          2: begin vector[1] = 0 end
          3: begin drive = out_value end
     END
```

Not all values need to be specified, but if they are not, they must not occur, otherwise an undefined logic state may occur. If all the possible states of the vector are not defined, the compiler may not be able to compile the design, since internally it always expands the logic before looking for redundancies to condense it. Large vectors, 8-bit or more, create too many situations for the optimiser to cope with and it may fail. As a general rule, using large bit vectors within a CASE statement in PALASM, is not a good idea. Ranges of vectors can be denoted by using two full-stops as illustrated below.

```
CASE (state[3..0])
    BEGIN
        0..3: begin drive A + B end
        4..8: begin output = 0 end
        9:   begin vector[3..0] = 6 end
        10..15: begin A = A end
    END
```

Non-vector variables can be concatenated together by the comma, so they can be used in CASE statements as shown below.

```
CASE (A, B, C)
    BEGIN
        0: begin drive = 0 end
        1: begin A = B end
        5: begin vector[3:0] = state[0.3] end
    END
```

Multiple logic equations can be grouped together after each condition using a BEGIN END pair, as illustrated below.

```
CASE (state[1..0])
    BEGIN
        0: begin
              vector[3] = 0
              vector[6:4] = data[4:2]
           end
        1: begin vector[2] = 0 end
        2: begin vector[1] = 0 end
        3: begin
              drive = out_value
              data1 = in_value
           end
    END
```

It is common to use binary numbers in the conditions, as this corresponds more closely with the Boolean variable vectors being used. For the example below binary numbers have been used in the guard conditions.

```
CASE (state[1:0])
    BEGIN
        #b00: begin
                    vector[3] = 0
                    vector[6..4] = data[4..2]
              end
        #b01: begin vector[2] = 0 end
        #b10: begin vector[1] = 0 end
```

```
        #b11: begin
                    drive  =  out_value
                    data1  =  in_value
              end
    END
```

So far, only logic equations have been executed within the CASE statement, but in fact, any valid PALASM statement can be included, such as IF THEN ELSE, and further CASE statements. As with large bit vectors, nesting CASE statements can easily cause the optimiser to fail. If all the possible values of the variable being tested in the case statement are not explicitly defined, the logic generated may create unpredictable results should one of the undefined states occur. This can be avoided by the use of the reserved word OTHERWISE as illustrated below.

Example

```
CASE (state[3..0])
    BEGIN
        0: begin drive  =  A+B end
        4: begin output  =  0 end
        15: begin A  =  A end
        OTHERWISE: begin C  =  A*B end
    END
```

A.4 STATE construct

The STATE construct used to implement state machines is not recommended for new designs using MACHXL. In PALASM, a state machine description begins with the reserved word

```
STATE
```

followed by the state of state machine

```
MOORE_MACHINE
MEALY_MACHINE
```

The difference between the two state machines is mainly in the outputs produced at each state. If the outputs at each state are always the same, that is, they never change even if the inputs are different, then it is a Moore state machine; whereas, if the outputs at each state can be different, depending on the values of the input signals, then it is a Mealy state machine. The same problems can be solved using Moore or Mealy state machines, the main difference being the number of states each machine requires. If for example a design has three states and, depending on the input values, each state can have three different sets of output values, then a Moore state machine would require nine states to be defined, whereas the Mealy state machine could be implemented with only three states. The three states of the Mealy machine could be implemented with only two registers to give binary codings between 0 and 2, whereas the Moore machine would require three registers to give binary codings between 0 and 8. Therefore, if registers are limited, Mealy state machines should be used.

A.4.1 Moore state machine

A Moore state machine description consists of four sections:

1) the header definition
2) the state assignments
3) the state transitions
4) the input conditions controlling transitions

A.4.2 Header

The header description consists of two mandatory reserved words:

1) STATE
2) MOORE_MACHINE

followed by up to three default options:

1) OUTPUT_HOLD This indicates those output values which are to be maintained unchanged even when they are not explicitly controlled.

2) DEFAULT_OUTPUT This indicates the values of the specified signals if a state machine operation cannot be identified.

3) DEFAULT_BRANCH This indicates which state to move to (rather than specific output values), when the next state is not explicitly identifiable. There are three options possible with this:

   1) a user specified state,
   2) HOLD_STATE maintains the current state,
   3) NEXT_STATE moves to the next state in the user defined list of states in the states assignment section.

Example

```
state
moore_machine
default_branch S1
```

A.4.3 State assignments

This section, which comes immediately after the state header, describes the output values that each state is to have. There are three main techniques for allocating output values to states:

1) binary
2) Gray code
3) one hot encoding

A.4.4 Binary

Binary coding uses an incrementing binary sequence as illustrated next.

```
S0   = /Q2 * /Q1 * /Q0
S1   = /Q2 * /Q1 *  Q0
S2   = /Q2 * /Q1 * /Q0
S3   = /Q2 * /Q1 * /Q0
S4   =  Q2 * /Q1 * /Q0
S5   =  Q2 * /Q1 *  Q0
S6   =  Q2 *  Q1 * /Q0
S7   =  Q2 *  Q1 *  Q0
```

A.4.5 Gray code

With Gray code there is only one bit is different between adjacent codes and this is used to prevent spurious outputs occurring when changing between adjacent states.

```
S0   = /Q2 * /Q1 * /Q0
S1   = /Q2 * /Q1 *  Q0
S2   = /Q2 *  Q1 *  Q0
S3   = /Q2 *  Q1 * /Q0
S4   =  Q2 *  Q1 * /Q0
S5   =  Q2 *  Q1 *  Q0
S6   =  Q2 * /Q1 *  Q0
S7   =  Q2 * /Q1 * /Q0
```

A.4.6 One hot encoding

One hot encoding uses one output per state and is useful when the output is used to select other logic functions; it avoids the need for a decoding state as it uses one flip-flop for each state.

```
S0   = /Q3 * /Q2 * /Q1 * /Q0   ; power up state
S1   = /Q3 * /Q2 * /Q1 *  Q0
S2   = /Q3 * /Q2 *  Q1 * /Q0
S3   = /Q3 *  Q2 * /Q1 * /Q0
S4   =  Q3 * /Q2 * /Q1 * /Q0
```

A.4.7 State transitions

Following the state assignments section comes the state transition section, which identifies when a state changes and what state it will change to. Each state is identified by :=, followed by the condition which will trigger a change of state. The conditions are described in the conditions section. After the condition (in the next example: change_state) comes the change state symbol, ->, followed by the state to change to, as illustrated in the example. Multiple conditions can be included for each state by using the + symbol and they effectively operate as a CASE statement.

Example

```
S1  :=  change_state -> S2
S2  :=  change_state -> SO
        + go_up -> S3
        + -> S4
```

If no condition is given, then an unconditional default state is created, and in the above example, if conditions change_state and go_up are not true then the default will be to go to state S0. This is a local default state and overrides the global default state given if the DEFAULT_STATE option was included in the state header.

A.4.8 Input conditions

The input conditions follow the state transitions section and are identified by the reserved word CONDITIONS. Conditions which were previously used in the state transition section need to be defined here.

Example

```
conditions

     change_state = nothing*/clear
     go_up        = /nothing*/clear
```

A.4.9 Mealy state machine

Mealy state machines are similar to Moore state machines with one major difference, which is that the outputs at each state can be altered by the inputs to the state machine. This is achieved in the Mealy definition of a state machine by adding a fourth section, called the output transition definition section. This statement is not described in this appendix.

A.5 The simulation section

Once the logic model for the selected PLD has been produced, it is necessary to simulate it before programming the PLD. This is achieved by designing test vectors which will put the inputs through all the required states and match the simulated output against the predicted output. The simulator operates by applying the specified inputs, calculating the outputs and comparing with the user predicted outputs. These are sometimes known as test vectors. The simulation section is identified by the use of the reserved word SIMULATION after the logic has been defined. It consists of two types of command:

1) basic, 2) flow control.

A.5.1 Basic commands

There are two basic commands, one to control combinatorial inputs and one to control registers. These are:

1) SETF Sets the specified inputs, which can be vectors, as either logic high or logic low. If a design consists only of combinational logic this is the only command required.

2) CLOCKF Defines a LOW/HIGH/LOW pulse on the clock signal specified, which is connected to the clock input of the registers. Used in combination with SETF for registered logic designs.

A.5.2 Example of a combinational simulation section

```
simulation

setf value_1   value_2   value_3
setf value_1   value_2   /value_3
setf value_1   /value_2  value_3
```

To set a combinational input to logic high its signal name is used; to set it to logic low, a forward slash is used in front of its signal name to indicate it is inverted. The sequence in which the setf instructions are defined, specifies the order for the test vectors to be applied to the logic design. All the logic design inputs and outputs are recorded in a simulation file with the file extension .HST, which is called the simulation history file.

A.5.3 Example of a registered simulation section

```
simulation

setf     value_1   value_2   value_3
clockf   clk
setf     value_1   value_2   /value_3
clockf   clk
setf     value_1   /value_2  value_3
clockf   clk
```

In the above example of a registered design, a clockf instruction has been inserted after each set of input vectors. This enables the inputs to be specified and then clocked into the registers. Only the clock signal connected to the registers being used needs to be specified. If a device with multiple clocks is being used, both clock signals may need to be defined.

A.5.4 Additional basic commands

In order to help with the basic simulation sequence, there are five additional commands:

1) TRACE_ON To obtain only a sub-set of the complete simulation history file, the TRACE_ON command can be used to specify signals whose values are to be recorded in a trace file (with the file extension .TRF).

2) TRACE_OFF Used to close the trace file. Only one pair of TRACE_ON and TRACE_OFF commands is allowed within a simulation definition.

3) VECTOR Enables a sequence of signals to be treated as a vector. This is a definition only, so it must appear before the vector sequence is to be used.

4) CHECK Enables the specified signals to be checked for specific logic values. If there is a difference, an error is flagged in the simulation history file. If check is not used, then the user has to scrutinise the simulation history manually looking for the correct values.

5) PRLDF Preloads registers (and hence state machines) to known initial values. This is only a simulation command and is not recommended for maximum reliability designs. It is better to assume an initial unknown power-on state and then devise a simulation sequence which will move the design into the required state. Flow control can be used to achieve this.

A.5.5 Example of the additional basic commands

```
simulation

vector       data_bus[7:0] := [Q3,Q2,Q1,Q0]
trace_on     output_7
setf         value_1 value_2 value_3
clockf       clk
check        output_1 output_2 output_3
setf         value_1 value_2 /value_3
check        /output_1 output_2 /output_3
clockf       clk
setf         value_1 /value_2 value_3
clockf       clk
trace_off
```

A.5.6 Flow control

The basic commands given above enable any sequence of test vectors to be devised and applied. However, if a large logic design has been implemented, this can result in a very large set of test vectors which can be tedious to enter into the file. An alternative approach is to use flow control.

A.5.7 Flow control commands

Flow control automates the application of test vector sequences to the simulation, using structured high level language constructs, as listed below:

1) BEGIN END — used to group simulation commands.
2) FOR TO DO — repeats a sequence of test vectors for a specific number of times.
3) WHILE DO — repeats a sequence of test vectors while a condition is true.
4) IF THEN ELSE — applies flow control simulation sequence if the condition is true, otherwise it applies the alternative sequence.

A.5.8 Example of flow control commands

Any of the basic and additional basic commands can also be used within the flow control commands, provided that the correct syntax rules are obeyed.

```
simulation

vector     data_bus[7..0] := [Q3,Q2,Q1,Q0]
trace_on   output_7
setf       value_1   value_2   value_3
clockf     clk
check      output_1  output_2  output_3
setf       value_1   value_2   /value_3
check      /output_1 output_2  /output_3
clockf     clk
setf       value_1   /value_2  value_3
clockf     clk


;sets data_bus equal to all logic zeros for 5 clock pulses and then all
;logic ones for 5 clocks.
for index := 1 to 10 do
  begin
    if (index <= 5) then
      begin
        setf data_bus[7..0] := #b00000000
      end
    else
      begin
        setf data_bus[7..0] := #b11111111
      end
    clockf clk
  end

;An example of using the WHILE DO command.
while (/output_7 + /output_6) do
  begin
    setf output_4 output_5 output_6
    clockf clk
  end

trace_off
```

The use of basic, additional and flow control simulation commands enables complex and sophisticated sets of test vectors to be created easily and compactly. However, it is still the responsibility of the user to ensure that the test vector sequences are correct and that they are interpreted correctly, before considering the simulation of a logic design to be correct.

A.6 A language reference summary

A list of the reserved words used by MACHXL and PALASM is given below. Not all versions of MACHXL and PALASM will implement all of them.

A.6.1 Reserved words

3VOLT
5VOLT
BEGIN
CHECK
CHIP
CLOCKF
CMBFBK
CMOS_LEVEL
COMB
COMBINATIONAL
CONDITIONS
DEFAULT_BRANCH
DEFAULT_OUTPUT
DEFAULT_VALUE
DEFMOD
DELAYCLK
DO
ELSE
END
ENDMOD
EQUATIONS
FILE
FOR
FUSE
GND
GROUP
HIGH
HOLD_STATE
IF
INPUT
INST
INSTANCE
LAT
LATCHED
LATFBK
LOW
MEALY_MACHINE
MODULE
MOOR_MACHINE
NC
NEXT_STATE
NODE
OPEN_DRAIN
OPTIONS
OR
OUTPUT
OUTPUT_HOLD
PIN
PINFBK
PRELOAD
PRLDF
REG
REGFBK
REGISTERED
SECURITY
SETF
SIGNATURE
SIMULATION
STATE
STRING
THEN
TO
TRACE_OFF
TRACE_ON
TREGFBK
T_TAB
TTL_LEVEL
VCC
VECTOR
WHILE

Appendix B VHDL

B.1 Introduction to VHDL

VHDL is a hardware description language originally developed to improve the design of large integrated circuits by enabling an abstract description of the circuits' operation to be produced which could be simulated to identify any defects or omissions in the specification. Following this, the same description could be converted into a gate level description which could be implemented as an integrated circuit. Because of this the full name of the language is Very high speed integrated circuit Hardware Description Language. Though originally only designed for digital systems, the language has proved to be so flexible, useful and widely adopted, that extensions to incorporate analogue circuits have been devised and are already available in a limited form from some software developers.

B.1.1 Layout level

The language is capable of describing the same digital circuit at a number of different levels of abstraction. The lowest level, with the least abstraction, is the layout level which enables the description of the silicon and how transistors are formed and connected to be produced. This is where the language originated, but is now hardly used for this purpose, as there are now compilers which can convert higher levels of abstraction into much more efficient layout descriptions than most human designers can achieve. The layout level enables the effect of the layout on silicon to be investigated and incorporates timing and analogue effects, for it has to be remembered that although these systems are called digital, they are implemented using transistors which are inherently analogue devices.

B.1.2 Logical level

The most used level of description at present is the logic level, as this corresponds most closely to the construction of digital systems from standard building blocks of logic such as gates and registers. This is called the logic level and an appropriate compiler is used to convert the description into the layout level. The conversion process is known as synthesis and it has to be realised that not all valid VHDL descriptions at the higher levels of abstraction can be synthesised into working layout descriptions. It is usual to implement a set of guidelines which are designed to prevent the designer from creating unsynthesisable descriptions.

B.1.3 Register transfer level

As designers become more familiar with the concepts of designing digital systems with logic levels of abstraction, they are also wanting to use even higher levels of abstraction, as this enables a higher level of productivity to be achieved and a higher level of error-free designing. This is implemented in the register transfer level of abstraction, which does not consider what logic may be required to implement the design, but considers instead the functions to be implemented and what registers may be required. Effectively, it is a description of how data values are transferred from one store or register to another and how they are altered or amended during this process. Register transfer languages were originally developed during the design of microprocessors to help with the design of instruction sets. Each instruction of a complex microprocessor consists of several smaller and simpler instructions which identify what data is transferred from what register to what other register and how it is altered. These instructions are sometimes known as microcode. Reduced Instruction Set Computers attempt to remove microcode and its associated time penalty, by making each micro-processor instruction out of a single register transfer level instruction.

Generally, register level designs are synchronous; that is, all actions take place at the same instant determined by some global signal known as the clock. Multi-clock systems are possible, as are asynchronous systems which do not use a global clock, and VHDL can be used to describe them all; however, it is much more difficult to design an error-free asynchronous digital system than a synchronous system. Therefore, most large digital systems are synchronous designs using only one global clock signal.

B.1.4 Behavioural level

The final level of abstraction available at present is the behavioural level, which does not even consider how any particular design could be implemented and does not make reference to logic gates or registers, or to the hardware architecture. It is purely concerned with the function to be implemented and is most useful for checking that the specification of a design is correct and complete. It is quite common for behavioural designs to be unrealisable, that is, they cannot be physically implemented, as the compilers to convert from behavioural to layout level do not yet exist.

This level is only really aware of the inputs, the expected outputs and the timing relationship between various input and output signals. The simulator is then used to verify that outputs change when and as required, determined by the input signals, the clock(s) and the past input states. This is a true abstract description of the hardware and its function. This level of abstraction is the most productive and is the one preferred by most designers; however, the difficulties of obtaining a layout description mean that it is not in widespread common use. The usual method is to implement a behavioural description to confirm the specification and then rewrite where necessary at the register transfer level (and if really necessary to the logic and layout levels) so that the design can be synthesised. At present, this level is usually only used to confirm the correctness and completeness of specifications of large systems, due to the synthesis problem. However, it is likely that before too long, true behavioural to layout level compilers will be devised and this level will then be increasingly used.

B.2 Data types and signals

To be useful, all abstract languages have to have the ability to manipulate data values which in turn requires the ability to define data variables. VHDL has a number of predefined data types, plus the ability for the user to define others. The predefined data types can be separated into four categories:

Boolean
numbers
characters
timing

Some of these data variables will correspond to the inputs and outputs of the design and can be considered to be electrical connections. However, some of them are intermediate variables, used to hold temporary values within parts of the design and which do not have an external connection; they are called signals. Signals can have the same data types as the input and output connections. To define an intermediate data variable, the reserved word signal is used, followed by the signal name and then the data type. A colon is used to separate the signal name from the signal data type and a semicolon is used to terminate the definition.

```
signal   weeks : integer;
```

B.2.1 Standard types

The simplest data type is the Boolean which has two values: TRUE and FALSE, and is typically used in conditional statements such as:

```
if (test = TRUE) then
  outp <= '1';
else
  outp <= '0';
endif
```

The definition of the intermediate variable or signal is as follows:

```
signal   test : boolean;
```

The most useful data types are the numbers and three number bases are pre-defined:

binary
integer
real

The binary values allowed: logic zero and logic one, are denoted by '0' and '1', which have single quotes either side and are similar to Boolean values. Integers are simply a sequence of numbers without any quote marks and real numbers are similar to integers except that they contain a decimal point. Both integer and real numbers can be positive and negative, although it has to be remembered that the numbers are manipulated in an underlying binary format based on the IEEE floating point and integer number representation standard. The definition of the signals is achieved as illustrated below:

```
signal   motor : bit;
signal   weeks : integer;
signal   average : real;
```

Variables can be allocated values as:

```
motor <= '0';
weeks <= 52;
average <= 11.23;
```

Alphanumeric characters can be defined in a similar manner, using either single character signals or multi-character sequences which are known as strings. Single character variables are defined using the data type **character** and sequences of characters using the data type **string**.

```
signal  initial : character;
signal  surname : string;
```

When allocating a single alphanumerical character, single quotes are used either side of the letter, whereas for strings, double quotes are used, as illustrated below:

```
initial <= 'R';
surname <= "Seals";
```

The final data type is different from all the others in that it is used to represent time rather than a value and can only really be used when timing constraints are being applied to a design. However, it is defined in exactly the same way as the other data variables, using the **time** reserved word.

```
signal  delay : time;
```

As the signal is designed to store time values which have a dimension, that is seconds, the values assigned to these signals must also include the time units as listed below:

fs	(femtosecond = 10-15)
ps	(picosecond = 10-12)
ns	(nanosecond = 10-9)
us	(microsecond = 10-6)
ms	(millisecond = 10-3)
sec	(seconds)
min	(minute = 60 seconds)
hr	(hour = 3600 seconds)

An example of using a signal of data type time is illustrated below:

```
delay <= 200 ns;
```

Note that some compilers may require a space to be present between the last digit of the numerical part and the first character representing the time units. Otherwise, it may be treated as a user defined variable or signal. If multiple signals are required which have the same data type, it is possible to define them on separate lines or on the same line using commas to separate the user defined names, as illustrated below.

```
signal  first, second, third : integer;
```

The above is exactly the same as the following:

```
signal  first : integer;
signal  second : integer;
signal  third : integer;
```

but the first method is quicker to input into the source file. However, if a comment is required to denote the purpose of each of the signals, the second method may be preferred.

```
signal  first : integer;    -- Used to denote the first person
                            -- in the queue.
signal  second : integer;   -- Used to maintain the second
                            -- person's age.
signal  third : integer;    -- Used to identify the third
                            -- character in the sequence.
```

Note that the double minus character sequence is used to indicate the beginning of a comment and the return at the end of the line is used to mark the end of the comment. Therefore, if comments are to extend over several lines of text, each new line must be marked with the double minus character sequence.

B.2.2 Bit vectors

VHDL includes a further predefined data type, called the vector, which uses the reserved word bit_vector and is used to describe a sequence of bit signal types. These are effectively one-dimensional arrays which are otherwise known as vectors. The use of bit_vectors enables groups of signals, usually buses to be manipulated as a whole rather than as individual bits, but still enables the individual bits to be accessed and treated as bit data types when required. As bit_vectors are sequences of bits, it is necessary to define the number of bits in the signal declaration. This is achieved by using the to and downto reserved words as illustrated below:

```
signal  data_bus : bit_vector(0 to 7);
```

The to and downto reserved words are used to identify whether the leftmost bit in the sequence is the most significant bit, using downto, or the least significant bit using to.

```
signal  data_bus : bit_vector(7 downto 0);  -- This is an 8 bit data
                                            -- bus with the left
                                            -- most bit in the
                                            -- sequence being the
                                            -- most significant.

signal  other_bus : bit_vector(0 to 7);     -- This is an 8 bit data
                                            -- bus with the left
                                            -- most bit in the
                                            -- sequence being the
                                            -- least significant.
```

Once the order of the sequencing of a bit vector has been defined in this way, the same sequencing order must be used whenever the variable is used throughout the program. When using bit vectors, the size of the vector used is that given in the signal definition, unless an override size is given.

```
signal  a,b : bit_vector(3 downto 0)        -- Two 4 bit vectors
a <= b;                                     -- default size is used.
```

When using the override length within the assignments, both source and destination must be the same number of bits long.

```
signal  a : bit_vector(3 downto 0);
signal  b : bit_vector(7 downto 0);

a(3 downto 1) <= b(6 downto 4);
```

Constant values can also be assigned to vectors in a similar manner, provided that the number of bits in the constant is the same as the number of bits in the vector. Note that bit sequences are required by this activity, rather than individual bits, denoted by having double quotes at the beginning and end of their value, as follows:

```
signal  a : bit_vector(7 downto 0);

a(3 downto 1) <= "110";
```

The only exception to this is that the constant can have fewer bits than the vector, when the compiler will assume that leading zeros should be inserted, as shown below:

```
signal  a : bit_vector(7 downto 0);

a <= "110101";  -- The constant is only 6 bits long but the vector is
                -- 8 so the compiler would insert two leading zeros.
```

Although these variables are being used as a single entity, it has to be remembered that they are in fact groups of bits and that using vectors is merely a convenient method of achieving this in a concise manner. The allocation of bits is determined by the sequence.

```
a (3 downto 0) <= "1101";
```

is equivalent to

```
a(3) <= '1';
a(2) <= '1';
a(1) <= '0';
a(0) <= '1';
```

and

```
a(3 downto 0) <= b(6 downto 3);
```

is equivalent to

```
a(3) <= b(6);
a(2) <= b(5);
a(1) <= b(4);
a(0) <= b(3);
```

One additional feature of bit vectors of interest is that signals originally defined as bit can be combined together to be assigned to a vector. This can be achieved in two ways, either using the concatenation operator, &, or grouping the bit variables together, using the open and close bracket symbols. Both these methods are illustrated below:

```
signal  a : bit_vector(3 downto 0);
signal  first, second, third, fourth : bit;

a(3 downto 0) <= fourth & third & second & first;
```

and

```
a(3 downto 0) <= (fourth, third, second, first);
```

which are both equivalent to

```
a(3) <= fourth;
a(2) <= third;
a(1) <= second;
a(0) <= first;
```

It should be noted that there are a number of other variations on how vectors can be defined and used which will not be explained in this simple description of the language. For a full description of the language the reader should consult one of the references given at the end of this appendix.

B.2.3 User defined data types

Although the predefined data types enable all the desired operations to be implemented, it is sometimes useful to be able to define new data types to make the program more concise, more understandable or more reliable. The user defined data types can help to produce programs that are more reliable by only allowing signals to hold specific values. The same effect can be achieved with the predefined data types, but they also allow unwanted values to be validly stored which is a potential source of error and hence the program is more unreliable. The reserved word type is used to identify that a user defined data type is to follow as illustrated below:

```
type state_type is (ready, blocked, running);
```

Type is followed by the user defined name for the new data type, which in the above example has been chosen to be state_type, which is then followed by the reserved word is and then the new data type names delimited by the brackets. Inside the brackets the names are separated by commas. State_type can now be used just like any of the predefined data types in signal definitions. Any signals defined in this way can only have the names specified in the type definition allocated to them, as illustrated below:

```
type state_type is (ready, blocked, running);

signal  status,high_status : state_type;

status <= ready;
high_status <= blocked;
```

The above user defined data types are known as enumerated types, as the compiler allocates a specific number to each of the names defined by the user within the brackets and then uses that number within the program. However, the user is unaware of this conversion process unless looking at specific outputs and logic values. The user defined numeric type enables the user to place limits on the predefined data types to achieve the improved reliability that is possible with reduced sets of signal values. These are defined in the same manner, except that the bracket containing the user specified names is replaced by the reserved word range followed by the allowed numeric values. An example using integers is given below:

```
type reduced_int is range 0 to 255; -- limits integers to 8 bit values.

signal  port_id : reduced_int;

port_id <= 255;
```

This particular user defined numeric type is not always supported by synthesis tools and is not often used in logic design, but it can be useful in behavioural designs when specifications are being validated. A number of other data types exist and methods of defining them which are beyond the scope of this simple introduction. Further information can be obtained from the references at the end of this appendix.

B.2.4 Standard logic IEEE 1164

Before a VHDL program can be compiled, it is necessary to specify any libraries that are required by the program. The library can contain any previously designed entity or data types and can be defined by the user. All programs require the inclusion of the standard library known as IEEE, as it was defined by the IEEE committee for VHDL which includes all of the predefined data types and the predefined logic operations. The library reserved word is used to indicate which libraries are being used. Multiple libraries can be defined on the same line provided that they are separated by commas. However, for the simple programs being designed here only the IEEE library will be included as illustrated below.

```
library IEEE;
```

Within the library there are a number of variations and the user has to indicate which ones are being used through the use reserved word as illustrated below:

```
library IEEE;
use IEEE.Std_logic_1164.all;
```

These two lines should be included at the beginning of all of the programs designed using this simple introduction and should enable all the programs developed to compile and simulate using any VHDL package. Further explanation of the library and use reserved words are beyond the scope of this introduction. See references for further information.

B.3 Operators

In order to be able to perform useful activities a wide variety of logical and arithmetic operators are available within VHDL, although only some of the more modern compilers may implement the less common ones. The most basic operator is assignment, which allocates the value on the right hand side of the assignment operator, which is the left angle bracket immediately followed by an equals symbol, to the signal or variable on the left hand side. Thus:

```
port_id <= 255;
```

allocates the constant value 255 (which would be converted to the binary "11111111") to the signal called port_id. The right hand side can be constant, another signal or variable, or a logical or arithmetic equation, provided that the compiler is able to determine that a constant value will result when the equation is implemented. Examples of this are:

```
first <= second;
second <= true;
```

The restrictions are that all the signals, variables or constants involved in an equation must all have the same data type, so the following would generate an error:

```
signal port_id : integer;

port_id <= 25.5;
```

B.3.1 Logical operators

The standard logical operators are implemented, although they are represented with a word rather than a mathematical symbol, as the symbols are reserved for use as arithmetic operators. There are six basic operators as listed below which operate on bits, bit vectors and Boolean:

```
and
or
```

```
nand    -- not and
nor     -- not or
xor     -- exclusive or
not
```

VHDL compilers created after 1993 should also include the followed more specialised logical operators

```
sll     -- shift left logical
srl     -- shift right logical
sla     -- shift left arithmetic
sra     -- shift right arithmetic
rol     -- rotate left
ror     -- rotate right
```

The difference between shifting and rotating is that with shifting the bit moved out of the end of the signal is lost, whereas with rotating it is added to the other end of the signal. Logical shifts always add logic zeros into the vacant bit and arithmetic shifts consider the most significant bit of the value to be the sign and maintain that value. So a shift right arithmetic will keep the value of the most significant bit the same, but a shift right logical will insert logic zeros in the vacant most significant bit. It should be noted that shift left logical and shift right logical are equivalent and both add logic zeros into the vacant least significant bit. Examples of using the basic logical operators are:

```
first <= "1101";
second <= "0011";
third <= first and second;
fourth <= first and (not second or third);
```

B.3.2 Conditional operators

As well as the six basic logic operators, there are six conditional operators which enable comparisons between values to be made, the results of which can be used to control the operation of the logic. These types of operators are also known as relational operators. Generally, these operators will return Boolean results, that is, true or false, and are used by the conditional statements available within VHDL, such as IF THEN ELSE. These are high level statements which enable complex Boolean equations to be simply and easily implemented, thereby improving programmer productivity. The six operators are denoted by various combinations of symbols:

<	less than
<=	less than or equal
>	greater than
>=	greater than or equal
=	equal to
/=	not equal to

The use of <= for assignment differentiates between assignment and the test for equality which uses the equals symbol on its own, rather than allowing the compiler to determine which should be implemented, as is common with other high level languages. An example using a conditional operator is:

```
signal  first, second : integer;
signal  biggest : boolean;

first <= 27;
second <= 34;
biggest <= (first < second);
```

Note that the use of the conditional operator returns a result which is Boolean from two signals which were defined as integer, allowing the result to be assigned to a Boolean signal.

B.3.3 Arithmetic operators

Where VHDL has a significant advantage over other hardware description languages is in the area of arithmetic operators. Most other HDLs do not incorporate arithmetic operators because of the difficulty the compiler has in converting the equations into an executable logic system. However, as VHDL is an international standard which has been designed to enable behavioural simulation for testing specifications where arithmetic operators are much more important, the compilers are able to handle arithmetic operators. However, it should be noted that not all VHDL compilers will implement all of the operators and some may limit their use to behavioural simulation rather than synthesising equivalent logic. The following arithmetic operators can usually be used in synthesisable designs:

+	addition
–	subtraction
*	multiplication
/	division

Note that all of these operators will work with integer or real numbers, but not a mixture in the same equation. The following additional operators can sometimes be used in behavioural designs but may not be synthesisable.

**	exponential
abs	returns the absolute value of a number
mod	modulus
rem	remainder

All of these operators can be used in the same way as for any other mathematical equations and simplify considerably the conversion of numerical algorithms into executable digital logic systems. Examples of the use of the four basic operators are:

```
signal  numb_a, numb_b, numb_c : integer;
signal  first, second, third : real;
```

```
numb_a <= (numb_b + numb_c) / 2;
first <= 3.2 * second - third;
```

B.4 Concurrent constructs

One of the major differences between hardware description languages and computer languages is that the majority of computer languages are sequential, that is, the execution starts at the top of the program and executes each statement in turn. The order of the statements then becomes important. However, for HDLs it has to be remembered that the compiler will be producing a hardware implementation for each statement and these will all be executing in parallel, so the order that the statements are written in does not have an effect on the hardware synthesised or on the function of the hardware. For example, the following two program fragments are equivalent:

```
signal  numb_a, numb_b, numb_c : integer;
signal  first, second, third : real;

numb_a <= (numb_b * numb_c) / 2;
first <= 3.2 * second - third;
```

and

```
signal  numb_a, numb_b, numb_c : integer;
signal  first, second, third : real;

first <= 3.2 * second - third;
numb_a <= (numb_b * numb_c) / 2;
```

Further difficulties arise because the way the statements are written does affect the hardware synthesised even though the function of the logic may be equivalent. For example, the following statement:

```
first <= (second and third) or (second and fourth);
```

would be implemented using two AND gates and an OR gate. But it is functionally equivalent to the following:

```
first <= second and (third or fourth);
```

which only requires one AND gate and one OR gate. This saves one AND gate, enabling more logic to be implemented in the same device or a smaller device to be used. Although these two statements are functionally equivalent, there is a timing difference. For the first solution, all the signals have to pass through two logic gates and therefore incur two propagation delays. For the second statement, the second signal only passes through one logic gate and therefore its timing characteristic will be slightly different. The difference may or may not have an affect on some other part of the system which could be identified from the simulation. It is recommended that designers should *not* incorporate implicit delays such as these, as they are too dependent on the compiler and the technology of the device used for implementation. Instead, they should explicitly include timing information using the wait statement and attempt to overcome possible problems due to propagation delays through the use of synchronous systems which coordinate all signal changes to a global clock.

B.5 Constructing a complete VHDL program

So far, only program fragments of VHDL have been considered in order to introduce the concepts and statements in a progressive sequence. To create a program which can be compiled and simulated, additional statements are required. The first of these is the entity statement which identifies the physical input and output signals that the logic function will have. These relate closely to the physical voltages that are connected to the device used. An example of an entity declaration to implement a 2-bit full adder is shown below:

```
entity  full_add_2bit is
port    (in1, in2, carry_in : in bit;
    sum, carry_out : out bit);
end full_add_2bit;
```

The entity reserved word is followed by the user defined name, followed by the reserved word is. On the next line the reserved word port is used to declare first the input signals and their data type, followed by the output signals and their data type. The reserved words in and out are used just before the signal data type identifiers. Finally, the entity declaration is completed by the reserved word end followed by the same user defined name used in the first line. All this is part of the approach VHDL takes of forcing the programmer to use structured programming methods as these are more likely to lead to a better design. The example given above has three input signals and two output signals and is represented in block diagram format in figure B.1.

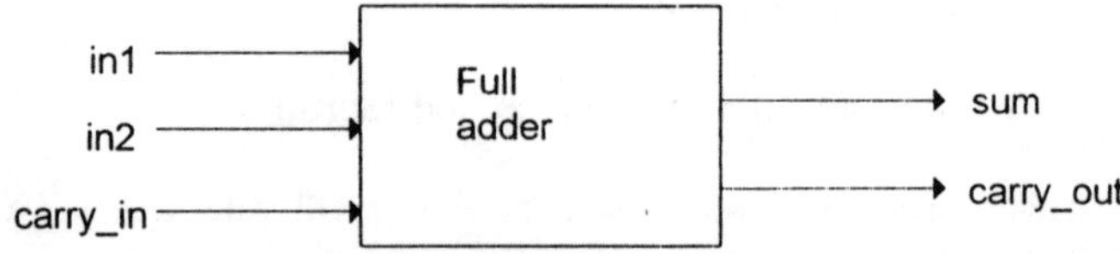

Figure B.1 Block diagram

The entity declaration is a block box definition that does not give any information about the internal operation. The internal operation is known as the architecture and should follow the entity declaration; it uses the reserved word architecture as illustrated below:

```
entity  full_add_2bit is
port    (in1, in2, carry_in : in bit;
    sum, carry_out : out bit);
end full_add_2bit;
```

```
architecture struct of full_add_2bit is

begin
  sum <= (not in1 and not in2 and carry_in) or
        (not in1 and in2 and not carry_in) or
     (in1 and not in2 and not carry_in) or
     (in1 and in2 and carry_in);
  carry_out <= (not in1 and in2 and carry_in) or
               (in1 and not in2 and carry_in) or
               (in1 and in2 and not carry_in) or
               (in1 and in2 and carry_in);
end struct;
```

The reserved word **architecture** is followed by a user defined name followed by the reserved word **of**, then the user name for the entity, followed by the reserved word **is**. Following this the rest of the architecture is defined between the **begin** and **end** reserved words. The **end** reserved word is followed by the user defined name for the architecture to complete the definition. This particular implementation of the full adder uses the full Boolean equations; alternative architectures which would have the same entity declaration could use the half adder approach to achieve the same functionality. If additional signals are required, they are defined between the line containing the **architecture** and the **begin** reserved words. For example, if the user decided to remove some of the redundancy by creating a single instance of the (in1 and in2 and carry_in) logical operation by using an intermediate signal, the following program would be derived:

```
entity  full_add_2bit is
port    (in1, in2, carry_in : in bit;
    sum, carry_out : out bit);
end full_add_2bit;

architecture struct of full_add_2bit is

signal  all_and : bit;

begin
  all_and <=(in1 and in2 and carry_in);
  sum <= (not in1 and not in2 and carry_in) or
        (not in1 and in2 and not carry_in) or
     (in1 and not in2 and not carry_in) or
        all_and;

  carry_out <= (not in1 and in2 and carry_in) or
               (in1 and not in2 and carry_in) or
               (in1 and in2 and not carry_in) or
                all_and;
end struct;
```

Again, both of these programs are functionally equivalent, but there may be small timing differences; there are also the differences in the number of logic gates used and how they are connected.

B.6 High level language constructs

There are three high level language constructs available within VHDL, designed to make the creation of programs easier. However, it should be remembered that these statements can be difficult for the compiler to convert into digital logic and some variations are best not used. For behavioural designs which are not going to be synthesised into logic, there are no restrictions on their use. The three constructs are:

IF THEN ELSE
CASE
FOR TO LOOP

and these are explained in the following sections.

B.6.1 The IF THEN ELSE construct

The syntax of the IF THEN ELSE construct is as given below with the ELSE being optional.

```
if (boolean test is true) then
  statements;
end if;
```

The first example does not have the optional ELSE part of the statement, whereas the following example includes it. Note that the end of the if statement is identified by the reserved word if after the last end.

```
if (boolean test is true) then
  statements;
else
 other_statements;
end if;
```

The if construct is useful for creating multiplexers and an example is:

```
if (select = '1') then
  out1 <= in1;
else
 out1 <= in2;
end if;
```

A demultiplexer can also be created in a similar way, although it must be remembered that all the outputs should be explicitly defined at all times if all output signal values are to be known at all times. Otherwise, the optimiser in the compiler may treat it as a don't care and some unpredictable results can occur.

```
if (select = '1') then
  out1 <= in1;
  out2 <= '0';    -- unused outs set to logic zero.
else
 out1 <= '0';
 out2 <= in1;
end if;
```

There is also the possibility of creating nested if constructs using the reserved word case as illustrated below. The following example also demonstrates the use of the conditional operators on integer numbers when determining the result of the Boolean test.

```
if (numba > 0 and numb <= 5) then
  out1 <= '0';
  out2 <= '0';
else if (numba > 5 and numb <= 8) then
  out1 <= '1';
  out2 <= '0';
else
  out1 <= '1';
  out2 <= '1';
end if;
```

However, a more efficient method of implementing the same functionality as using nested if constructs is to use the CASE construct.

B.6.2 The CASE construct

The case construct allows one of a different number of statements to be executed, determined by the value of an expression. The expression can be any signal capable of having multiple values, such as a bit_vector or an integer. However, real numbers should not be used due to the problems of obtaining a correct match. Even bit data types can be used, but as they have only two possible values, this would be equivalent to an if construct and therefore would have no advantage in being used. The syntax of the case construct is given below and starts with the case reserved word, followed by the expression (usually treated as an integer but can be a bit_vector) followed by the reserved word is.

```
case expression is
  when value1 =>
    statements;
  when value2 =>
    other_statements;
  when choice3 =>
    more_statements;
end case;
```

On the next line the reserved word when is used to identify what value the expression is being tested for. After the value there are the reserved symbols equals immediately followed by the right angle bracket (=>) followed by the other VHDL construct or constructs required to be executed for that particular situation. The when reserved word is used to identify further values that the expression can have and what constructs should be executed. After the last when there is the reserved word end followed by the reserved word case. All possible values of the expression must be included otherwise the operation of the logic will be unpredictable. Therefore either limited integer signals must be used or the others reserved word following the last when as illustrated below:

```
case expression is
  when value1  =>
    statements;
  when value2  =>
    other_statements;
  when choice3  =>
    more_statements;
  when others  =>
    final_statements;   -- Any values of the expression not covered
end case;               -- previously are detected here.
```

An example using the case construct for a 1-to-4 demultiplexer is:

```
case channel is
  when 0  =>
    out1 <= in1;
    out2 <= '0';
    out2 <= '0';
    out3 <= '0';
  when 1  =>
    out1 <= '0';
    out2 <= in1;
    out2 <= '0';
    out3 <= '0';
  when 2  =>
    out1 <= '0';
    out2 <= '0';
    out2 <= in1;
    out3 <= '0';
  when others  =>
    out1 <= '0';
    out2 <= '0';
    out2 <= '0';
    out3 <= in1;
end case;
```

The use of the others reserved word with the last choice is an example of good design technique. The expression should never have any values other than 0, 1, 2 and 3 but, by adding the others to the last when, if any alternative value such as 5 accidentally appear, the logic will still operate. The decision as to what should happen with the spurious values is decided by the user. In this example, it has been decided that it will always be out3. An alternative, which might be preferred in some situations, would be to turn all of the outputs off, as illustrated below and activate an error signal. Allocating error signals in this way consumes hardware resources, but is useful for systems where errors have to detected and recorded so that user intervention can take place. This is often used in high reliability systems.

```
case channel is
  when 0 =>          -- selects first output channel
    out1 <= in1;
    out2 <= '0';
    out2 <= '0';
    out3 <= '0';
    error <= '0';
  when 1 =>          -- selects second output channel
    out1 <= '0';
    out2 <= in1;
    out2 <= '0';
    out3 <= '0';
    error <= '0';
  when 2 =>          -- selects third output channel
    out1 <= '0';
    out2 <= '0';
    out2 <= in1;
    out3 <= '0';
    error <= '0';
  when 3 =>          -- selects fourth output channel
    out1 <= '0';
    out2 <= '0';
    out2 <= '0';
    out3 <= in1;
    error <= '0';
  when others =>     -- error detection test
    out1 <= '0';
    out2 <= '0';
    out2 <= '0';
    out3 <= '0';
    error <= '1';    -- An error situation has occurred
end case;
```

B.6.3 The FOR TO LOOP construct

The for loop allows an efficient method of repeating a sequence of statements a known number of times. Examples might be to set all the bits in a bit_vector to logic 1 or to output an incrementing integer. The syntax of the construct is given below and starts with the for reserved word followed by a signal name, then the reserved word in followed by the range of values that the signal can have:

```
for signal_name in lower_limit to upper_limit loop
  statements;
end loop;
```

This is then followed by the statements which are to repeatedly executed and then the reserved words end and loop.

B.7 Processes and sequential statements

So far, only statements which are all executed in parallel have been considered, but VHDL has the facility to execute statements sequentially, as most other programming languages do, using the process construct. The process construct sets aside a group of statements to be execute sequentially, starting with the one nearest the top and ending with the one nearest the bottom of the declaration. If more than one process is declared in a program, the processes operate in parallel but within the processes the statements are executing sequentially. The process construct is a complex one and only a simple example of the syntax and examples will be given. Further details can be obtained from the references. The process is declared using the reserved word process followed by the begin reserved word and then the statements to be executed. The declaration is completed by the reserved words end and process. An example of the syntax is:

```
process

begin
  statements;
end process;
```

One feature of processes that is particularly useful is that the declaration may contain a sensitivity list which specifies that if any of the listed signals alters the process will be executed. This enables a number of processes to be declared, but they will only execute if one of the signals is changed. An example of a process with a sensitivity list is:

```
process (first, second, third)

begin
  first < = second and third;
end process;
```

Whenever any of the signals, first, second or third is altered, the process will execute.

B.8 Clocked designs

So far all of the designs have been combinational, that is, they have not relied on the presence of a global synchronising signal. VHDL does not explicitly require synchronous designs to be specified, but instead requires the designer to indicate which signal will be used to coordinate actions. One method of achieving this is to use the wait command.

This is indicated by the use of the wait reserved word then the until reserved word, followed by the condition to be waited for. The syntax is:

```
wait until (my_sig = '1');
```

This construct will cause the function to remain at that point in the program until the signal my_sig becomes equal to a logic 1. When compiled and synthesised this is implemented as a registered signal with my_sig being the clock connected to the register. An example of a two bit counter is:

```
entity twobit_counter is
  port( clk : in bit;
     cnter : out bit_vector(1 downto 0));
end twobit_counter;

architecture struct of twobit_counter is

signal state1 : bit_vector(1 downto 0);

process

begin
  wait until (clk = '1');
  case state1 is
    when "00" =>
      cnter <= "01";
      state1 <= "01";
    when "01" =>
      cnter <= "10";
      state1 <= "10";
    when "10" =>
      cnter <= "11";
      state1 <= "11";
    when others =>
      cnter <= "00";
      state1 <= "00";
  end case;
end process;
end struct;
```

B.9 Other constructs

So far, only a limited number of VHDL constructs have been described in a simplified way. There is a significant number of other constructs which have not been described which are beyond the scope of this introduction. Many of them are related to creating behavioural designs which it may not be possible to synthesise into hardware. Because of this they are not described. However, further information can be obtained from the references given below or from any good book on VHDL design.

B.10 A complete VHDL program

A simple complete VHDL program which implements a simple memory address decoder for a microprocessor based computer is listed below.

```
-- R C Seals
-- 23 July 1996
-- University of Greenwich
-- A simple address decoder

library IEEE;
use IEEE.Std_logic_1164.all;

entity decoder is
  port(a15, a16, a17, a18, a19 : in  bit;
       cs_rom1, cs_rom2, cs_ram1, cs_ram2 : out bit);
end decoder;

architecture micro of decoder is

begin
  cs_rom1 <= not (a15 and a16 and a17 and a18 and a19);
  cs_rom2 <= not (not a15 and a16 and a17 and a18 and a19);
  cs_ram1 <= not (not a15 and not a16 and not a17 and not a18 and not a19);
  cs_ram2 <= not (a15 and not a16 and not a17 and not a18 and not a19);
end micro;
```

B.11 References

1. IEEE Standard VHDL Language Reference Manual, IEEE Std 1076-1987, New York, IEEE publication No. SH11957.

2. IEEE Standard VHDL Language Reference Manual, IEEE Std 1076-1993, New York, IEEE publication No. SH16840, ISBN 1-55937-376-8.

Glossary

Adder	Logic device which adds two binary numbers together to form a sum, with optional carry.
Algorithm	A list of statements which when executed sequentially will implement the required process.
ALU	Arithmetic Logic Unit. A collection of digital circuits which implement the basic logic and arithmetic operations such as AND, OR, NOT, add, subtract and so on.
AND gate	A collection of transistors which implements the Boolean AND function.
AND-OR architecture	A standard PLD circuit construction, with all the inputs being connected to AND gates and the outputs of the AND gates being connected to the inputs of OR gates. The outputs from the OR gates implement the AND-OR Boolean function.
Antifuse	When an antifuse is programmed, a connection that was previously 'not conducting' is made to conduct. (The opposite to a fuse.)
Architecture	The internal interconnection of a digital system indicating how data is transfered between various functions.
ASIC	Application Specific Integrated Circuit. A name used to describe an IC which has been designed at transistor level to implement a specific function, and cannot be used for anything else.
Asynchronous	Used to describe events which can occur at any time, that is, they are time independent.
Ball grid array	Method of making solder connections between an IC and a PCB, using small balls of solder preformed on the IC.
Barrel shifter	Efficient form of shift register.
Benchmark	A standardised method of 'doing something'. The aim is to provide a method which allows different processes and

	designs to be compared. To be widely accepted, they should be manufacturer independent.
Bi-directional	Describes either a connection or a logic circuit which allows electrical signals to travel in either direction.
Bipolar	A method of constructing transistors, which produces fast switching transistors but which consume a relatively high amount of power, most of which is dissipated as heat.
Boolean	Usually used to describe the state of some variable which can have only two values, called either true and false, or for digital circuits, logic 1 and logic 0.
Boolean logic	A method of combining Boolean values using a set of logical rules.
Buffer	A logic circuit which is connected between a signal source and its destination to provide protection and additional current and/or voltage capability.
Bus	A collection of digital signals with a consistent function, for example, memory address.
CAD	Computer Aided Design. In this context, used to describe the software tools used to create the logical designs and then convert them so that they can be programmed into the PLDs and FPGAs.
Clock	A repeated digital waveform with a regular mark and space, which has fast rise and fall times that is used to synchronise logic devices in different parts of a system.
CMOS	Complementary Metal Oxide Semiconductor. A semiconductor production process which creates digital circuits that have a very low power consumption.
Combinational	Used to describe a logic circuit in which the instantaneous output(s) is completely and always determined by the instantaneous inputs. Such systems do not have any registers and have no method of memory storage.
Combinatorial	See combinational.

CQFP	Ceramic Quad Flat Pack. A type of IC encapsulation made from a ceramic material which has external connections along each of four sides (usually a square package shape is used).
Critical path	The path within a digital circuit along which a signal will travel which has the most important parameter, for that particular design. Typically, time is the most important parameter, so the longest path is the critical one as high speed operation is required.
Custom	Design of a specific digital circuit for a specific function. See also ASIC.
D type	A type of flip-flop where the output is determined solely by the value present at the input at the instant of a valid clock pulse. The output logic value remains valid until the next clock pulse.
Datapath	The physical path that signals take in a circuit.
DRAM	Dynamic Random Access Memory. A form of read/write memory which needs constant refreshing to maintain the correct data values, but which requires only low power, and uses a minimal number of transistors to implement. It is particularly suited for the production of very large, cheap, solid state memories for computer systems.
EDIF	Electronic Data Interchange Format. A standardised representation of data which is independent of specific manufacturers and is designed to allow the transfer of information between otherwise incompatible software systems.
Electronically configurable	Where the logic function implemented by a programmable logic device can be changed electronically, without having to remove the device from the PCB so that is can be erased by UV light or other means.
Enable	A signal which allows or disallows a digital signal to output from some part of a digital system to another part of the system.
EPROM	Erasable Programmable Read Only Memory. A component used to store binary values in a large number of internal locations which is non-volatile. By exposing the memory cells

to high power UV light, the contents of the memory locations can be erased so that new values can be stored there.

Exclusive OR gate	A logic circuit which implements the Boolean exclusive-OR logic function.
Fan-in	The maximum number of digital signals that can be connected together at one input of a digital circuit.
Fan-out	The maximum number of digital signals that can be connected together at one output of a digital circuit.
FET	Field Effect Transistor. A low power consumption, easily made transistor which does not occupy too much silicon, allowing large numbers of transistors to be placed on a single IC.
Flip-flop	A logic circuit which has two stable output logic states, logic 0 and logic 1. By applying the correction stimulus to the inputs, the output can be made to change from one stable state to another. When the input stimulus is removed, the output remains at the last programmed value. A flip-flop is the basis of memory components, with each flip-flop able to store one bit of information.
Footprint	The area of PCB occupied by a particular IC.
FPGA	Field Programmable Gate Array. Array of blocks of logic which can be programmed to implement a wide selection of logic functions, with programmable interconnections.
Fuse	An originally conducting connection point which can be made to become open circuit permanently by the application of large currents for short periods of time, until the connection literally melts and evaporates. The process is non-reversible.
Gate	The smallest digital circuit possible, usually an AND or OR gate.
Glue logic	The various gates used to make the necessary timing and logic conversions to enable two or more larger components to be effectively connected together.

Granularity	A description of the relative smallness of the basic logic building block of a programmable logic device.
Input	The physical point at which the digital voltages and signals enter the IC packaging.
Interconnection	Physical low impedance path between logic elements.
Invertor	Logical NOT operation.
JTAG	Joint Test Action Group. An IEEE standard describing a method of testing the interconnections and operations of a PCB based digital system.
Latch	A registered element where the output changes with the input while the enable is active high. When the enable is deactivated, the last valid logic level on the input is maintained on the output until the next activation.
LCA	Logic Cell Array (Xilinx name for FPGA).
Library	Collection of similar elements and basic building blocks for logic system designs.
Look-up table	An addressable memory system used to convert one value into another.
Macro	Group of statements or actions to be executed.
Mapper	Converts the logical operations required by the design into a suitable format for programming on to the physical component to be used.
Mapping	The process of converting the logical design and placing it into the chosen component.
Minimisation	The process where Boolean equations are reduced to their most compact and efficient form.
MOSFET	Metal Oxide Semiconductor Field Effect Transistor. A robust and low power implementation of a FET.
Multi-chip module	Two or more silicon chips bonded on to a substrate and connected using gold or silver loaded paints.

Multiplexer — Logic function to convert multiple input signals into a single output signal.

Multiplier — A logical function to perform the arithmetic multiply operation.

Netlist — A description of the interconnections between the components or logic blocks in an electronic system.

NRE — Non Recurring Engineering costs.

One hot coding — A method of designing state machines where there is a separate register for each specific state.

Optimisation — The process during which both the speed of operation of the logic system is increased and the number of logic gates needed to implement the logic system is decreased until a satisfactory compromise is reached. Typically, the fewer gates there are, the slower the system will operate.

OR gate — Logical OR operation.

Output — The result of a logical operation.

Packaging — The physical protection added to an integrated circuit to provide mechanical strength, protection from the environment and heat dissipation.

Partitioning — The process where a large design is separated into a number of smaller interconnected modules.

PGA — Pin Grid Array, a method of connecting an IC package to the PCB.

Pin out — The allocation of internal logical functions on a component to the physical pins on the packaging.

Place and route — The process where the required logical functions are allocated to the available logic operations on the physical component and their subsequent interconnection.

PLD — Programmable Logic Device. A limited array of blocks of logic which can be programmed to implement a small selection of logic functions.

PLCC	Plastic Leadless Chip Carrier; a form of IC packaging which does not have any pins but which is soldered directly to the PCB.
PQFP	Plastic Quad Flat Pack; a form of IC packaging which has a low profile, has connections along all four sides of the device and is constructed from plastic.
Primary memory	Memory used by a computer to store programs (and data) while being executed.
Product term sharing	The process whereby logical OR terms from adjacent logic functions within an FPGA are combined in order to produce a larger product term equation than either of them can produce individually.
PROM	Programmable Read Only Memory; a non-volatile form of memory component which can be programmed only once.
Propagation	The time taken for an electronic pulse or signal to travel from some identified start position to some other identified stop position.
Prototype	Initial construction of a design in order to determine if there are any unforeseen problems.
Pull-down	A component, usually a resistor, which is used to force an undriven logical signal to a logic low.
Pull-up	A component, usually a resistor, which is used to force an undriven logical signal to a logic high.
RAM	Random Access Memory; an inaccurate, but commonly used term to describe a volatile memory component capable of having its internal data accessed in any sequence and altered any number of times during the digital system operation.
Reconfigurable	A type of logic function which can be altered as the system is executing.
Register	The smallest type of memory storage, where the output is altered on the active edge of the clock signal and remains valid until the next active edge.

Reset	The process whereby logic signals are returned to their initial power on values.
ROM	Read Only Memory; a form of non-volatile memory component.
Routing	The selection of the interconnection between logic functions that have been mapped to a target device.
Secondary storage	Off-line program and data storage, usually hard disks.
Self-timing	A description of a type of asynchronous logic system design.
Simulation	The process of imitating the operation of a logic system before it is constructed in order to verify that it will operate as required.
Slew rate	The rate of change of an electronic signal, usually a voltage.
Slew rate limited	A description of a logic output which limits the rate at which the signal can change.
SRAM	Static Random Access Memory; a type of RAM which does not require a clock signal in order to maintain its data values.
SSI	Small Scale Integration; a term used to describe logic components containing less than 100 logic gate equivalents.
State machine	A term for a diagrammatic method of describing the operation of a clocked or synchronous digital system, where each stable set of outputs is a state. The transfer of the outputs from one stable state to another is determined by the description.
Sum of products	A term used to describe the Boolean equation output by an AND-OR logic gate structure.
Synchronous	Description of a system where all the outputs change at the same time, determined by a global clock signal.
Synthesis	The process of converting a program description of a digital system into the hardware to implement it.

T type	A toggle register, where the output changes to the opposite logic state at every clock pulse.
TTL	Transistor-Transistor Logic; a term used to describe the output configuration of transistors on a logic device implemented using bipolar transistors.
Tri-state	A logical output which is capable of being in one of three valid states, logic 0, logic 1, or high impedance.
UNIX	Operating system in widespread use, particularly for work stations.
Usable gates	A description of the number of equivalent logic gates in a digital component that can be utilised within a design.
Verification	The process of confirming that a product meets the original specification.
VLSI	Very Large Scale Integration; used to describe logic systems containing more than 10,000 logic gate equivalents.
Workstation	Powerful personal computer with high resolution display, large primary memory and very large secondary storage.
Worst case	The combination of parameters and situations which causes the worst possible result to occur.

Index